Diffraction and
Imaging Techniques
in Material Science

Diffraction and Imaging Techniques in Material Science

Volume I: Electron Microscopy

Second, revised edition

Editors

S. Amelinckx, R. Gevers, J. Van Landuyt
State University of Antwerp, Belgium

1978

NORTH-HOLLAND PUBLISHING COMPANY • AMSTERDAM – NEW YORK – OXFORD

North-Holland ISBN   Volume I : 0 444 85128 3
                     Volume II: 0 444 85129 1
                     Set   : 0 444 85130 5

Publishers:

NORTH-HOLLAND PUBLISHING COMPANY – AMSTERDAM – NEW YORK – OXFORD

Sole distributors for the U.S.A. and Canada:

ELSEVIER NORTH-HOLLAND, INC.
52 VANDERBILT AVENUE
NEW YORK, N.Y. 10017

First edition 1970
Second, revised edition 1978

Library of Congress Cataloging in Publication Data
Main entry under title:

Diffraction and imaging techniques in materials science.

    Comprises new contributions and revised and updated papers originally presented at the International Summer Course on Material Science, Antwerp, 1969, and published in 1970 under title: Modern diffraction and imaging techniques in material science.
    Includes bibliographical references and index.
    CONTENTS: v. 1.   Electron microscopy.--v. 2.   Imaging and diffraction techniques.
    1. Electron microscopy--Congresses. 2. Electrons--Diffraction--Congresses. 3. Imaging systems--Congress-es. I. Amelinckx, Severin. II. Gevers, R. III. Lan-duyt, J. van. IV. International Summer Course on Material Science, Antwerp, 1969. Modern diffraction and imaging techniques in material science.
TA417.23.D54   620.1'127   78-22081
ISBN 0-444-85130-5

PRINTED IN THE NETHERLANDS

PREFACE TO THE FIRST EDITION

This book contains the proceedings of a summer school sponsored by NATO and held at the University of Antwerp during the period from July 28th to August 8th, 1969. The objective of the school was to teach at an advanced level the recent developments in "Diffraction and Imaging Techniques" which are increasingly being used in the study of materials.

The school attracted wide interest and a number of applicants had unfortunately to be refused in view of the limited accommodation facilities. It was therefore felt that the proceedings should be published rapidly and in a permanent form making them accessible not only to the participants but also to people which had not been able to attend the course so as to give them an opportunity to benefit from the lectures given by the best experts in their respective fields.

Although the book reflects inevitably the diversity of viewpoints of the different authors, the arrangement of the material is such that it will constitute a consistent treatment requiring a minimum of background knowledge. In most cases this background knowledge is provided in introductory lectures.

The organizing committee is grateful to the different authors for their collaboration in editing this book.

We also gratefully acknowledge the financial help of NATO, and the help of the University of Antwerp in providing the necessary facilities for lecturing and for housing the students.

The Organizing Committee

PREFACE TO THE SECOND EDITION

The first edition of this book has been very well received by the scientific community; it has been widely used as a textbook for courses on diffraction and solid state electron microscopy. However the first edition was completely sold out a few years ago and many orders have had to be refused.

It was therefore felt that a new, revised and completed edition would be very much welcomed by the many users.

Nearly all authors have updated and reworked their contributions and new contributions in recently developed fields have been added so as to maintain the spirit and scope of the original edition. It has therefore become necessary to publish the book in two volumes.

The editors wish to express their appreciation to the authors for making a real effort to make the book an up to date textbook once again.

It is hoped that this second edition will meet with the same success as the first one.

The Editors

CONTENTS

VOLUME I: ELECTRON MICROSCOPY

INTRODUCTION

TRANSMISSION ELECTRON MICROSCOPY

PARTICULAR ASPECTS OF ELECTRON DIFFRACTION

VOLUME II: IMAGING AND DIFFRACTION TECHNIQUES

HIGH VOLTAGE ELECTRON MICROSCOPY

LOW ENERGY ELECTRON DIFFRACTION

X-RAY AND NEUTRON DIFFRACTION AND TOPOGRAPHY

MIRROR ELECTRON MICROSCOPY

FIELD EMISSION MICROSCOPY

INTRODUCTION

Diffraction and Imaging Techniques in Material Science,
eds. S. Amelinckx, R. Gevers and J. van Landuyt
© *North-Holland Publishing Company, 1978*

GENERAL REVIEW OF THE EXPERIMENTAL METHODS
FOR THE DETERMINATION OF ATOMIC STRUCTURES

A.GUINIER

Laboratoire de Physique des Solides, Université Paris-Sud, Orsay, France

The different chapters of this book are devoted to various methods able to furnish information on the atomic structure of matter at an atomic scale. Generally speaking, all these methods are based upon some interaction of matter with radiations of different kinds.

The necessary condition is that the resolving power of any of these devices be sufficient to allow the localization of the individual atoms. A general rule in optics is that the limiting value of the resolving power (i.e. the shortest distance between two points which can be distinguished) is of the order of the wave-length of the radiation used. Every atom having a diameter of the order of 1 Å, that implies that one must use radiations of a wave-length of 1 Å or shorter.

1. Classification of methods

We can now classify the possible methods of observation by making a list of radiations within this range of wave-lengths.

(1) Among the electromagnetic radiations, we find X-rays and fortunately the desired wave-lengths (0.1–1 Å) correspond to radiations which are both easy to produce, easy to detect and have a suitable interaction with matter. X-rays of longer wave-length (10 to 100 Å) are so easily absorbed in the matter that they cannot reach the sample to be studied and X-rays of shorter wave-length (0.01 to 0.1 Å) require the use of cumbersome and expensive high-tension generators.

(2) Besides these electromagnetic radiations, we have at our disposal the radiations associated to beams of various particles, the wave-length of which is given by the de Broglie formula

$$\lambda = \frac{h}{mv} \quad \text{or} \quad \lambda = \frac{h}{\sqrt{2m}\sqrt{E}} \tag{1}$$

E being the kinetic energy of the particle of mass m. Numerically, for electrons, with E expressed in electron-volts ($E=eV$) and λ in Ångstroms (Å)

$$\lambda = 12.5/\sqrt{V}.$$

So for *electrons*, the 1 Å wave-length corresponds to electrons accelerated by a tension of a few hundred volts. Such electrons are stopped by one or two atomic layers: thus they can only be used for the observation of the structures of surfaces (LEED methods, p. 553). With an increasing acceleration tension, the electrons are able to pass through layers of 100 to 1000 Å which allows the observation of a three dimensional structure. The wavelength of such electrons is of the order of 0.1 Å; it is well known that technically the production and the detection of 10 to 100 kV electrons do not encounter special difficulties. In fact, *electrons* are now the agents of very effective means for the observation of atomic structures (p. 355).

(3) For heavy particles, the same wave-length is obtained, according to formula (1) when the particles have much lower energy. For instance in a neutron beam of 1 Å wave-length, the neutron has a velocity of 4000 m/sec and an energy of 0.08 eV. This is the energy of particles in thermal equilibrium at a temperature of 600°K. *Neutrons* have a special interest for the study of atomic structures because their interaction with the atoms is of a quite different nature from the interaction of atoms with photons or charged particles. Thus the neutrons "see" different aspects of the atoms (p. 593). Furthermore the absorption of neutrons in matter is very low. Thus an entire specimen of very large size may be observed (a few centimeters instead of a fraction of millimeters for X-rays, or a fraction of microns for electrons). Of course, the use of neutrons cannot be general in every Solid State Physics laboratory, since it is restricted to the laboratories attached to the few big research reactors in operation in the world.

(4) Some charged heavy particles are also utilized but *protons* have a serious inconvenience; they produce serious damages in the matter under examination and so the observed structure may not be the primitive one. But helium ions are used in a very interesting instrument (field-ion microscope, p. 811).

2. Image formation and diffraction techniques

The value of the wave-length of the radiation gives an unavoidable limitation of the resolving power but the physical properties of the radiation must make possible the realisation of a practical device able to approach as far as possible the theoretical limit.

The most obvious method is the formation of an *image*, as in an optical instrument, with a magnification high enough to show distinctly the details which can be separated. But with some of the radiations which enter the category of the "possible" radiations, no image forming device may be realised. Thus X-rays propagate in straight line and can be deviated neither by reflection nor by refraction at the interface of two material mediums. So, the rays issued from a point source cannot be focused in a point image and − at least up to now − no X-ray microscope is available. In fact, reflection of X-rays indeed occurs on a plane surface, but only if the angle of incidence is lower than a few minutes and the attempts to construct an X-ray microscope with an interesting resolving power have not been successful. The situation is the same for the neutrons.

On the other hand, the trajectory of a charged particle may be altered by the forces exerted by electrical or magnetic fields. Combination of such fields may lead to an image-forming system and so microscopes, even with a very high magnification, are possible. These instruments (electron microscopes and ion-microscopes) are now essential tools for Solid State physicists (pp. 107 and 811).

The formation of images is not the only way to collect information about the structure of an object. There is a second possibility, much more general since it is applicable for all kinds of radiations, the phenomena of *diffraction*. The object is bathed in a coherent plane wave; the different atoms receiving this primary radiation become sources of scattered radiation; the total diffracted radiation results from the interferences between the ensemble of the coherent secondary sources. The repartition of the diffracted radiation in the different directions of space depends upon the nature of the interaction of the atoms and the primary beam and on the arrangement of the atoms in the object. Thus the knowledge of the diffracted radiation gives information on the atomic structure of the object and, even in some cases, that is sufficient to build a model of the structure; but this is possible only because the wave-length of the primary beam is short enough, the concept of the resolving power used in the case of image being also valid for the diffraction phenomena. But in the general case, the information contained in the diffraction data do not allow to give an unambiguous structural model. Nevertheless diffraction is in the present state of the technique the most direct approach to this model (pp. 593, 374 and 399).

The scattering due to the individual atoms being provoked by the incident beam, the energy of the scattered radiation is substracted from the incident energy. The characteristics of the diffraction phenomena depend on the value of the ratio of these two energies. If the scattered energy is very small relative to the incident energy, one can admit that the wave-field after diffraction is simply the addition of the incident unperturbed wave plus the scattered radiation. That is called in quantum mechanics the Born approximation and for diffraction the *"kinematical"* case. This approximation is generally valid for X-rays but there are some exceptions, rare but very interesting: when the diffracting body is a large and perfect crystal, i.e. when the atoms, in volumes of the order of $[10$ to $100\,\mu m]^3$ are located at the nodes of one single lattice, the intensities of the diffracted beam and of the incident beam become comparable. Another theory of diffraction — called dynamical — is then valid: the diffraction phenomena are profoundly altered (pp. 43 and 462). In electron diffraction, the cases where the dynamical theory has to be applied are much more frequent.

In electron microscopy, the image formation is not independent from the diffraction phenomena. The contrast in the image corresponds to variations from point to point of the transmission factor of the electrons through the object, and the diffraction of the direct beam is a very important cause of absorption.

In conclusion, table 1 gives the summary of this rapid review.

Table 1

Nature of radiations		Methods of observation	
Particles	Wave-length		
X-ray photons	1Å		diffraction
Electrons { high energy	0.05Å	microscopy	diffraction
low energy	1Å		diffraction
Neutrons	1–10Å		diffraction
Ions		microscopy	

TRANSMISSION ELECTRON MICROSCOPY

Diffraction and Imaging Techniques in Material Science,
eds. S. Amelinckx, R. Gevers and J. van Landuyt
© *North-Holland Publishing Company, 1978*

KINEMATICAL THEORY OF ELECTRON DIFFRACTION

R.GEVERS

Laboratoria van het SCK, Mol-Donk, Belgium

1. Introduction

It is well-known that accelerated electrons incident on a sufficiently thin crystal in a parallel monochromatic beam are not only transmitted without change in direction, but also emerge at the back surface in a number of discrete directions.

The task of the theory is to calculate the relative number of the electrons in each of the so-called "diffracted beams".

It is also known that this property is shared by X-ray photons and by neutrons, and that the phenomenon is due to the translation symmetry of the crystalline matter. Nevertheless it turns out that the details of the observations are different for the three types of radiation. This is rather fortunate, since it allows to gather complementary informations about the substance under study by the use of the three different techniques.

1.1. *The Bragg-law*

The common feature of the diffraction of the three different types of particles is the direction of the diffracted beam with respect to the incident direction and the orientation of the crystal plate. This is rather evident since it is only determined by the translation symmetry of the crystal.

The wave vectors $\mathbf{k}_o$ and $\mathbf{k}$ of the incident and the scattered beam satisfy the well-known Bragg law.

$$\mathbf{k} - \mathbf{k}_o = \mathbf{g} \tag{1}$$

where $\mathbf{g}$ is any reciprocal lattice vector.

Since only elastic scattering is considered, one has

$$k_o = |\mathbf{k_o}| = |\mathbf{k}| = 1/\lambda \tag{2}$$

where λ is the wave length.

The Bragg law expresses that the scattering amplitudes of the scattering events by a very large number of scattering centres, arranged at the nodes of a regular lattice, are perfectly in phase with each other.

1.2. *Reflection sphere construction*

The Bragg law (1) can be interpreted with the help of the widely used Ewald or reflection sphere (see fig. 1). The latter is a sphere with radius $1/\lambda$. If C is its centre and if $\overrightarrow{CO} = \mathbf{k_o}$, then O must be thought to be the origin of the reciprocal lattice. To any reciprocal lattice node G, defined by the reciprocal lattice vector $\mathbf{g}$, lying on the reflection sphere, corresponds then a diffracted beam with wave vector $\mathbf{k} = \overrightarrow{CG}$.

The angle between $\mathbf{k_o}$ and $\mathbf{k}$ is noted as $2\theta_B$, and θ_B is called the Bragg angle.

1.3. *Bragg reflection on lattice planes*

An alternative way of interpreting (1) is as follows.

The reciprocal lattice vector $\mathbf{g}$ can be written as

$$\mathbf{g} = h\mathbf{A} + k\mathbf{B} + l\mathbf{C} \tag{3}$$

where $\mathbf{A, B, C}$ are the base vectors of a unit cell of the reciprocal lattice.

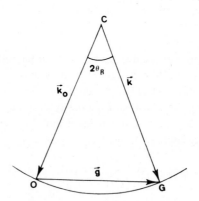

Fig. 1. Reflection sphere construction.

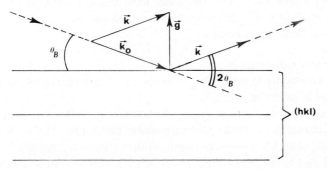

Fig. 2. Schematic representation of the reflection of electrons on a family of lattice planes (hkl). $(\mathbf{g} = h\mathbf{A} + k\mathbf{B} + l\mathbf{C}.)$

The vector $\mathbf{g}$ is then perpendicular to the family of lattice planes with Miller indices (hkl) and its length is a multiple of the reciprocal of the interplanar spacing d_{hkl}.

From fig. 2 follows then immediately that (1) expresses that the particles in the beam $\mathbf{k}$ can be considered as obtained by reflection on the lattice planes (hkl). The reflections on the successive planes of the family have to be perfectly in phase, and this occurs only if the angle between the incident beam and the lattice plane equals the Bragg angle.

1.4. Condition for diffraction

The Bragg angle is obtained by squaring (1). One finds:

$$k^2 + k_o^2 - 2\mathbf{k} \cdot \mathbf{k}_o = g^2 ,$$

or

$$\frac{1}{\lambda^2}(2 - 2\cos 2\theta_B) = \left(\frac{n}{d_{hkl}}\right)^2 .$$

Finally

$$2d_{hkl} \sin \theta_B = n\lambda , \qquad \sin \theta_B = \frac{n\lambda}{2d_{hkl}} = \frac{g}{2k_o} . \qquad (4)$$

One notices immediately that diffraction can only occur if

$$\lambda < 2(d_{hkl})_{max} . \qquad (5)$$

This condition puts an upper limit to the wave length. There is also a practical lower limit, since the Bragg angles must remain larger than a certain critical value, in order to be observed.

1.5. *Order of magnitude of wave length*

The order of magnitude of λ is of importance for the details of the observations to be expected.

If λ is comparable with $(d_{hkl})_{max}$ the radius of the reflection sphere and the mesh of the reciprocal lattice have comparable dimensions. This is the case for X-rays and neutrons where wavelengths of the order of magnitude of 1 to 2 Å are used. As a consequence Bragg angles will not be small. For an arbitrary orientation of the crystal with respect to the incident beam, one needs luck to have a reciprocal lattice node on or at least very close to the reflection sphere. One has to imagine methods for bringing reciprocal lattice nodes on this sphere, and only very rarely more than one diffracted beam is observed at the same time. If the diffracted beams are registered, one obtains in general a deformed image of the reciprocal lattice, leading sometimes to indexing problems.

Generally, the incident electrons in electron transmission microscopy have been accelerated by a potential of 100 kV. The corresponding wavelength is 37×10^{-3} Å, yielding a k_o value of about 25 Å^{-1}. This value has to be compared with the mesh of the reciprocal lattice, mostly about hundred times smaller.

A consequence of this relatively small value of λ is that the Bragg angles are small for low index reflections, a few degrees at most. This is an advantageous situation for the electron microscopist, since small deformations in a crystal will lead to local orientation differences of the lattice planes which are not negligibly small as compared to the Bragg angle itself. The induced local and relatively important changes in diffraction conditions make this deformation then visible by a local change in transmitted and diffracted intensity.

Due to the small dimensions of the reciprocal lattice as compared to the radius of the reflection sphere, there will always be many reciprocal lattice nodes close to that sphere, giving rise to many diffracted beams at the same time.

In electron transmission microscopy one considers only the Laue case, i.e. all diffracted beams emerge at the back surface of the crystal plate.

Since one has $k_o \cong |\mathbf{k}_o + \mathbf{g}|$ and $k_o \gg g$ for all diffracted beams, all **g**-vectors defining diffracted beams are nearly perpendicular to the incident beam direction. The diffracted beams are obtained by the reflection of electrons on the lattice planes of a single zone, the incident beam being nearly parallel to the

zone axis [*uvw*] . If these beams are registered on a photographic plate held
normal to the incident beam, one obtains a direct image of this zone of the
reciprocal lattice, with negligible deformation since the Bragg angles are small.
This zone can be easily indexed, enabling the determination of crystallographic characteristics of the features under observation.

1.6. *Strength of the interaction*

There is a second possibility for differences to occur between X-ray, neutron-
and electron diffraction, namely the different strength of the interaction with
the crystalline substance. One must be prepared for significant differences
since this interaction is of different nature for the three different types of
radiation. Whereas neutrons interact only with the nuclei (if magnetic scattering is not considered), photons only with the electron clouds (the interaction
with the heavy nuclei can be neglected), the electrons interact both with the
nuclei and with the electron clouds, through strong electrostatic Coulomb
forces.

The crystal potential felt by the accelerated electron when passing through
the crystal slab, due to the nuclei and the electron clouds, is noted $V(\mathbf{r})$ and
it is of course three-dimensionally periodic. It can thus be developed in a
Fourier series, following

$$V(\mathbf{r}) = V_0 + \sum_{\mathbf{g}} V_{\mathbf{g}} \exp i2\pi \mathbf{g} \cdot \mathbf{r} \tag{6}$$

where the sum runs over all reciprocal lattice vectors. The Fourier coefficients
can be computed with the help of the wave functions of the atoms and ions
making up the crystal. The mean potential V_0 can be estimated to lie mostly
in the range of 10–20 V, and it is responsible for the refraction of the incident
beam when entering and leaving the crystal. Since V_0 is very small as compared
to 100 kV (the accelerating potential), this effect is very small and can mostly
be neglected.

The fluctuations around this mean potential are described by the further
Fourier coefficients $V_{\mathbf{g}}$ which can be estimated to be a few volts for low index
$\mathbf{g}$.

Each term of (6) is responsible for a reflection on a family of lattice planes.
The coefficient $|V_{\mathbf{g}}|$ is small as compared to the accelerating potential, but
there is a very large number of scattering centres. Therefore, for a favourable
phase relationship, i.e. if one nearly satisfies (1), one can nevertheless expect
strong diffraction. This will be shown in the next sections.

The main consequence is that one has to take dynamical interaction into account. This means that one can mostly not neglect the possibility that an electron is scattered many times, when passing through the crystal. This will be discussed in detail by Professor Whelan.

The electron-crystal interaction is also too strong to overlook the inelastic scattering events by which phonons, plasmons, X-rays etc. are created. This leads to the so-called absorption effect, also to be discussed in other contributions. This effect is responsible for the fact that the crystal plate has to be sufficiently thin, say thinner than 1.000 to 2.000 Å for 100 keV-electrons, in order to remain transparent for the electrons.

1.7. *Deviation from the exact Bragg orientation*

Due to the small thickness of the crystal and to the dynamical interactions, the intensities of the different diffracted beams can remain appreciable even if one deviates rather drastically from the condition (1), called the exact condition for Bragg reflection. Therefore, one has to introduce a parameter which describes this deviation adequately. One chooses the distance s_g from the reciprocal lattice point G to the reflection sphere, perpendicular to the entrance

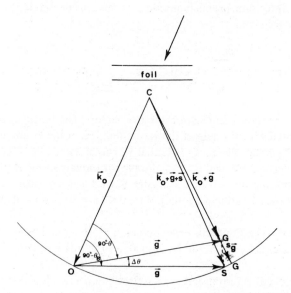

Fig. 3. Reflection sphere construction illustrating the geometrical relationship between s_g, g, and θ, θ_B for the case $s_g > 0$; for $k_0 \gg g \gg s_g$, one has OG $\cong$ OS and CS $\cong$ CG.

surface of the crystal plate, measured in the direction of propagation of the electrons (fig. 3).

This parameter s_g is called the deviation from the exact Bragg orientation, or also the excitation error.

There are two possiblities (1) $s_g > 0$, i.e. the reciprocal lattice node G lies inside the reflection sphere, (2) $s_g < 0$, i.e. it lies outside the sphere. In the first case the angle θ formed by the incident beam and the reflection planes is larger than the Bragg-angle θ_B (fig. 3); in the second case one has $\theta < \theta_B$.

Noting

$$\Delta\theta = \theta - \theta_B \tag{7}$$

one has for small s values, in good approximation

$$\Delta\theta = s_g/g \tag{8}$$

as can be derived from fig. 3.

2. The kinematical approach

2.1. *The kinematical assumptions*

The kinematical treatment is the most simple approach for calculating the amplitudes of the different beams. It involves, however, very daring assumptions, the validity of which must be controlled afterwards. They are:

(1) An electron can only be scattered once;

(2) The depletion of the incident beam when progressing into the crystal can be ignored.

It is clear that one can only hope that these approximations are good, if the scattering is sufficiently weak. One has only to find out what "sufficiently" means here.

Since one does not allow an electron to be scattered more than once, i.e. one assumes that these events are so rare that they can be ignored, no dynamical interaction between beams are taken into account.

2.2. *Schrödinger equation – Born approximation*

The usual kinematical treatment, as performed in the case of X-rays and neutrons, consist in considering the scattering by each individual scattering centre arranged on a lattice, and by summing up the amplitudes of the events, taking their phase-relationship into account.

However, we prefer to develop for the case of electrons, a different but equivalent method, showing clearly how the extension to the dynamical situation must be made. This method is the Born approximation applied to the Schrödinger equation describing the movement of the accelerated electron in the crystal. For an electron with kinetic energy much higher than the energies of the electrons of the crystal it is a good approximation to consider it as moving in the given crystal potential $V(\mathbf{r})$ defined by (6) (no inelastic scattering is considered). Its wave function ψ satisfies the Schrödinger equation

$$\left[-\frac{h^2}{8\pi^2 m} \Delta - eV(\mathbf{r}) \right] \psi = eE\psi \tag{9}$$

where m is the electron mass; $-e$ is the electronic charge ($e>0$); h is Planck's constant; E is the accelerating potential ($E>0$). Since the mean interaction is attractive, $-eV_o < 0$, i.e. V_o is defined as positive. By putting

$$E' = E + V_o \,, \qquad eE' = \frac{h^2 k_o^2}{2m} \,, \qquad (k_o=1/\lambda) \tag{10},(11)$$

one can rewrite (9) as follows

$$\Delta\psi + 4\pi^2 k_o^2 \, \psi = -\frac{8\pi^2 me}{h^2} \, V'(\mathbf{r}) \, \psi \tag{12}$$

with

$$V'(\mathbf{r}) = V(\mathbf{r}) - V_o \,. \tag{13}$$

The parameter k_o is the magnitude of the wave vector of the incident wave corrected for refraction. Introducing the further notation

$$U(\mathbf{r}) = \frac{2me}{h^2} \, V'(\mathbf{r}) \tag{14}$$

or

$$U(\mathbf{r}) = \sum_{\mathbf{g}} U_{\mathbf{g}} \exp i2\pi \mathbf{g} \cdot \mathbf{r},$$

$$U_{\mathbf{g}} = \frac{2me}{h^2} V_{\mathbf{g}}, \qquad U_{\mathrm{o}} = 0 \qquad\qquad (15),(16)$$

one obtains finally the Schrodinger equation in the following form

$$\Delta \psi + 4\pi^2 k_{\mathrm{o}}^2 \psi = -4\pi^2 U(\mathbf{r}) \psi . \qquad\qquad (17)$$

If one ignores the scattering, i.e. one neglects the second member, the integral of (17) is

$$\psi_{\mathrm{o}} = \exp i2\pi \mathbf{k}_{\mathrm{o}} \cdot \mathbf{r} \qquad\qquad (18)$$

the wave function describing the incident beam with wave vector $\mathbf{k}_{\mathrm{o}}$ (corrected for refraction).

As well known, the Born approximation consist in replacing ψ in the second member by ψ_{o}, i.e. the wave function unperturbed by the perturbation potential. It is clear that the term $U\psi_{\mathrm{o}}$ in the second member describes now only electrons scattered out of the incident beam ψ_{o}, which moreover is not influenced by the scattering. These are nothing else than the kinematical assumptions. One has thus to consider the equation

$$\Delta \psi + 4\pi^2 k_{\mathrm{o}}^2 \psi = -4\pi^2 U(\mathbf{r}) \psi_{\mathrm{o}} \qquad\qquad (19)$$

or, more explicitely:

$$\Delta \psi + 4\pi^2 k_{\mathrm{o}}^2 \psi = -4\pi^2 \sum_{\mathbf{g}} U_{\mathbf{g}} \exp i2\pi (\mathbf{k}_{\mathrm{o}} + \mathbf{g}) \cdot \mathbf{r} . \qquad\qquad (20)$$

From the theory of linear, inhomogeneous differential equations it follows that the integral of (20) is given by

$$\psi = \psi_{\mathrm{o}} + \sum_{\mathbf{g}} \psi_{\mathbf{g}}$$

where ψ_g must satisfy the equation

$$\Delta\psi_g + 4\pi^2 k_o^2 \psi_g = -4\pi^2 U_g \exp i2\pi(\mathbf{k_o}+\mathbf{g})\cdot\mathbf{r} \tag{21}$$

with the boundary condition that ψ_g must vanish at the entrance surface.

Each ψ_g represents one of the diffracted beams, the beam **g**, *inside* the crystal. The linear structure of (19) results in the independence of the different beams, as should be in a kinematical treatment.

One can always substitute:

$$\psi_g(\mathbf{r}) = \phi_g(\mathbf{r}) \exp i2\pi(\mathbf{k_o}+\mathbf{g})\cdot\mathbf{r} . \tag{22}$$

Before proceeding to further calculations, we first stress the meaning of (22). One can always write for $\phi_g(\mathbf{r})$.

$$\phi_g(\mathbf{r}) = \int A(\boldsymbol{\sigma}) (\exp i2\pi\boldsymbol{\sigma}\cdot\mathbf{r}) d^3\sigma \tag{23}$$

where $A(\boldsymbol{\sigma})$ in the Fourier transform of $\phi_g(\mathbf{r})$. Introducing (23) into (22) gives

$$\psi_g = \int A(\boldsymbol{\sigma}) [\exp i2\pi(\mathbf{k_o}+\mathbf{g}+\boldsymbol{\sigma})\cdot\mathbf{r}] d^3\sigma . \tag{24}$$

The physical meaning of (24) is straight-forward: the total diffracted beam **g** is obtained by the superposition of different plane waves, with wave vectors $(\mathbf{k_o}+\mathbf{g}+\boldsymbol{\sigma})$ and amplitudes $A(\boldsymbol{\sigma})$. One expects of course that the σ-values for which $|A(\boldsymbol{\sigma})|$ is non zero or non negligible will be small as compared to the dimensions of the reciprocal lattice.

One can now calculate either $A(\boldsymbol{\sigma})$ or $\phi_g(\mathbf{r})$. It will turn out that the calculation of ϕ_g is more easy. Once ψ_g known, $A(\boldsymbol{\sigma})$ can be obtained by Fourier transformation. Since

$$\Delta[\phi_g \exp i2\pi(\mathbf{k_o}+\mathbf{g})\cdot\mathbf{r}] = [\Delta\phi_g] \exp i2\pi(\mathbf{k_o}+\mathbf{g})\cdot\mathbf{r} + 2 \operatorname{grad} \phi_g$$

$$\times \operatorname{grad} [\exp i2\pi(\mathbf{k_o}+\mathbf{g})\cdot\mathbf{r}] + \phi_g[\Delta \exp i2\pi(\mathbf{k_o}+\mathbf{g})\cdot\mathbf{r}]$$

and

$$\operatorname{grad} [\exp i2\pi(\mathbf{k_o}+\mathbf{g})\cdot\mathbf{r}] = i2\pi(\mathbf{k_o}+\mathbf{g}) [\exp i2\pi(\mathbf{k_o}+\mathbf{g})\cdot\mathbf{r}]$$

$$\Delta \exp i2\pi(\mathbf{k_o}+\mathbf{g})\cdot\mathbf{r} = -4\pi^2(\mathbf{k_o}+\mathbf{g})^2 \exp i2\pi(\mathbf{k_o}+\mathbf{g})\cdot\mathbf{r}$$

one has

$$\Delta\phi_{\mathbf{g}} \left[\exp i2\pi(\mathbf{k}_o+\mathbf{g})\cdot\mathbf{r}\right] = \left[\Delta\phi_{\mathbf{g}} + i4\pi(\mathbf{k}_o+\mathbf{g})\right.$$

$$\cdot \text{ grad } \phi_{\mathbf{g}} - 4\pi^2(\mathbf{k}_o+\mathbf{g})^2\phi_{\mathbf{g}}\left.\right] \left[\exp i2\pi(\mathbf{k}_o+\mathbf{g})\cdot\mathbf{r}\right] . \tag{25}$$

Introducing (25) into (21), one obtains, after dividing the two members of the equation by $\exp i2\pi(\mathbf{k}_o + \mathbf{g})\cdot\mathbf{r}$

$$\Delta\phi_{\mathbf{g}} + i4\pi(\mathbf{k}_o+\mathbf{g})\cdot \text{ grad } \phi_{\mathbf{g}} + 4\pi^2[k_o^2 - (\mathbf{k}_o+\mathbf{g})^2]\,\phi_{\mathbf{g}} = -4\pi^2 U_{\mathbf{g}} \tag{26}$$

Let us choose the z-axis along the normal of the entrance surface, in the sense of propagation of the electrons, and the x- and y-axis in the entrance surface. Moreover, we choose the x-axis along the projection of $(\mathbf{k}_o+\mathbf{g})$ on the entrance surface. One has then

$$(\mathbf{k}_o+\mathbf{g}) \cdot \text{ grad } \phi_{\mathbf{g}} = [(\mathbf{k}_o+\mathbf{g}) \cdot \mathbf{e}_z] \frac{\partial\phi_{\mathbf{g}}}{\partial z} + [(\mathbf{k}_o+\mathbf{g})\cdot\mathbf{e}_x] \frac{\partial\phi_{\mathbf{g}}}{\partial x}$$

or if α is the angle between $(\mathbf{k}_o + \mathbf{g})$ and $\mathbf{e}_z$

$$(\mathbf{k}_o+\mathbf{g}) \cdot \text{ grad } \phi_{\mathbf{g}} = |\mathbf{k}_o+\mathbf{g}|\left(\cos\alpha \frac{\partial\phi_{\mathbf{g}}}{\partial z} + \sin\alpha \frac{\partial\phi_{\mathbf{g}}}{\partial x}\right) . \tag{27}$$

Next, one introduces a further, but very good, approximation into (26). Since $|\mathbf{k}_o+\mathbf{g}|$ is very large, it will be very good to neglect the first term with respect to the second one. This approximation will be further discussed in other contributions. If one introduces this approximation into (26), and substitutes then (27) into (26) and divides the two members by $i4\pi|\mathbf{k}_o + \mathbf{g}|\cos\alpha$, one finds

$$\frac{\partial\phi_{\mathbf{g}}}{\partial z} + \tan\alpha \frac{\partial\phi_{\mathbf{g}}}{\partial x} - i2\pi \frac{k_o^2-(\mathbf{k}_o+\mathbf{g})^2}{2|\mathbf{k}_o+\mathbf{g}|\cos\alpha}\phi_{\mathbf{g}} = i\pi \frac{U_{\mathbf{g}}}{|\mathbf{k}_o+\mathbf{g}|\cos\alpha} . \tag{28}$$

2.3. Discussion of the parameters appearing in the equation

Let us now consider the two parameters showing up in (28). From the reflection sphere construction of fig. 4, it follows that

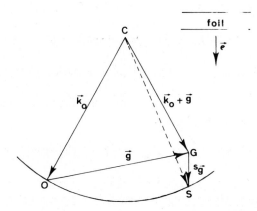

Fig. 4. Construction used for calculating s_g and showing that $|k_o+g+s_g e_z| = k_o$.

$$(k_o+g+s_g e_z)^2 = k_o^2 \, ,$$

or

$$(k_o+g)^2 + 2s_g|k_o+g| \cos\alpha + s_g^2 = k_o^2 \, .$$

The deviation parameter s_g is smaller than the dimension of the reciprocal lattice, and, a fortiori, very much smaller than $|k_o + g| \cong k_o$. Therefore the third term can be neglected with respect to the second one. One finds then

$$s_g = \frac{k_o^2 - (k_o+g)^2}{2|k_o+g| \cos\alpha} \, . \tag{29}$$

The second parameter has the dimension of a reciprocal length, and one can define

$$\frac{1}{\xi_g} = \frac{|U_g|}{|k_o+g| \cos\alpha} \, . \tag{30}$$

Taking (16) into account one finds explicitely for ξ_g

$$\xi_g = \frac{h^2|k_o+g| \cos\alpha}{2me} \frac{1}{|V_g|} \, . \tag{31}$$

Since $k_o \gg g$, it is a good approximation to put now

$$|\mathbf{k_o + g}| \simeq k_o .$$

Then

$$\xi_{\mathbf{g}} = \frac{h^2 k_o \cos\alpha}{2me \ |V_{\mathbf{g}}|} . \tag{32}$$

Taking (10),(11) into account, one can also write for ξ_g

$$\xi_{\mathbf{g}} = \frac{1}{k_o} \frac{E' \cos\alpha}{|V_{\mathbf{g}}|} \sim \frac{\lambda E \cos\alpha}{|V_{\mathbf{g}}|} . \tag{33}$$

The parameters $\xi_{\mathbf{g}}$ (for $\cos\alpha \simeq 1$) are called the *extinction distances*.

Whereas the s_g-values describe the illumination conditions, i.e. the orientation of the crystal with respect to the incident beam, the extinction distances depend on the strength of the different reflections

A strong interaction, i.e. $|V_{\mathbf{g}}|$ is large, corresponds to a small extinction distance, whereas a weak interaction gives rise to a large extinction distance.

The parameters $\xi_{\mathbf{g}}$ depend also on the accelerating potential, they increase with E (like $E^{\frac{1}{2}}$ if relativistic corrections are left out). This corresponds to the classical fact that more accelerated particles are less deflected by the same potential. Bringing into (33) estimated values for $|V_{\mathbf{g}}|$, leads to $\xi_{\mathbf{g}}$ values for low order reflections and for 100 keV-electrons, ranging from about hundred Å to about thousand Å. The extinction distances will be further discussed in other contributions.

2.4. *Integration of the equation*

Noting further

$$V_{\mathbf{g}} = |V_{\mathbf{g}}| \exp i\theta_{\mathbf{g}} \tag{34}$$

one can rewrite (28) as, if one introduces (29) and (30)

$$\frac{\partial \phi_{\mathbf{g}}}{\partial z} + \tan\alpha \frac{\partial \phi_{\mathbf{g}}}{\partial x} - i2\pi s_g \phi_{\mathbf{g}} = \frac{i\pi}{\xi_{\mathbf{g}}} \exp i\theta_{\mathbf{g}} . \tag{35}$$

If one considers a plate-shaped foil, there is no reason why $\phi_{\mathbf{g}}$ should depend on x, i.e.

$$\frac{\partial \phi_g}{\partial x} = 0 \quad \text{and} \quad \frac{\partial \phi_g}{\partial z} = \frac{d\phi_g}{dz} .$$

The eq. (35) becomes then

$$\frac{d\phi_g}{dz} - i2\pi \, s_g \phi_g = \frac{i\pi}{\xi_g} \exp i\theta_g . \tag{36}$$

If one substitutes

$$\phi_g = S_g \, (\exp i2\pi \, s_g z) \tag{37}$$

one has finally

$$\frac{dS_g}{dz} = \frac{i\pi}{\xi_g} (\exp i\theta_g)(\exp -i2\pi \, s_g z) . \tag{38}$$

After integration, taking the boundary condition $S_g(0) = 0$ into account, one finds (the entrance surface is at $z=0$)

$$S_g = \frac{i\pi}{\xi_g} (\exp i\theta_g) \int_0^z (\exp -i2\pi \, s_g z) dz .$$

Finally

$$S_g = (\exp i\theta_g)(\exp -i\pi \, s_g z) \frac{i \sin \pi \, s_g z}{s_g \xi_g} \tag{39}$$

or

$$\phi_g = (\exp i\theta_g)(\exp i\pi \, s_g z) \frac{i \sin \pi \, s_g z}{s_g \xi_g} . \tag{40}$$

3. Discussion of the kinematical results

3.1. *Variation of the intensity with crystal thickness*
The intensity

$$I_g = |\phi_g|^2 = \frac{\sin^2 \pi \, s_g z_0}{(s_g \xi_g)^2} \tag{41}$$

(z_0 is crystal thickness), gives the number of electrons leaving the back surface per unit surface and per unit time for unit incident beam (for simplicity we have assumed that $\cos\alpha \simeq 1$). This result can however, only be trusted if $I_g \ll 1$, since one has assumed the depletion of the transmitted beam to be not important.

Let us first suppose that s_g is fixed but that z_0 increases. The diffracted intensity varies then in a periodical way, the depth-period Δz_0 being given by

$$\Delta z_0 = 1/s_g . \tag{42}$$

For $z_0 = n/s_g$ (n : integer), I_g vanishes, whilst I_g becomes maximal for thicknesses $z_0 = (n+\frac{1}{2})/s_g$ (fig. 5). Furthermore

$$I_g (z_0)_{max} = \frac{1}{(s_g \xi_g)^2} . \tag{43}$$

The fluctuating behaviour of the intensity with crystal thickness is a consequence of the interference of the two plane waves which form inside the crystal the total diffracted beam. From (40) follows that

$$\psi_g = \phi_g \exp i2\pi(k_0+g)\cdot r = \frac{\exp i\theta_g}{2s_g\xi_g} (\exp i2\pi(k_0+g+se_z)\cdot r$$

$$- \exp i2\pi(k_0+g)\cdot r] . \tag{44}$$

The two plane waves have wave vectors (k_0+g+se_z) and $k_0 + g$, and opposite amplitudes. The $A(\sigma)$-function from formulae (23) is thus

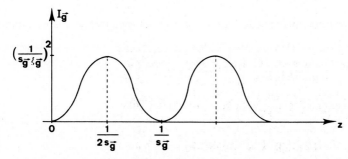

Fig. 5. Periodical variation of the intensity of the diffracted beam I_g as a function of crystal thickness z.

$$A(\sigma) = A\delta(\sigma - se_z) - A\delta(\sigma) \, ,$$

$$A = \frac{\exp i\theta_g}{2s_g\xi_g} \, . \tag{45}$$

For a plate-shaped parallel foil these two plane waves combine again into a single plane wave at the back surface, the diffracted beam outside the foil, with wave vector $k_o + g + se_z$ and amplitude S_g as a consequence of the continuity of the wave function at that surface.

3.2. Variation of the intensity with crystal orientation

Next we keep the crystal thickness constant, but increase the deviation from the exact Bragg orientation. Since $I_g(s_g)$ is an even function of s_g we can restrict ourselves to $s_g > 0$, i.e. the scattering angle is larger than $2\theta_B$.

The intensity I_g has its maximum value for $s_g = 0$, i.e. at the exact Bragg orientation and is then given by

$$I_g(s_g=0) = (\pi z_0/\xi_g)^2 \, . \tag{46}$$

If one leaves the exact orientation, I_g will decrease rapidly and will obtain its absolute minimum value zero for

$$s_g = 1/z_0 \, . \tag{47}$$

If s_g increases further, I_g fluctuates, becoming zero for

$$s_g = n/z_0 \qquad (n, \text{ integer}) \tag{48}$$

and having maxima approximately halfway between two successive minima, i.e. for

$$s_g = (n+\tfrac{3}{2})/z_0 \qquad (n=0,1,2,...) \, . \tag{49}$$

These maxima decrease with k, approximately like

$$I_g(s_g)\big|_{\max} \simeq \frac{1}{(s_g\xi_g)^2} = \left(\frac{z_0}{\xi_g}\frac{1}{n+\frac{3}{2}}\right)^2 \, . \tag{50}$$

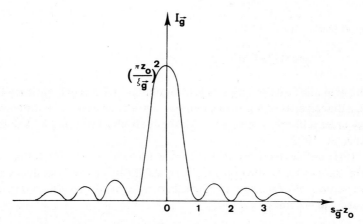

Fig. 6. Schematic graph of the variation of the intensity of the diffracted beam I_g as a function of crystal orientation.

These subsidiary maxima are much smaller than the main maximum at $s_g = 0$, e.g.

$$\frac{I_g(n=0)}{I_g(s_g=0)} = \left(\frac{\frac{2}{3}z_0/\xi_g}{\pi z_0/\xi_g}\right)^2 = \frac{4}{9\pi^2} \simeq 0.04 \; .$$

See also fig. 6.

3.3. Validity of the kinematical theory

For the discussion of this section it is better to express the crystal thickness in extinction distances. Let

$$z_0 = y\xi_g \; . \tag{51}$$

The condition for the validity of the kinematical approach is

$$I_g \ll 1 \tag{52}$$

since one must respect the assumption that the depletion of the transmitted beam is not very important. Is it possible that the approximation remains good up to $s_g = 0$? If yes, one must satisfy the condition, following (52), (46), (51)

$$\pi^2 y^2 \ll 1, \quad \text{or} \quad y \ll 1/\pi$$

say at least

$$y < 1/3\pi \simeq 0.1 \ .$$

This is in most cases a very stringent condition, and it is only satisfied for very thin crystals of less than about one tenth of an extinction distance. For low order reflections this means thicknesses from a few times 10Å to something like 100Å.

It is possible that a crystal has to be considered as very thin for one reflection, but not for another one. If the crystal is tilted away from the exact Bragg orientation into a position of a subsidiary maxima, the condition is much released and becomes

$$y^2 \ll (n+\tfrac{3}{2})^2 \ .$$

For a thin crystal, say $y = \tfrac{1}{2}$, this condition is fairly well satisfied for the first subsidiary maximum ($n=0$). However, for a thick crystal, say $y = 4$, one can only satisfy the condition for very large n-values; the kinematical theory breaks down completely. The kinematical theory can only be accepted as a first approximation

(1) if the crystal is very thin: there are then not enough scattering centres to build up an important diffracted beam.

(2) if the crystal is far from the exact Bragg orientation.

The scattering events with the different scattering centres are so strongly out of phase that the mutual partial annihilation of the scattered wavelets prevents the construction of a strong diffracted beam.

In all other cases an important diffracted beam will already be built up at a depth under the entrance surface still far from the back surface. From (46) it follows that one can expect ξ_g to be a measure for this depth.

Electrons which have been scattered from the transmitted beam $\mathbf{k}_0$-direction into the scattered beam $(\mathbf{k}_0+\mathbf{g})$-direction, can later equally be scattered back into the former direction. One can ignore this only if there are only few electrons in the scattered beam. Our discussion learns that this will mostly not be the case. The kinematical theory must be replaced by the more refined dynamical one, taking into account that electrons can be scattered many times between transmitted and scattered beam, and possibly between different scattered beams, before leaving the crystal at the back side. This will be discussed in detail in the lectures by Whelan and by Howie in this volume.

3.4. *Relevant features of the kinematical theory*
3.4.1. Introduction

As will be pointed out in the lectures of Professor Whelan, it is possible to realize a so-called "two beam" situation. By this is meant that there is, apart from the transmitted beam, only one strongly diffracted beam **g**. It becomes then a good approximation to neglect the weaker beams.

The results of this dynamical "two-beam" theory must tend asymptotically to those of the kinematical theory if $|s_g|$ becomes large. The qualitative properties predicted by the latter theory, must remain true for small $|s_g|$-values, although important quantitative corrections will become necessary.

3.4.2. Variation with crystal thickness

The kinematical treatment predicted a periodic variation of the intensity of the scattered beam, and thus also of the transmitted beam, with crystal thickness, the depth-period being $|1/s_g|$. The more refined dynamical theory must lead to the same qualitative conclusion: a periodic variation of intensity with thickness. The period will be a function of s_g tending asymptotically to $|1/s_g|$ for large $|s_g|$. For small $|s_g|$ it must deviate strongly from the kinematical result since the latter diverges if s tends to zero. Moreover, one suspects that the period for $s_g = 0$ will be a simple function of ξ_g.

The maxima of I_g, as given by (43) diverge for $s_g \rightarrow 0$. One expects drastic dynamical corrections for small $|s_g|$. It is even plausible that the diffracted beam can become very important at certain thicknesses, resulting in a completely or nearly completely exhausted transmitted beam.

3.4.3. Variation with crystal orientation

The subsidiary maxima of the kinematical expression for the intensity lie approximately on the curve

$$I(s) = 1/(s\xi)^2 . \tag{53}$$

which diverges for $s = 0$. For $s = 0$ itself I equals $(\pi z_0/\xi)^2$. In general this curve will rise very much above one, and $I(s=0) \gg 1$. This can not be, and, consequently, the dynamical treatment must lower this curve very strongly, in order to bring it completely under the value one. However, for large $|s|$ the correct curve must tend to the kinematical one, given by (53). This enables us to estimate roughly the width of this curve, i.e. the interval for the deviation from the exact Bragg position for which the scattered intensity at the positions for maximal scattering is not yet negligible with respect to one. Somewhat arbitrarily we choose $I = 0.1$ as a limit. From (53) follows that $I(s)$ will become smaller than about one tenth of the incident intensity for orientations

$$|s| > \sim 3/\xi .$$ (54)

Following (8) this corresponds to a deviation from the exact Bragg angle given by

$$|\Delta\theta| > \sim 3/g\xi = \Delta\theta_o .$$ (55)

On the other hand the Bragg angle is given by, following (4)

$$\sin \theta_B = \theta_B = g/2k_o .$$ (56)

From (56) and (55) one calculates:

$$\Delta\theta_o/\theta_B \cong \sim 6k_o/g\xi .$$ (57)

If one introduces in (57) realistic values for low order reflections, say $k_o = 25 \text{Å}^{-1}, g^2 = 3 \times 10^{-1} \text{Å}^{-2}, \xi = 3 \times 10^2 \text{Å}$, one finds that $\Delta\theta_o/\theta_\Delta$ is of the order of magnitude of one. One concludes thus that the scattered intensity can remain important even for deviations from the Bragg angle comparable with this angle itself. For accelerated electrons one must not strictly satisfy the Bragg-condition (1), in order to obtain important scattered beams. Stated otherwise: the reciprocal lattices nodes must not lie strictly on the reflection sphere. This, together with the fact that the radius of this sphere is large as compared to the dimensions of the reciprocal lattice, leads to the appearance of many scattered beams of a same zone obtained from the transmitted beam. Moreover, the scattered beams for which $|s_g|$ is small can become very important inside the crystal. Electrons can then be scattered out of these beams into other and weaker beams. The discussion of this multiple beam effect falls beyond the scope of this lecture and will be treated elsewhere.

The kinematical treatment led to the prediction that the subsidiary maxima were much lower than the main maximum at $s = 0$. This can no longer be expected from a dynamical treatment, since the unreasonable kinematical value of $I(0)$ will be suppressed to a value below one. If $|s|$ increases one expects still that $I(s)$ will fluctuate. However, for thick crystals the values of the maxima will vary rather slowly. Many fluctuations can be expected before the scattered intensity becomes very small. The dynamical treatment will introduce important corrections for the positions of maxima and minima, and for the values of the maxima, for small $|s|$.

3.4.4. Conclusion

The foregoing discussion of the kinematical treatment demonstrates that one can not accept its quantitative results, except if the crystal is very thin, or if the crystal orientation is very far from the exact Bragg orientation.

Nevertheless, its qualitative predictions have to remain true in a more realistic two-beam dynamical treatment: the periodic dependence of the intensity with varying crystal orientation.

One is not only warned that dynamical interaction will be important, but also that multiple beam effects can become important.

We propose to call the kinematical theory, as discussed in these first two lectures, the "one-beam" kinematical theory, since it describes scattering of electrons out of a single beam.

In the last of our lectures we will consider a more general kinematical theory, leading to results which can be realistic in good approximation.

Before that, we indicate in the next section how the scattered intensities have to be calculated for a deformed crystal, in particular for crystals containing defects.

4. Deformed crystals

Hirsch, Howie and Whelan [1] have first introduced the following elegant way for treating the diffraction by a deformed crystal.

These authors assumed that the deformation could be described by a displacement function $\mathbf{R}(\mathbf{r})$, the deviation of an elementary volume element from its normal position at $\mathbf{r}$.

For small $\mathbf{R}$ one has then as a good approximation

$$V'(\mathbf{r}+\mathbf{R}) \equiv V(\mathbf{r}), \quad \text{for all } \mathbf{r}$$

where V' is the crystal potential in the deformed crystal, or

$$V'(\mathbf{r}) \equiv V(\mathbf{r}-\mathbf{R}) . \tag{58}$$

If one introduces (6) into (58) one obtains

$$V'(\mathbf{r}) = V_0 + \sum_{\mathbf{g}} V_{\mathbf{g}} \exp i2\pi \mathbf{g} \cdot (\mathbf{r}-\mathbf{R})$$

or

$$V'(\mathbf{r}) = V_0 + \sum_{\mathbf{g}} [V_{\mathbf{g}} \exp -i2\pi\mathbf{g}\cdot\mathbf{R}(\mathbf{r})] \; [\exp i2\pi\mathbf{g}\cdot\mathbf{r}] \; . \qquad (59)$$

Strictly speaking, the series (59) is no longer a Fourier series, since the coefficients have become functions of $\mathbf{r}$. This is due to the disturbance of the perfect translation symmetry of the crystal. For small $\mathbf{R}$, however, one can still justify the reasoning of section 2, and one obtains the same result provided one makes the substitution

$$U_{\mathbf{g}} \rightarrow U_{\mathbf{g}} \exp -i2\pi\mathbf{g}\cdot\mathbf{R}(\mathbf{r}) \; . \qquad (60)$$

The deformation must be sufficiently small in order still to be able to recognize a lattice, although its dimensions and orientation change slightly with the position in the crystal.

This means mathematically the following. The Fourier transform of the unperturbed potential $V(\mathbf{r})$ is a sum of delta-functions situated at the nodes of the reciprocal lattice. The perturbed potential $V'(\mathbf{r})$ must then have a Fourier transform consisting of peak functions centered around the reciprocal lattice nodes and with *negligible* overlap. For a perfect plate-shaped crystal foil the σ-vector occuring in (23) has only two values. For a foil containing a defect this will no longer be true: the $A(\sigma)$ function will become a true function with a width still much smaller than the dimension of the reciprocal lattice.

Introducing (60) into (35) leads then to the equation

$$\frac{\partial\phi_{\mathbf{g}}}{\partial z} + \tan\alpha \; \frac{\partial\phi_{\mathbf{g}}}{\partial x} -i2\pi s_{\mathbf{g}}\phi_{\mathbf{g}} = (\exp i\theta_{\mathbf{g}}) \frac{i\pi}{\xi_{\mathbf{g}}} (\exp -i\alpha_{\mathbf{g}}) \qquad (61a)$$

if one notices

$$\alpha_{\mathbf{g}}(\mathbf{r}) = 2\pi\mathbf{g}\cdot\mathbf{R}(\mathbf{r}) \; . \qquad (61b)$$

For simplicity we consider only the case of an incident beam nearly normal to the foil surface. The angle α is then very small, of the order of magnitude 10^{-2}. As a consequence the second term can be estimated as being very small as compared to the first one, and it becomes a good approximation to neglect this second term. This means that x and y are considered in (61) as parameters and not as integration variables. This is known as the "column approximation". The latter will be discussed in more detail in the other chapters.

The partial differential eq. (61a) simplifies then to the ordinary differential equation

$$\frac{d\phi_g}{dz} - i2\pi s_g \phi_g = (\exp i\theta_g) \frac{i\pi}{\xi_g} (\exp -i\alpha_g) . \tag{62}$$

The physical meaning of (62) becomes clearer if one makes the substitution

$$\phi_g = {}_*\phi_g (\exp -i\alpha_g) . \tag{63}$$

Bringing (63) into (62), and taking (61b) into account, gives

$$\frac{d_*\phi_g}{dz} - i2\pi \left(s_g + g \cdot \frac{dR}{dz} \right) {}_*\phi_g = (\exp i\theta_g) \frac{i\pi}{\xi_g} \tag{64}$$

This equation is the same as the eq. (36) for a perfect crystal provided one substitutes

$$s_g \rightarrow s_g^{(eff.)} = s_g + g \cdot \frac{dR}{dz} . \tag{65}$$

The deviation parameter s_g, constant for a perfect crystal, has to be replaced by a position dependent parameter which describes the local lattice dimension and lattice orientation. More explicitly: at a position r one can still recognize the reflecting (hkl)-planes, however, with a lattice parameter d_{hkl} and an orientation which differ slightly from the parameter and the orientation in the non-deformed crystal. At that position one can calculate the local deviation parameter $s_g^{(eff.)}$ and the result is given by (65). Even for a small deformation, the orientation differences can become comparable with the Bragg angle. Taking this fact into account and also the fact that the scattering interval is large, leads one to expect a strong effect, confirmed by actual calculations. The scattered intensity

$$I_g = |\phi_g|^2 \tag{66}$$

can be observed at the back surface by allowing only this scattered beam to enter the optical system of the electron microscope. This intensity will be a function of x and y, since α_g depends on these parameters,

$$I_g = I_g(x,y) . \tag{67}$$

One observes a (dark field) strain contrast image of the deformation associated with the defect in the crystal. Introducing the substitution (37) into (62) gives

$$\frac{dS_g}{dz} = (\exp i\theta_g)\left(\frac{i\pi}{\xi_g}\right)\exp -i(2\pi s_g z + \alpha_g) \ . \tag{68}$$

After integration

$$I_g = |S_g|^2 \ ,$$

$$S_g = (\exp i\theta_g)\left(\frac{i\pi}{\xi_g}\right)\int_0^z \{\exp -i[2\pi s_g z + \alpha_g(\mathbf{r})]\}dz \ . \tag{69}$$

Most images are made in a dynamical situation, and the result (69) is then of no great use and can even lead to erroneous conclusions.

The result (69) can only have some value if one satisfies the kinematical conditions for the perfect foil. Even then one has to check if I_g remains much smaller than one over the entire image. In actual cases this is mostly not the case, the quantitative result (69) can then not be considered as a good approximation over the entire image. Nevertheless, the same arguments as in 3.4.3 lead one to believe that certain qualitative and semi-quantitative properties of the kinematical images must remain true for the dynamical images.

We illustrate this for the images of dislocations for large s_g-values. Except for very small Burgers vector, the kinematical results give unreasonable high values for the scattered intensity near the maximum of the image profile. However, at distances where the kinematical theory predicts a faint contrast, the kinematical result must be a good approximation for the dynamical one. This means that the kinematical theory leads to a fair estimate for the image width, for large $|s_g|$-values.

The kinematical theory learns also that the image centre does not coincide with the dislocation itself and gives a rule for determining the side of the image. Moreover the image profile is skewed. Here also one may believe that these properties will remain true if dynamical corrections are taken into account.

The detailed discussion of the images of defects is beyond the scope of these introductory lectures and will be discussed in other chapters.

5. Multiple beam kinematical theory

5.1. *Introduction*

The "one-beam" kinematical treatment mostly breaks down, since the assumption that an electron is scattered only once is not satisfied. This does not mean that a kinematical approach is unsuitable to calculate, in good approximation, the amplitudes of the weak beams. However, some refinements must then be introduced into the theory.

Suppose that there are n reciprocal lattice nodes close to the reflection sphere with not very large extinction distances. There exist then, apart from the transmitted beam, n strongly scattered beams in the crystal. As a first approximation, one neglects all other weak beams which are also present. One has then to solve a $(n+1)$-multiple beam dynamical problem. The solution in this problem is assumed to be known, i.e. one knows the wave function of the electrons

$$\psi^{(0)}(\mathbf{r}) = \{\phi_0(\mathbf{r}) + \sum_{i=1}^{n} \phi_i(\mathbf{r}) \exp i2\pi\mathbf{g}_i\cdot\mathbf{r}\}\exp i2\pi\mathbf{k}_0\cdot\mathbf{r} \qquad (70)$$

inside the crystal.

All other reciprocal lattice nodes lie very far from the reflection sphere or (and) have associated extinction distances which are very large.

The electrons which leave the crystal in one of the weak beam directions can be considered as obtained by scattering out of the $(n+1)$ strong beams. Moreover, the kinematical assumption becomes plausible, i.e. it is a good approximation to neglect the possibility that such an electron will be scattered back into one of the strong beam directions, since the coupling between the system of strong beams and the system of weak beams is small.

An electron is scattered many times between the different strong beams on its way through the crystal plate, always remaining in its wave field. There is a small probability that the electron will be scattered at a certain moment into a weak beam direction. There is little chance that this electron will be scattered back later on into one of the strong beam directions. The kinematical approach neglects this possibility. Moreover, it assumes that one can ignore the depletion of the strong beams for calculating the relative numbers of electrons in the weak beams.

5.2. *(n+1) beam kinematical theory*

This kinematical treatment can be developed in the same way as the one-beam kinematical treatment as a Born approximation.

However, instead of replacing ψ in the second member of the Schrödinger eq. (17) by ψ_o given by (18) one introduces now the wave function $\psi^{(o)}$ given by (70).

The second member of (20) has then to be replaced by

$$- 4\pi^2 \, U(\mathbf{r}) \, \psi^{(o)}(\mathbf{r}) = - 4\pi^2 \sum_{\mathbf{g}} \left[\sum_{i=0}^{n} U_{\mathbf{g}-\mathbf{g}_i} \phi_i(\mathbf{r}) \right] \exp i2\pi(\mathbf{k}_o + \mathbf{g}) \cdot \mathbf{r} \tag{71}$$

leading in the same way as in sect. 2 to the differential equation for $\phi_{\mathbf{g}}$

$$\frac{d\phi_{\mathbf{g}}}{dz} - i2\pi s_{\mathbf{g}} \phi_{\mathbf{g}} = i\pi \sum_{i=0}^{n} \frac{U_{\mathbf{g}-\mathbf{g}_i}}{|\mathbf{k}_o + \mathbf{g}|_\perp} \phi_i(\mathbf{r}) ,$$

$$(\mathbf{k}_o + \mathbf{g})_\perp = |\mathbf{k}_o + \mathbf{g}| \cos\alpha , \qquad |\mathbf{k}_o + \mathbf{g}|_\perp \cong (\mathbf{k}_o)_\perp \tag{72}$$

which replaces the eq. (36).

As pointed out in other lectures, each beam $\mathbf{g}_i$ is the superposition of $(n+1)$ plane waves with slightly different wave vectors $\mathbf{k}_o + \mathbf{g}_i + \frac{1}{2}\beta_j \mathbf{e}_z$ $(j=0,1,...,n)$, each plane wave belonging to a Bloch wave numbered by the index j.

Therefore each ϕ_i can be written as

$$\phi_i(z) = \sum_{j=0}^{n} A_{ij} \exp i\pi\beta_j z . \tag{73}$$

Introducing (73) into (72) enables us to rewrite the latter equation as follows

$$\frac{d\phi_{\mathbf{g}}}{dz} - i2\pi s_{\mathbf{g}} \phi_{\mathbf{g}} = \sum_{j=0}^{n} \left(\sum_{i=0}^{n} i\pi A_{ij} \frac{U_{\mathbf{g}-\mathbf{g}_i}}{(\mathbf{k}_o)_\perp} \right) \exp i\pi\beta_j z \tag{74}$$

or, making the substitution (37)

$$\frac{dS_{\mathbf{g}}}{dz} = i\pi \sum_{j=0}^{n} \left(\sum_{i=0}^{n} A_{ij} \frac{U_{\mathbf{g}-\mathbf{g}_i}}{(\mathbf{k}_o)_\perp} \right) \exp -i2\pi(s_{\mathbf{g}} - \frac{1}{2}\beta_j)z . \tag{75}$$

The eq. (75) suggests us to introduce the following notations

$$\frac{1}{\xi'_{g,j}} = \sum_{i=0}^{n} \frac{U_{g-g_i}}{(k_o)_\perp} A_{ij}$$ (76)

and

$$s_g^{(j)} = s_g - \tfrac{1}{2} \beta_j .$$ (77)

Eq. (75) reads then

$$\frac{dS_g}{dz} = \sum_{j=0}^{n} \frac{i\pi}{\xi'_{g,j}} \exp -i2\pi s_g^{(j)} z .$$ (78)

After integration, one obtains finally

$$S_g = \sum_{j=0}^{n} (\exp -i\pi s_g^{(j)} z) \frac{i \sin \pi s_g^{(j)} z}{s_g^{(j)} \xi'_{g,j}} .$$ (79)

5.3. Discussion and remarks

The structure of eq. (78) shows clearly that the most adequate description consists in considering the kinematical scattering of electrons out of each wave field separately. The term number j of (78) and (79) represents the scattering of electrons out of the jth strong wave field, containing electrons moving in all the strong beam directions, into the weak beam. For this type of scattering one is able to define an effective extinction distance, given by (76), and an effective deviation parameter, given by (77).

The wave vector of each wave field has a direction which slightly differs from the direction of the incident beam (corrected for refraction). The deviation from the exact Bragg orientation must thus be defined with respect to the direction of the wave vector of the wave field under consideration, leading to the introduction of the effective deviation parameter, as given by (77). The directions of the wave vectors of the different wave fields are different with respect to each other and depend on the actual crystal orientation. This is included in the formula (77), since the β_j are orientation dependent.

The reciprocal effective extinction distance, given by (76), is a weighed sum of the reciprocal extinction distances (taking also their phase factors into account) corresponding to the different possible scatterings out of one of the strong beam directions, contained in the wave field, into the considered weak beam direction. The weight factors A_{ij} describe how the electrons in a given wave field j are distributed over the different beams $\mathbf{g}_i$ in a semi-infinite crystal.

Since an electron cannot be scattered directly from one strong wave field into another strong wave field, and since the kinematical approach neglects the indirect scatterings, strong field → weak beam → strong field, the scattering events between the different wave fields and the weak beam are independent, resulting in the linear structure of eqs. (78) and (79).

The parameters present in (79) depend critically on the illumination conditions.

The terms of (79) represent the kinematical scatterings from a wave field into a given beam, independent with respect to each other. They have in fact the same structure as the one beam kinematical result, provided one uses the adequate definitions of extinction distance and deviation parameter.

The theory as developed here ignores possible dynamical interactions between the weak beams themselves. By using more sophisticated mathematical methods it is, however, also possible to allow for these interactions. They are mostly not important.

5.4. The "two-beam" kinematical treatment

The most simple illumination condition is the two-beam one.

One can now use the wave function (70) calculated in the lecture of Professor Whelan.

Let $\mathbf{G}$ be the dynamical beam, s and ξ the corresponding deviation parameter and extinction distance.

One has then

$$\beta_0 = s + \frac{1}{\xi}(1+\omega^2)^{\frac{1}{2}}, \quad \beta_1 = s - \frac{1}{\xi}(1+\omega^2)^{\frac{1}{2}}, \quad \omega = s\xi \quad (80\text{a,b,c})$$

and

$$A_{00} = \frac{1}{2}\left(1 - \frac{\omega}{\sqrt{1+\omega^2}}\right), \quad A_{01} = \frac{1}{2}\left(1 + \frac{\omega}{\sqrt{1+\omega^2}}\right) \quad (81\text{a,b})$$

$$A_{10} = \frac{1}{\sqrt{1+\omega^2}}\exp i\theta_{\mathbf{G}}, \quad A_{11} = \frac{-1}{\sqrt{1+\omega^2}}\exp i\theta_{\mathbf{G}}. \quad (81\text{c,d})$$

Introducing (80) and (81) into (76) and (77), gives

$$\frac{1}{\xi'_{g,o}} = \frac{1}{2} \left\{ \left(1 - \frac{\omega}{\sqrt{1+\omega^2}}\right) \frac{U_g}{(k_o)_\perp} + \frac{\exp i\theta_G}{\sqrt{1+\omega^2}} \frac{U_{g-G}}{(k_o)_\perp} \right\} \tag{82a}$$

$$\frac{1}{\xi'_{g,1}} = \frac{1}{2} \left\{ \left(1 + \frac{\omega}{\sqrt{1+\omega^2}}\right) \frac{U_g}{(k_o)_\perp} - \frac{\exp i\theta_G}{\sqrt{1+\omega^2}} \frac{U_{g-G}}{(k_o)_\perp} \right\} \tag{82b}$$

$$s_g^{(o)} = s_g - \frac{1}{2}\left(s + \frac{\sqrt{1+\omega^2}}{\xi}\right), \quad s_g^{(1)} = s_g - \frac{1}{2}\left(s - \frac{\sqrt{1+\omega^2}}{\xi}\right) \tag{83a,b}$$

and for the amplitude of the weak beam, one obtains

$$S_g = (\exp -i\pi s_g^{(o)}z) \frac{i \sin \pi s_g^{(o)}z}{s_g^{(o)}\xi'_{g,o}} + (\exp -i\pi s_g^{(1)}z) \frac{i \sin \pi s_g^{(1)}z}{s_g^{(1)}\xi'_{g,1}}. \tag{84}$$

5.5. Discussion and observation
One can rewrite (84) as follows

$$S_g = A^{(o)} + A^{(1)} - A^{(o)} (\exp -i2\pi s_g^{(o)}z) - A^{(1)}$$

$$\times (\exp -i2\pi s_g^{(1)}z) \tag{85}$$

where

$$A^{(o)} = \frac{1}{2} \frac{1}{s_g^{(o)}\xi'_{g,o}}, \quad A^{(1)} = \frac{1}{2} \frac{1}{s_g^{(1)}\xi'_{g,1}} \tag{86}$$

and one is particularly interested in

$$I_g = |S_g|^2. \tag{87}$$

Let us discuss the variation of I_g with crystal thickness, i.e. the extinction thickness contours to be expected in the weak beam dark-field for a wedge-shaped crystal.

If (85) is brought into (87), one obtains a superposition of terms with different depth-periods, namely (1) the period $1/s_g^{(o)}$, (2) the period $1/s_g^{(1)}$, (3) the period $1/(s_g^{(o)} - s_g^{(1)}) = \xi/\sqrt{1+\omega^2}$.

Since one assumed that

$$|s_g| \gg |s| , \ 1/\xi \tag{88}$$

the first and second period differ only slightly. The superposition of the terms with these two periods will still be nearly periodic with a period not deviating very much from $1/s_g$, the usual kinematical period.

The fringe system with depth-period $\approx 1/s_g$ will, however, be modulated by the term with period $\xi/\sqrt{1+\omega^2}$, the latter period being mostly several times the first one. The result is a modulated fringe pattern, the fringe spacing being approximately the kinematical one, whereas the contrast modulation period corresponds to the depth period of the bright and the strong dark field images.

In fig. 7 the dark field image is shown of a wedge-shaped MgO-crystal in the weak kinematical spot $(00\bar{2})$, the dynamical spot being (002), for $s \cong 0$. One observes the expected characteristics of the fringe pattern. Comparison with the bright field image confirms that the modulation period and the bright field fringe spacing are in fact equal. The ratio of the modulation period and the fine spacing is also, in very good approximation, equal to s_g/ξ.

We discuss now a very special prediction of the theory and which can be checked by observation.

For crystals with a centre of symmetry, the Fourier coefficients are all real, if one takes the origin of reciprocal space in such a centre. Moreover for crystals like fcc, bcc metals and NaCl-structures, these coefficients are positive.

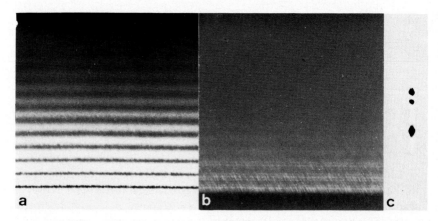

a   b   c

Fig. 7. Extinction contours at a wedge shaped MgO-crystal. a. Bright field image. b. Dark field image in a weak spot. Notice the modulated fringe pattern. c. Enlargement of the spot used for the dark field in b. (Courtesy R.De Ridder.)

In that case, one has

$$\theta_G = 0, \quad \frac{U_g}{(k_o)_\perp} = \frac{1}{\xi_g}, \quad \frac{U_{g-G}}{(k_o)_\perp} = \frac{1}{\xi_{g-G}}. \tag{89}$$

From (82) follows then

$$\frac{1}{\xi'_{g,o}} = \frac{1}{2}\left[\left(1 - \frac{\omega}{\sqrt{1+\omega^2}}\right)\frac{1}{\xi_g} + \frac{1}{\sqrt{1+\omega^2}}\frac{1}{\xi_{g-G}}\right] \tag{90}$$

$$\frac{1}{\xi'_{g,1}} = \frac{1}{2}\left[\left(1 + \frac{\omega}{\sqrt{1+\omega^2}}\right)\frac{1}{\xi_g} - \frac{1}{\sqrt{1+\omega^2}}\frac{1}{\xi_{g-G}}\right]. \tag{91}$$

If one changes the crystal orientation continuously, i.e. if ω varies, the first extinction distance $\xi'_{g,o}$ will always remain finite. On the other hand the second one, $\xi'_{g,1}$ becomes infinite for the orientation

$$\omega = s\xi = \frac{1}{2}\left(\frac{\xi_{g-G}}{\xi_g} - \frac{\xi_g}{\xi_{g-G}}\right). \tag{92}$$

Since it follows from (82) that

$$\frac{1}{\xi'_{g,o}} + \frac{1}{\xi'_{g,1}} = \frac{1}{\xi_g} \tag{93}$$

one has for this particular crystal orientation

$$\xi'_{g,o} = \xi_g, \qquad \xi'_{g,1} = \infty. \tag{94}$$

Bringing (94) into (84) gives then, for this particular orientation

$$S_g = (\exp -i2\pi s_g^{(o)}z)\,\frac{i\sin \pi s_g^{(o)}z}{s_g^{(o)}\xi_g}. \tag{95}$$

The physical meaning is as follows.

The scattering amplitudes for the scattering of electrons out of the transmitted and strongly diffracted beam into the weak beam, are in phase for the first wave field, but in anti-phase for the second wave field. For the first wave field extinction can never occur. For the second wave field, however, there is partial destructive interference. By adjusting the amplitudes of the transmitted and diffracted wave in the second wave field by tilting the crystal plate, one can achieve complete annihilation, i.e. if one satisfies (92). For this situation no electrons in the weak beam come from the second wave.

The intensity for this particular orientation is, from (95)

$$I_g = \frac{\sin^2 \pi s_g^{(o)} z}{(s_g^{(o)} \xi_g)^2} \tag{96}$$

i.e. the same expression as in the one-beam kinematical theory, provided one replaces the deviation parameter by a corrected one.

The formula (96) describes a non-modulated, strictly periodical variation of the intensity with crystal thickness, with depth-period $1/s_g^{(o)}$. The weak dark field image is like the one predicted by the dynamical two-beam theory, indicating that it is a consequence of the scattering of electrons between two entities. However, these are no longer two beams, but a wave field and a beam.

Fig. 8 shows again the weak dark field of a wedge-shaped MgO crystal in the $(00\bar{2})$-spot, the dynamical spot being (002). However, the crystal is now tilted into the orientation (92). One observes now in fact a perfectly non-modulated fringe pattern. The fringe spacing corresponds very well to the value obtained from theory.

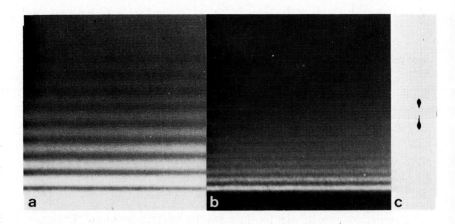

Fig. 8. The same wedge shaped MgO crystal as in fig. 7 slightly changed in orientation.
a. Bright field image. b. Dark field image in a weak spot. Notice the different aspect of the fringe pattern and the complete absence of modulation. c. Enlargement of the same weak spot as in 7c used for the dark field in b. (Courtesy R.De Ridder.)

For a very thick crystal, for which absorption becomes very important, the second term of (85) will be exponentially damped, whereas the third term will be exponentially enhanced. This expresses that the electrons are scattered out of a strongly absorbed and a easily transmitted wave field.

For a very thick crystal the third term of (85) becomes much more important than the other two terms. As an approximation one has then

$$I_g \cong \tfrac{1}{4} \left(\exp - 2\pi\mu^{(1)}z \right) \frac{1}{\left| s_g^{(1)} \xi'_{g,1} \right|^2} \tag{97}$$

where $\mu^{(1)}$ is the (amplitude) absorption coefficient of the easily transmitted wave field.

The expression (97) for I_g becomes a good approximation if the following assumptions are valid: (i) the electrons moving in the strongly absorbed wave field have already all disappeared long before the back surface, (ii) the electrons which are scattered into the weak beam directions at positions still far from the exit surface, do not reach this surface in that direction, due to the uniform absorption.

The expression (97) counts then the number of electrons which have survived first in the easily transmitted wave field up to close to the exit surface, and which are next scattered into the weak beam direction.

Formula (97) describes an exponential decrease of the intensity with respect to the crystal thickness. The approximation leading to (97) is, however, very drastic. Even for a rather thick crystal, the other terms of (95) will contribute somewhat to the intensity, giving rise to small fluctuations of the intensity with respect to the crystal thickness.

Reference

[1] P.B.Hirsch, A.Howie and M.J.Whelan, Phil. Trans. Roy. Soc. A252 (1960) 499.

Diffraction and Imaging Techniques in Material Science,
eds. S. Amelinckx, R. Gevers and J. van Landuyt
© *North-Holland Publishing Company, 1978*

DYNAMICAL THEORY OF ELECTRON DIFFRACTION

M.J.WHELAN

Department of Metallurgy, University of Oxford, England

1. The dynamical theory of diffraction of fast electrons

By fast electrons we mean electrons in the energy range from a few keV up to several hundred keV, the energy range useful in transmission electron microscopy. The formulation of the theory we are going to present here is similar to the method originally employed by Darwin [1] for the case of X-ray diffraction, and our approach will be to some extent complementary to that which will be given for X-ray diffraction by Authier in this volume. In this chapter we will be concerned with the two-beam theory (fig. 1), where besides the transmitted beam of amplitude ϕ_0, only one strong diffracted beam of amplitude ϕ_g is imagined to be excited in a slab crystal of thickness t. The incident beam amplitude is taken as unity at the top surface of the crystal. This situation is relevant to the calculation of bright-field and dark-field image intensities in electron microscopy, where the corresponding experimental situation is determined by the position of the objective aperture as shown in fig. 1. Generalisation of the theory to cover more than one strong diffracted beam will be given in this volume by Howie.

1.1. *Limitations of the kinematical theory*

Before embarking on the dynamical theory it is useful to consider the range of applicability of the kinematical theory, which has been outlined by Gevers and which gives much qualitative insight into the mechanism of diffraction contrast from defects in transmission electron microscopy. The geometrical conditions are defined in fig. 2. $\mathbf{K}$ and λ are the wave vector and wave length ($K=\lambda^{-1}$); $\mathbf{g}$ is the reciprocal lattice vector of the operating Bragg reflection; s is the deviation parameter denoting the distance by which the reciprocal lattice point $\mathbf{g}$ lies off the Ewald sphere in a direction normal to the

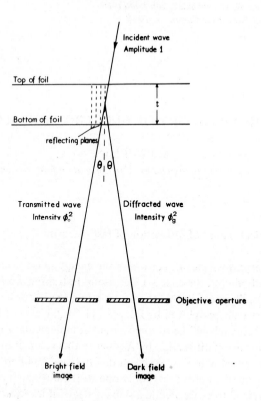

Fig. 1. Illustrating the symmetrical Laue case of transmission electron diffraction through a plate crystal of thickness t. The reflecting planes are perpendicular to the surface. The Bragg angle θ is very small ($\approx 10^{-2}$ rad), so that in practice the symmetrical Laue case is useful for discussing normal incidence.

crystal surface. The kinematical theory leads to the following result for the absolute intensity of the diffracted beam.

$$|\phi_g|^2 = \frac{\pi^2}{\xi_g^2} \frac{\sin^2 \pi t s}{(\pi s)^2} \,. \tag{1}$$

ξ_g is the extinction distance given by

$$\xi_g = \frac{\pi K \Omega \cos\theta}{f(\theta)} = \frac{K \cos\theta}{U_g} \,, \tag{2}$$

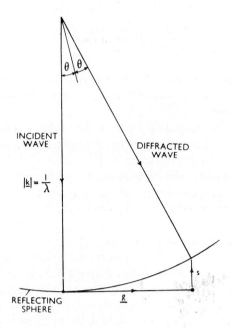

INCIDENT
WAVE

DIFFRACTED
WAVE

$|\underline{k}| = \dfrac{1}{\lambda}$

s

REFLECTING
SPHERE

$\underline{g}$

Fig. 2. Ewald sphere construction for determining the direction of the diffracted waves.

Ω is the volume of the unit cell; $f(\theta)$ is the atomic scattering amplitude for electrons; U_g is the Fourier coefficient of a suitably scaled crystal lattice potential experienced by the fast electron. We have assumed that there is only one atom per unit cell. If this is not the case f must be replaced by a structure amplitude of the form $\Sigma_i f_i(\theta) \exp(-2\pi i \mathbf{g} \cdot \mathbf{r}_i)$, where f_i is the atomic scattering amplitude of atom i at position $\mathbf{r}_i$ in the unit cell.

Eq. (1) shows that when $s = 0$

$$|\phi_g|^2 = \pi^2 t^2 / \xi_g^2 . \tag{3}$$

Thus the intensity of the diffracted beam increases quadratically with t, but evidently eq. (3) cannot hold if $\pi^2 t^2 / \xi_g^2 > 1$ (incident intensity), i.e. if $t >$ about $\xi_g/3$. For typical materials with 100 kV electrons ξ_g is in the range 150 to 500 Å for low order reflections. Thus the crystal has to be very thin ($\ll 100$ Å) for kinematical theory to be valid at $s = 0$. We may note here that for X-rays the condition is less stringent since

$$\frac{\xi_g, \text{X-rays}}{\xi_g, \text{electrons}} \simeq \frac{\lambda_e \, f_e}{\lambda_x \, f_x} \simeq 400 \ast \text{ or more .} \tag{4}$$

Thus extinction distances for X-rays are typically in the range 10 to 100 μm, and crystals in the micron range of thickness generally behave kinematically for X-ray diffraction.

Breakdown of the kinematical theory is also evident in other aspects, for example the widths of dislocation images derived from this theory and the spacing of thickness fringes (Hirsch et al. [2]) varies as s^{-1}. For $s \to 0$ fringe spacings become infinite, whereas in practice it is known they tend to a finite limit. It is worth noting, however, that for $s \neq 0$, the kinematical theory is a good approximation provided $\xi_g s \gg 1$, even for thick crystals.

1.2. Dynamical equations in the Laue case

By the Laue case is meant the case where the incident beam and diffracted beam enter and leave the crystal slab at opposite surfaces. This is distinguished from the so-called Bragg case, studied by Darwin [1] , where incident and diffracted beams enter and leave by the same surface. The solution of the dynamical equations for these two cases are quite different. In particular we shall study the symmetrical Laue case, shown in fig. 1, where the reflecting planes are perpendicular to the surface.

Consider an electron with free-space wave vector χ incident on a slab crystal so that a Bragg reflection g is excited. Let the amplitude of the transmitted wave as a function of depth z be $\phi_0(z)$ and that of the diffracted wave $\phi_g(z)$. As the wave ϕ_0 propagates into the crystal, its amplitude will be depleted by diffraction and the amplitude ϕ_g will increase, i.e. there is coupling between ϕ_0 and ϕ_g. We can describe the coupling by the following differential equations.

---

* This magnitude can be established by writing

$$f_e(\theta) = \frac{me^2\lambda^2}{2h^2} \frac{(Z-F(\theta))}{\sin^2 \theta} \text{ (Born approximation) ,}$$

$$f_x(\theta) = \frac{-e^2}{mc^2} F(\theta)$$

where $F(\theta)$ is the atomic scattering factor tabulated in the International Crystallographic Tables. Assuming hydrogen like wave functions, the ratio f_e/f_x may be shown to be approximately $(\hbar c/e^2)^2 = 137^2$ at $\theta = 0$.

$$\frac{d\phi_0}{dz} = \frac{i\pi}{\xi_0} \phi_0 + \frac{i\pi}{\xi_g} \phi_g \exp(2\pi isz)$$

$$\frac{d\phi_g}{dz} = \frac{i\pi}{\xi_g} \phi_0 \exp(-2\pi isz) + \frac{i\pi}{\xi_0} \phi_g .$$ (5)

The first of these equations states that the change in ϕ_0 in depth dz is partly due to forward scattering by the atoms in the slice dz, and partly due to scattering from the diffracted beam. A similar interpretation may be given to the second equation. It is to be noted that the coupling constants are proportional to ξ_0^{-1} and ξ_g^{-1} which themselves are proportional to $f(0)$ and $f(\theta)$. Moreover there is a phase change of $\pi/2$ (represented by the factor i) caused by the scattering. Such phase changes arise through the reconstruction of plane wave fronts from waves scattered by single atoms taking due account of phase, and they are well known in problems in physical optics. If in the second of eqs. (5) ϕ_g is small and ϕ_0 is assumed to be approximately unity, the equation may be integrated approximately to give the kinematical result (1) with the correct absolute scaling factor.

A variety of equations like (5) may be obtained by making suitable phase transformations. For example put

$$\phi_0'(z) = \phi_0(z) \exp(-i\pi z/\xi_0)$$

$$\phi_g'(z) = \phi_g(z) \exp(2\pi isz - \pi iz/\xi_0) .$$ (6)

We find from (5)

$$\frac{d\phi_0'}{dz} = \frac{i\pi}{\xi_g} \phi_g'$$

$$\frac{d\phi_g'}{dz} = \frac{i\pi}{\xi_g} \phi_0' + 2\pi is \, \phi_g' .$$ (7)

The solutions of (5) and (7) differ only by phase factors, and therefore, since we are only interested in intensities, both systems of equations will give the same result. The transformation (6) is equivalent to making allowance for the mean refractive index of the crystal, because the directly transmitted wave may be described as

$$\phi_0(z) \exp\left(2\pi i \boldsymbol{\chi} \cdot \mathbf{r}\right) \text{ or as } \phi_0'(z) \exp\left(2\pi i\left(\boldsymbol{\chi} \cdot \mathbf{r} + \frac{z}{2\xi_0}\right)\right).$$

The argument of the exponential of the latter expression shows that a major part of the z-dependence of ϕ_0 of the former expression is accounted for by a change of wave vector to $\mathbf{K}$, where $K_z = \chi_z + 1/2\xi_0$. $\mathbf{K}$ is the wave vector of the electron wave inside the crystal after allowing for the mean inner potential. It is easy to show that this is equivalent to a mean refractive index

$$\mu = \frac{|\mathbf{K}|}{|\boldsymbol{\chi}|} = 1 + \frac{\lambda \cos\theta}{2\xi_0} = 1 + \frac{\lambda^2}{2\pi} N f(0) \tag{8}$$

where N is the number of atoms per unit volume. μ is slightly greater than unity for electron wave refraction. Typically $\mu - 1 \cong 10^{-4}$ for 100 kV electrons.

1.3. Solution of the dynamical equations for a perfect crystal

We choose to solve the eqs. (7) and (dropping primes) we eliminate ϕ_g by differentiating the first equation with respect to z and by substituting for $d\phi_g/dz$ and ϕ_g from the second and first equations respectively. We obtain

$$\frac{d^2\phi_0}{dz^2} - 2\pi i s \frac{d\phi_0}{dz} + \left(\frac{\pi}{\xi_g}\right)^2 \phi_0 = 0. \tag{9}$$

By elimination of ϕ_0 it may be shown that ϕ_g satisfies the same equation. We try a solution of (9) of the form $\exp(2\pi i\gamma z)$. Substitution in (9) gives

$$\gamma^2 - s\gamma - (1/2\xi_g)^2 = 0. \tag{10}$$

Eq. (10) is quadratic and has two roots

$$\gamma^{(1)} = \tfrac{1}{2}\left(s - \sqrt{s^2 + \xi_g^{-2}}\right) \tag{11}$$

$$\gamma^{(2)} = \tfrac{1}{2}\left(s + \sqrt{s^2 + \xi_g^{-2}}\right). \tag{12}$$

Consider first the root $\gamma^{(1)}$. We may then write

$$\phi_0(z) = C_0^{(1)} \exp(2\pi i\gamma^{(1)}z) \tag{13}$$

$$\phi_g(z) = C_g^{(1)} \exp(2\pi i\gamma^{(1)}z) \tag{14}$$

where $C_0^{(1)}$ and $C_g^{(1)}$ are constants to be determined by noting that (13) and (14) must satisfy the original coupled differential eqs. (7). Substitution of (13) and (14) in the first of eqs. (7) gives

$$C_g^{(1)}/C_0^{(1)} = 2\xi_g\gamma^{(1)} = \xi_g s - \sqrt{1 + \xi_g^2 s^2} = w - \sqrt{1 + w^2} \tag{15}$$

where $w = \xi_g s$ is a dimensionless parameter which denotes deviation from the Bragg reflecting position, the so-called "deviation parameter" of the dynamical theory of diffraction. It is usual to choose the coefficients C_0, C_g so that $|C_0|^2 + |C_g|^2 = 1$. From (15) we then find

$$C_0^{(1)} = \left\{ \frac{1}{2} \left(1 + \frac{w}{\sqrt{1 + w^2}} \right) \right\}^{\frac{1}{2}} \tag{16}$$

$$C_g^{(1)} = - \left\{ \frac{1}{2} \left(1 - \frac{w}{\sqrt{1 + w^2}} \right) \right\}^{\frac{1}{2}}. \tag{17}$$

Similarly we may find a solution corresponding to the root $\gamma^{(2)}$

$$C_g^{(2)}/C_0^{(2)} = 2\xi_g\gamma^{(2)} = w + \sqrt{1 + w^2} \tag{18}$$

$$C_0^{(2)} = \left\{ \frac{1}{2} \left(1 - \frac{w}{\sqrt{1 + w^2}} \right) \right\}^{\frac{1}{2}} \tag{19}$$

$$C_g^{(2)} = \left\{ \frac{1}{2} \left(1 + \frac{w}{\sqrt{1 + w^2}} \right) \right\}^{\frac{1}{2}}. \tag{20}$$

For the root $\gamma^{(i)}$ ($i=1,2$) we can now use the expressions (13) and (14) to write down the wave function propagating in the crystal

$$B^{(i)}(\mathbf{r}) = \phi_0^{(i)} \exp(2\pi i\mathbf{K}\cdot\mathbf{r}) + \phi_g^{(i)} \exp(2\pi i(\mathbf{K}+\mathbf{g})\cdot\mathbf{r})$$

$$= C_0^{(i)} \exp(2\pi i\mathbf{k}_0^{(i)}\cdot\mathbf{r}) + C_g^{(i)} \exp(2\pi i(\mathbf{k}_0^{(i)}+\mathbf{g})\cdot\mathbf{r}) \tag{21}$$

where

$$(k_o^{(i)})_z = K_z + \gamma^{(i)} .$$

(22)

There will be two functions $B^{(1)}$ and $B^{(2)}$ corresponding to the two values of γ. The functions $B^{(i)}$ are two-beam approximations to Bloch functions.

1.4. *The dispersion surface*

The two Bloch functions have wave vectors $k_o^{(i)}$ given by eq. (22), and we may use this equation to construct a surface which is the locus of the end of the vector $k_o^{(i)}$ as the orientation of the incident beam is varied, i.e. as K varies. There are two branches of this surface corresponding to $i = 1, 2$, as shown in fig. 3. The vector AO represents the incident wave vector K. The reflecting sphere and the distance $s(=s_g)$ are shown. The locus of K is the sphere of radius $|K|$ centred at O. $\gamma^{(i)}$ is the distance of A (parallel to the z direction) from the two branches of the dispersion surface. As A varies over the sphere of radius $|K|$, the wave vectors $k_o^{(i)}$ trace out the two branches of the dispersion

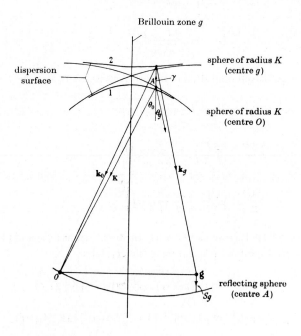

Fig. 3. Illustrating the construction of the dispersion surface.

surface. In practice $|\mathbf{K}| \cong 50 |\mathbf{g}|$, so that the sphere of radius $|\mathbf{K}|$ is practically a plane in the vicinity of the Brillouin zone boundary which bisects the reciprocal lattice vector $\mathbf{g}$. In this case the two branches of the dispersion surface on the two-beam theory are generated by rotation of two branches of a hyperbola about $\mathbf{g}$. The hyperbolic surface is asymptotic to the aforementioned sphere centred at O and to a similar sphere centred at $\mathbf{g}$.

The concept of the dispersion surface is particularly useful as a geometrical aid for describing wave vectors of Bloch functions in the crystal. In general, as we shall see, the incident beam excites two Bloch functions in the Laue case, one on each branch of the dispersion surface. If the dispersion surface is known we can find the crystal wave vectors $\mathbf{k}_0^{(i)}$ simply by constructing a normal to the crystal surface (i.e. along z) through the end of the wave vector $\mathbf{K}$ at A in fig. 3. The intersections of the normal with the branches of the surface give the "wave-points" of the vectors $\mathbf{k}_0^{(i)}$.

The dispersion surface is usually introduced in the wave-mechanical treatment of electron diffraction, following the methods of Bethe [3] , MacGillavry [4] and others. In this treatment the dispersion surface enters as a surface of constant energy for crystal wave functions with energy equal to that of the incident electron wave. The construction described above for determining crystal wave vectors arises from the condition of continuity of components of wave vectors parallel to the crystal surface as in problems of wave matching at interfaces in electromagnetic theory. Our method of derivation of the dispersion surface, starting from eqs. (5) or (7), demonstrates that the surface is not a direct consequence of a quantum-mechanical treatment, since the result was obtained from a simple geometrical treatment of scattering. In fact the only point where quantum mechanics needs to be used in our treatment is in calculation of atomic scattering amplitudes (eq. (2)).

The concept of the dispersion surface can be generalised to include the case of more than one strong Bragg reflection. This will be dealt with in a later chapter by Howie, but we should note here that if n-waves are considered, the dispersion surface consists of n-branches asymptotic to spheres of radius $|\mathbf{K}|$ centred at the n reciprocal lattice points.

1.5. Solution in the Laue case

It is useful to introduce a notation due to Takagi for describing deviations from the exact Bragg condition. We introduce a parameter β by the relation

$$w = \cot \beta . \tag{23}$$

In fig. 3, $w = +\infty$ (β=0) corresponds to the point A being far to the right of the Brillouin zone boundary. $w = 0$ ($\beta = \pi/2$) occurs when A is at the zone boundary, which is the exact Bragg position. $w = -\infty$ ($\beta = \pi$) occurs when A is far to the left of the zone boundary. It is usual to take s positive if the reciprical lattice point is inside the reflecting sphere and negative in the reverse situation. In terms of β we have

$$C_o^{(1)} = C_g^{(2)} = \cos\tfrac{1}{2}\beta \; ; \qquad C_o^{(2)} = -C_g^{(1)} = \sin\tfrac{1}{2}\beta \; . \qquad (24)$$

Suppose there is only one wave incident on the top surface of the crystal. We write the total crystal wave as

$$\psi(\mathbf{r}) = \psi^{(1)} B^{(1)}(\mathbf{r}) + \psi^{(2)} B^{(2)}(\mathbf{r}) \; . \qquad (25)$$

$\psi^{(1)}$ and $\psi^{(2)}$ represent the amplitude of the two Bloch waves excited in the crystal. Using (21), eq. (25) becomes

$$\psi(\mathbf{r}) = \psi^{(1)} C_o^{(1)} \exp(2\pi i \mathbf{k}_o^{(1)} \cdot \mathbf{r}) + \psi^{(2)} C_o^{(2)} \exp(2\pi i \mathbf{k}_o^{(2)} \cdot \mathbf{r})$$

$$+ \psi^{(1)} C_g^{(1)} \exp(2\pi i (\mathbf{k}_o^{(1)} + \mathbf{g}) \cdot \mathbf{r}) + \psi^{(2)} C_g^{(2)}$$

$$\times \exp(2\pi i (\mathbf{k}_o^{(2)} + \mathbf{g}) \cdot \mathbf{r}) \; . \qquad (26)$$

The first two terms on the right of (26) represent the directly transmitted wave in the crystal; the second two terms on the right represent the diffracted wave. We choose the origin of coordinates at the top surface of the crystal and equate the amplitude of the directly transmitted wave at the top to unity (the incident beam amplitude), and that of the diffracted wave to zero

$$\psi^{(1)} C_o^{(1)} + \psi^{(2)} C_o^{(2)} = 1 \; ; \qquad \psi^{(1)} C_g^{(1)} + \psi^{(2)} C_g^{(2)} = 0 \; . \qquad (27)$$

Using (24), eq. (27) gives

$$\psi^{(1)} = \cos\tfrac{1}{2}\beta \qquad\qquad (28)$$

$$\psi^{(2)} = \sin\tfrac{1}{2}\beta \; . \qquad\qquad (29)$$

We may now evaluate the amplitudes of the directly transmitted and diffracted waves for a crystal of thickness t. We have

$$\phi_0(t) = \sum_{i=1,2} \psi^{(i)} C_0^{(i)} \exp(2\pi i \gamma^{(i)} t)$$

$$\phi_g(t) = \sum_{i=1,2} \psi^{(i)} C_g^{(i)} \exp(2\pi i \gamma^{(i)} t) .$$ \hfill (30)

Apart from an unimportant phase term, eqs. (30) may be simplified with the aid of eqs. (11), (12), (23), (24), (28) and (29). We obtain the result

$$\phi_0(t) = \cos\left(\frac{\pi t}{\xi_g}\sqrt{1+w^2}\right) - \frac{iw}{\sqrt{1+w^2}}\sin\left(\frac{\pi t}{\xi_g}\sqrt{1+w^2}\right) \hfill (31)$$

$$\phi_g(t) = \frac{i\sin\left(\frac{\pi t}{\xi_g}\sqrt{1+w^2}\right)}{\sqrt{1+w^2}} . \hfill (32)$$

1.6. Examination of the Laue solution

From (32) we find that the diffracted beam intensity can be written as

$$|\phi_g|^2 = \frac{\pi^2}{\xi_g^2}\frac{\sin^2 \pi t \bar{s}}{(\pi \bar{s})^2} \hfill (33)$$

where $\bar{s}$ is an effective value of s

$$\bar{s} = \sqrt{s^2 + \xi_g^{-2}} . \hfill (34)$$

Eq. (33) is directly comparable with eq. (1), the kinematical solution. We see that it differs from the kinematical result only by the replacement of s by an effective value $\bar{s}$, which has a minimum value equal to ξ_g^{-1} at the Bragg position. Thus the limitations of the kinematical theory when $s \to 0$ mentioned in sect. 1.1 are effectively removed in the dynamical treatment. The expression (33) is the Bragg reflection "rocking curve" of the crystal obtained from the two-beam dynamical theory. Fig. 4 shows schematic diagrams of rocking curves on (a) the kinematical theory and (b) the dynamical theory. It is worth noting that the width of the central maximum of the rocking curve on the s-scale given by kinematical theory is $2/t$ and decreases with increasing t, a well known result

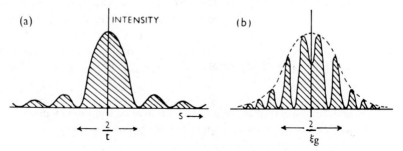

Fig. 4. Schematic diagram of the intensity distribution around a reciprocal lattice point. (a) on the kinematical theory, (b) on the dynamical theory.

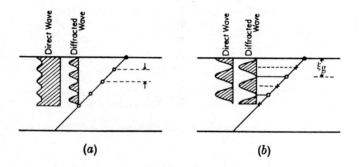

Fig. 5. Schematic diagram of the "Pendellösung" effect, (a) in the kinematical region where the diffracted beam is weak, (b) in the dynamical region where $s = 0$. The depth periodicity of the oscillations of crystal wave intensities is equal to the extinction distance ξ_g.

for particle-size broadening in X-ray diffraction. However, the dynamical rocking curve is more complicated. For $t \ll \xi_g$ the curve approaches the kinematical result. However, for $t > \xi_g$ the behaviour is as illustrated in fig. 4(b). The envelope of the oscillations has a half-width $2/\xi_g$ independent of the crystal thickness.

Fig. 5 illustrates the "Pendellösung" effect for incident and diffracted intensities as given by eqs. (31) and (32). In this diagram we plot schematically the intensities $|\phi_0|^2$ and $|\phi_g|^2$ as a function of depth in the crystal. At the Bragg position the intensities of direct and diffracted waves oscillate with depth as shown in fig. 5(b). The intensity varies between zero and unity with a depth periodicity ξ_g. The coupling of the direct and diffracted intensities is known as "extinction" because in a depth $\frac{1}{2}\xi_g$ the intensity of the direct wave is completely extinguished by scattering into the diffracted beam. Extinction was first noted as an important effect in X-ray diffraction by Darwin [2], particularly for strong X-ray reflections. Extinction effects are even more important in electron diffraction because of the greatly increased atomic scattering amplitude for electron waves. Extinction is responsible for the so-called "thickness extinction contours" observed on bright-field and dark-field electron micrographs of wedge shaped crystals, and they were discussed by Hillier and Baker [5], Heidenreich and Sturkey [6] and others. It is worth noting that "Pendellösung" may be thought of as being due to beating between the wave vectors of Bloch waves on the two branches of the dispersion surface of fig. 3.

Fig. 5(a) illustrates the nature of the kinematical approximation. Away from the Bragg position, the depth periodicity of the crystal waves is reduced to $\xi_g/\sqrt{1 + w^2}$. When w is large this approaches s^{-1}, as given by the kinematical theory. Thus in fig. 5(a) the intensity of the direct wave is close to unity, while the diffracted intensity is small.

1.7. Dynamical equations in the Bragg case

It is instructive to mention this case here in order to emphasise the entirely different nature of the crystal wave. In the symmetrical Bragg case, reflection takes place from planes parallel to the crystal surface. Equations analogous to eq. (7) can be derived. As before z is depth below the surface. The equations are

$$\frac{d\phi_o}{dz} = i\pi s \cot\theta \, \phi_o + \frac{i\pi}{\xi_g} \cot\theta \, \phi_g$$

$$\frac{d\phi_g}{dz} = -\frac{i\pi}{\xi_g} \cot\theta \, \phi_o - i\pi s \cot\theta \, \phi_g . \qquad (35)$$

It is left as an exercise to the student to show that solutions of the above equation of the form $\exp(-\gamma z)$ exist, where $\gamma = \pi \cot\theta \sqrt{1 - w^2}/\xi_g$.

The ratio ϕ_g/ϕ_o at any depth may be calculated and is found to be

$$\frac{\phi_g}{\phi_o} = \frac{-1}{w + i\sqrt{1 - w^2}} . \qquad (36)$$

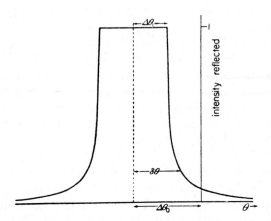

Fig. 6. Rocking curve in the Bragg case. The region where the reflected intensity is unity
is given by $|w| \leqslant 1$.

The rocking curve given by (36) is shown in fig. 6. Over the region $|w| < 1$
there is total reflection of the incident wave. The Bragg case was first studied
for X-ray diffraction by Darwin [1]. The case is important in the theory of
grazing angle electron diffraction. The exponential solution for the crystal
waves shows that evanescent waves are excited in the crystal. At the Bragg
position ($w=0$), the waves may decay rapidly in a few atomic layers. The crystal wave in this case is not unlike the evanescent wave existing at an interface
where total internal reflection of light occurs.

2. Treatment of absorption in the dynamical theory of electron diffraction

The theory as developed in the previous lecture considered the effect of
elastic scattering only and led to the idea of the "Pendellösung" solution of
the dynamical theory (fig. 5 of sect. 1), where direct and diffracted intensities oscillate with a depth periodicity ξ_g at the Bragg reflection position. It
should be noted that for elastic scattering only, this depth oscillation should
persist indefinitely, i.e. the visibility of thickness extinction contours on
bright-field or dark-field electron micrographs of wedge shaped crystals should
be independent of crystal thickness. That this is not the case in practice is evident from micrographs like fig. 7, where it is seen that the intensity of thickness fringes dies away in the thicker regions of the crystal. Only about four or

Fig. 7. Thickness extinction contours in a bright-field image of a wedge crystal of
Cu + 7% Al alloy.

five dark fringes are visible on this micrograph, and ultimately the contrast in
the thick regions is practically uniform, even though there is good transmission
in such regions. Evidently the dynamical theory as developed so far does not
give a sufficiently good description of results. We shall meet other examples in
the next section where the theory including elastic scattering only is at variance
with experiment.

It is well known that a theory treating elastic scattering is a first approximation only. Besides being scattered elastically, the incident electron wave may
also be scattered inelastically by creating various excitations in the crystal, such

as single electron excitations, plasmons, phonons etc. Inelastic scattering phenomena will be discussed in a later chapter by Howie, but we wish to emphasize here that such scattering can give rise to an apparent absorption of the elastically scattered wave by virtue of the fact that the inelastic waves may be scattered outside the aperture of the objective of an electron microscope and hence are prevented from reaching the image. The inelastic scattering appears as a diffuse background between Bragg spots on the electron diffraction pattern.

Yoshioka [7] first showed in a formal quantum-mechanical treatment that the effect of inelastic scattering on the elastic scattering could be represented by the addition of a small imaginary part to the crystal lattice potential, which gives rise to "absorption" of the elastic wave in much the same way as a complex refractive index gives rise to absorption of electromagnetic waves. A similar mechanism had been postulated (Molière [8]) to account for electron diffraction effects in the Bragg case, and a similar theory was also applied in X-ray diffraction by von Laue [9] to explain the experiments of Borrmann [10] (see also Zachariasen [11]).

We intend to give an account of the treatment of absorption due to inelastic scattering in this section, but we wish to emphasize from the start that the theory to be outlined is only a first approximation because the effect of any inelastic scattering which passes through the objective aperture is neglected. Not all the inelastic scattering appears in regions of the diffraction pattern between Bragg spots. Some of the inelastic scattering is concentrated close to the Bragg spots, particularly for single electron and plasmon scattering, and will therefore be included in the electron microscope image for typical aperture sizes. Such scattering can produce image contrast effects which must be added to that due to elastic scattering. Thus the situation can in practice be quite complicated, i.e. the "absorption" itself can be a function of aperture size.

2.1. *A uniform absorbing potential*

Consider an electron wave with free-space wave vector χ, which enters a crystal with inner potential V_0 volts. If the energy of the electron is E eV, we have

$$E = \frac{h^2}{2me} \chi^2 \tag{37}$$

$$E + V_0 = \frac{h^2}{2me} \mathbf{K}^2 , \tag{38}$$

where $\mathbf{K}$ is the wave vector inside the crystal and e is the electronic charge. To satisfy continuity of the wave function at the plane boundary, we require

$$K_t = \chi_t \tag{39}$$

where these quantities are the tangential components of the wave vectors parallel to the boundary. Hence we find for the refractive index μ

$$\mu = \frac{|\mathbf{K}|}{|\chi|} = \left\{1 + \frac{V_0}{E}\right\}^{\frac{1}{2}} \simeq 1 + \frac{1}{2}\frac{V_0}{E} \tag{40}$$

since $V_0 \ll E$. This equation is equivalent to eq. (8) of sect. 1 since V_0 is related to $f(0)$ by

$$V_0 = \frac{h^2}{2\pi me} N f(0) . \tag{41}$$

Now suppose we add a small imaginary part to V_0, i.e.

$$V_0 \to V_0 + i V_0' . \tag{42}$$

Then in place of (38) we should write

$$E + V_0 + i V_0' = \frac{h^2}{2me} (K_t^2 + (K_z + i\delta)^2) \tag{43}$$

where K_z is the perpendicular component of $\mathbf{K}$ in (38), and δ is a small imaginary addition to K_z due to V_0'. The wave in the crystal will now be of the form

$$\exp(2\pi i \mathbf{K} \cdot \mathbf{r}) \exp(-2\pi\delta z) \tag{44}$$

the exponential decay describing absorption.

From (43) we can show (neglecting $O(\delta^2)$) that

$$\delta = \frac{me}{h^2 K_z} V_0' . \tag{45}$$

Hence the absorption coefficient for amplitude, κ, is given by

$$\kappa = 2\pi\delta = \frac{2\pi me}{h^2 K_z} V_0' . \tag{46}$$

Absorption can be described equally well by allowing the atomic scattering amplitude for electron waves to become complex;

$$f(\theta) \to f(\theta) + if'(\theta) \tag{47}$$

since V_0' will be related to $f'(0)$ by an expression similar to (41). We then find

$$\kappa = \frac{N f'(0)}{K_z} . \tag{48}$$

In keeping with the notation of the previous section, we define "absorption distances", ξ_0', ξ_g' by an expression similar to eq. (2) of sect. 1

$$\xi_g' = \frac{\pi K \Omega \cos \theta}{f'(\theta)} . \tag{49}$$

We then have for a uniform absorbing potential

$$\kappa = \pi/\xi_0' . \tag{50}$$

2.2. Anomalous absorption

We note from above that the effect of a uniform absorbing potential in a crystal lattice would be to attenuate all Bloch waves to the same extent. Thus thickness extinction contours in a wedge crystal should decrease in intensity with increasing thickness t like $\exp(-2\pi t/\xi_0')$. However the visibility of the fringes $((I_{max}-I_{min})/(I_{max}+I_{min}))$ would not depend on thickness. The effect of uniform absorption is simply to decrease the scale of the intensity of fringes in thick regions of the crystal. That this is not the case in practice is evident from micrographs like fig. 7, where even though the fringes fade out, there is still very good transmission in thick regions. We may explain the observations if there is selective absorption of the two Bloch waves in the two-beam theory. The selective absorption is referred to as "anomalous absorption", even though the description "anomalous" is really a misnomer, and the physical explanation of the effect is illustrated in fig. 8. This shows the wave patterns of the two Bloch waves belonging to branches 1 and 2 of the dispersion surface at the Bragg position ($w=0$). Eqs. (16), (17), (19), (20) and (21) of sect. 1 show that for $w = 0$

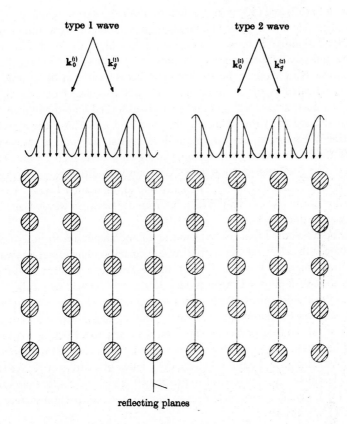

Fig. 8. Schematic diagram illustrating "anomalous absorption" at the Bragg position. The current flow vector is parallel to the reflecting planes. Absorbing regions at atoms are shaded. The type 2 wave is absorbed more than the type 1 wave.

$$B^{(i)}(\mathbf{r}) = \frac{1}{\sqrt{2}} \{\exp(2\pi i \mathbf{k}_0^{(i)} \cdot \mathbf{r}) + (-1)^i \exp(2\pi i (\mathbf{k}_0^{(i)} + \mathbf{g}) \cdot \mathbf{r})\}. \qquad (51)$$

We may express this as

$$B^{(1)}(\mathbf{r}) = -i\sqrt{2} \exp(2\pi i |\mathbf{k}_0^{(1)} + \tfrac{1}{2}\mathbf{g}|z) \sin \pi g x \qquad (52)$$

$$B^{(2)}(\mathbf{r}) = \sqrt{2} \exp(2\pi i |\mathbf{k}_0^{(2)} + \tfrac{1}{2}\mathbf{g}|z) \cos \pi g x \qquad (53)$$

where x is a coordinate in the surface parallel to $\mathbf{g}$. The current flow corresponding to (52) and (53) is in the direction of $k_o^{(i)} + \frac{1}{2}g$ (i.e. parallel to the Bragg planes) and is modulated laterally as $\sin^2 \pi g$ or $\cos^2 \pi g$ as shown in fig. 8. The lateral modulation causes the current for the branch 1 Bloch wave to be located mid-way between planes of atoms and vice versa for the branch 2 Bloch wave. Now suppose the absorption effect is located at the atomic positions as indicated by the shaded regions in fig. 8. It is clear from this diagram that the branch 2 wave will be more strongly absorbed than the branch 1 wave because it is located with maxima at the atomic planes. This is the physical explanation of anomalous absorption. In thick crystals the branch 2 wave will be effectively removed by absorption, leaving only the branch 1 wave. Thus we may have good transmission in thick regions with diffraction contrast effects from dislocations (see fig. 7) mainly due to the branch 1 wave. Thickness extinction contours which are due to interference between waves 1 and 2 will fade away in thick regions.

It should be noted that the explanation of anomalous absorption of electrons given here is the electron counterpart of the corresponding effect known in X-ray diffraction as the Borrmann effect. In the X-ray case absorption is due mainly to K-shell photo-electron production, and hence will be localised very close to the atomic centres. This gives rise to a rather extreme effect whereby one type of wave is hardly absorbed at all, leading to good transmission in thick crystals set at the Bragg reflecting position. One difference with the X-ray case should be noted. The symmetry of types 1 and 2 waves (fig. 8) is interchanged for X-rays. This arises because the refractive index of matter for X-rays is slightly less than unity, whereas for electrons it is slightly greater than unity. Hence for X-rays the wave on the lower branch of the dispersion surface is more strongly absorbed.

The selective absorption of electrons has been referred to as "channelling". Howie will be dealing with this in a later chapter, but we wish to note that channelling effects can be important in situations where multiple Bragg reflections are excited. The channelling properties of all the n Bloch waves excited need to be considered.

2.3. Dynamical equations describing absorption

Absorption may be included in the theory given in the first lecture by allowing the crystal potential to have a small periodic imaginary part or by allowing the atomic scattering amplitude to become complex (eq. (47)). This is equivalent to making the following substitutions in eq. (5) of the previous section

$$\frac{1}{\xi_o} \rightarrow \frac{1}{\xi_o} + \frac{i}{\xi'_o} \tag{54}$$

$$\frac{1}{\xi_g} \rightarrow \frac{1}{\xi_g} + \frac{i}{\xi'_g} . \tag{55}$$

We start with the equations in the form

$$\frac{d\phi_o}{dz} = i \frac{\pi}{\xi_o} \phi_o + i \frac{\pi}{\xi_g} \phi_g$$

$$\frac{d\phi_g}{dz} = i \frac{\pi}{\xi_g} \phi_o + i \left(\frac{\pi}{\xi_o} + 2\pi s \right) \phi_g \tag{56}$$

which can be derived from (5) of section 1 by putting $\phi'_g = \phi_g \exp(2\pi i s z)$. In eqs. (56) we must make the substitutions (54) and (55).

We put

$$\phi'_o = \phi_o \exp\left(-i\pi z \left(\frac{1}{\xi_o} + \frac{i}{\xi'_o} \right) \right)$$

$$\phi'_g = \phi_g \exp\left(-i\pi z \left(\frac{1}{\xi_o} + \frac{i}{\xi'_o} \right) \right) \tag{57}$$

in (56), and note that besides accounting for mean refraction by the term in ξ_o^{-1} as before, these equations now contain a mean absorption term $\exp(\pi z/\xi'_o)$. We then find

$$\frac{d\phi'_o}{dz} = i\pi \left\{ \frac{1}{\xi_g} + \frac{i}{\xi'_g} \right\} \phi'_g$$

$$\frac{d\phi'_g}{dz} = i\pi \left\{ \frac{1}{\xi_g} + \frac{i}{\xi'_g} \right\} \phi'_o + 2\pi i s \, \phi'_g \tag{58}$$

which are eqs. (7) of section 1 in the case of absorption. Proceeding as before we find that ϕ'_o and ϕ'_g both satisfy the differential equation

$$\frac{d^2\phi'_o}{dz^2} - 2\pi i s \frac{d\phi'_o}{dz} + \pi^2 \left\{ \frac{1}{\xi_g^2} - \frac{1}{\xi_g'^2} + \frac{2i}{\xi_g \xi'_g} \right\} \phi'_o = 0 . \tag{59}$$

We try a solution of (59) of the form $\exp(2\pi i \gamma z)$ and find

$$\gamma^{(1)} = \frac{1}{2}\left(s - \frac{1}{\xi_g}\sqrt{1 + w^2} + 2i\frac{\xi_g}{\xi_g'} \right)$$

$$\simeq \frac{1}{2}\left(s - \frac{1}{\xi_g}\sqrt{1 + w^2} - \frac{i}{\xi_g'\sqrt{1 + w^2}} \right)$$

$$= \frac{1}{2\xi_g}(w - \sqrt{1+w^2}) - \frac{i}{2\xi_g'\sqrt{1 + w^2}} . \tag{60}$$

We have neglected $\xi_g'^{-2}$ and assumed that ξ_g/ξ_g' is small compared with unity. Similarly we find for $\gamma^{(2)}$

$$\gamma^{(2)} = \frac{1}{2\xi_g}(w + \sqrt{1+w^2}) + \frac{i}{2\xi_g'\sqrt{1 + w^2}} . \tag{61}$$

We note that eqs. (60) and (61) differ from (11) and (12) of sect. 1 only by the appearance of a small imaginary part describing absorption. To obtain the actual absorption coefficient we must take account of the mean absorption term in (57). We find that the amplitude absorption coefficients for the two Bloch waves are

$$\kappa^{(1)} = \pi\left(\frac{1}{\xi_0'} - \frac{i}{\xi_g'\sqrt{1 + w^2}} \right)$$

$$\kappa^{(2)} = \pi\left(\frac{1}{\xi_0'} + \frac{i}{\xi_g'\sqrt{1 + w^2}} \right) . \tag{62}$$

The wave on branch 1 of the dispersion surface has a lower absorption co-efficient than that of the branch 2 wave. At the reflecting position ($w=0$), the difference between the two absorption coefficients is a maximum, and the effect is most extreme when $\xi_g' = \xi_0'$. In this case the wave on branch 1 has zero absorption coefficient, while that on branch 2 has twice the average absorption coefficient. The conditions $\xi_g' = \xi_0'$ implies through eq. (49) that $f'(\theta) = f'(0)$, i.e. the absorptive power is distributed in the crystal lattice like δ-functions at the atomic positions in fig. 8. For X-ray diffraction $f'(\theta)$ is very nearly equal to $f'(0)$ because the absorption is due to K-shell photoelectric processes concentrated close to the atomic centres. For electrons it has often been assumed that $\xi_0' = \xi_g'$ and that $\xi_g' \cong 10\xi_g$ in calculations of diffraction contrast. Absorption parameter have been estimated by Hashimoto [12] and by Metherell and Whelan [13] using experimental profiles of thickness extinction contours. For aluminium ξ_0'/ξ_g' is about 30. Thus the rough estimates mentioned above may not be very reliable. Calculations of ξ_g'/ξ_g for various elements as a function of temperature and g have been made by Humphreys and Hirsch [14] on the basis of single electron and phonon scattering.

2.4. The Laue solution with absorption

Having estimated the amplitude absorption coefficients (62) for the two crystal Bloch waves, we can proceed as in sect. 1.4 to evaluate direct and diffracted waves from a crystal of thickness t. In place of (25) of sect. 1 we have

$$\psi(\mathbf{r}) = \psi^{(1)} B^{(1)}(\mathbf{r}) \exp(-\kappa^{(1)}z) + \psi^{(2)} B^{(2)}(\mathbf{r}) \exp(-\kappa^{(2)}z) . \quad (63)$$

The boundary conditions at the top surface of the crystal are applied in the same way. We find the same values for the excitation amplitudes $\psi^{(1)}$ and $\psi^{(2)}$. Eventually we obtain

$$\phi_0(t) = \exp(-\pi t/\xi_0') \left\{ \cos X - \frac{iw}{\sqrt{1 + w^2}} \sin X \right\} \quad (64)$$

$$\phi_g(t) = \exp(-\pi t/\xi_0') \frac{i \sin X}{\sqrt{1 + w^2}} \quad (65)$$

where

$$X = \frac{\pi t}{\xi_g} \sqrt{1 + w^2} + \frac{i\pi t}{\xi_g' \sqrt{1 + w^2}} . \quad (66)$$

We see that the solution including absorption is formally similar to that without absorption (eqs. (31), (32) of sect. 1).

Absorption is included simply by allowing the arguments of the sines and cosines to become complex according to (66) and by multiplying by the term $\exp(-\pi t/\xi_0')$ which represents the average absorption.

2.5. Examination of the Laue solution with absorption

Figs. 9 and 10 show examples of "rocking curves" computed from eqs. (64) and (65). Fig. 9 shows the effect of increasing absorption for a crystal of constant thickness ($t=4\xi_g$). Fig. 9a is for the case of no absorption and we see that the bright-field (full curve) and dark-field (broken curve) rocking curves are

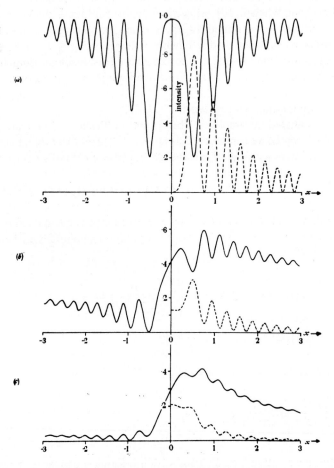

Fig. 9. "Rocking curves" computed from the two-beam theory for $t = 4\xi_g$. Full curves refer to bright field; broken curves refer to dark field.(a) No absorption, (b) $\xi_g/\xi_g' = 0.05$, (c) $\xi_g/\xi_g' = 0.10$. $\xi_0' = \xi_g'$.

complementary, as expected for no absorption. With increasing absorption, i.e. increasing ξ_g/ξ_g', the bright-field curve becomes asymmetrical about $w = 0$. The dark-field curve remains symmetrical. Note also that the amplitude of the oscillations of the curves decreases with increasing absorption and increasing thickness (fig. 10). In fig. 10 oscillations are visible for $t = 1.5\xi_g$ but are no longer visible when $t = 10\xi_g$. The decrease in amplitude of the oscillations is a direct consequence of the preferential absorption of the branch 2 wave.

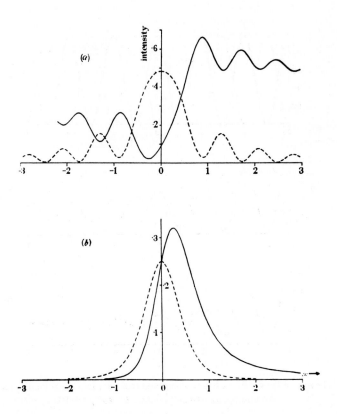

Fig. 10. "Rocking curves" computed from the two-beam theory. Full curves refer to bright field; broken curves refer to dark field. $\xi_g/\xi_g' = 0.10$, $\xi_0' = \xi_g'$. (a) $t = 1.5\xi_g$, (b) $t = 10\xi_g$.

Fig. 11 shows the effect of absorption on thickness extinction contours at the Bragg position. In fig. 11a Pendellösung fringes persist indefinitely in the thick regions, whereas in figs. 11b and c they are seen to fade out more rapidly with increasing absorption.

Figs. 7, 12 show examples of extinction contours in various materials illustrating the effects predicted by the theory. We have already discussed the significance of the fading-out of fringes in fig. 7 and we can understand this in terms of the theory of Pendellösung fringes including anomalous absorption (figs. 11b and c). Fig. 12 is an example of a bend extinction contour in an aluminium foil whose thickness increases over the field of view. The contour

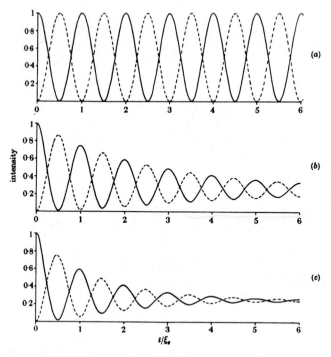

Fig. 11. Profile of Pendellösung fringes computed from the two-beam theory. $\xi'_0 = \xi'_g$. (a)
No absorption, (b) $\xi_g/\xi'_g = 0.05$ (c) $\xi_g/\xi'_g = 0.10$.

is due to a pair of Bragg reflections, 111 and $\bar{1}\bar{1}\bar{1}$. Because of the smallness of
the Bragg angle, a region of the foil where the 111 reflections is strongly excited will only be separated by a small distance from the adjacent region
where $\bar{1}\bar{1}\bar{1}$ is excited for moderate bending of the foil. These contours are
therefore due to pairs of Bragg reflections like 111 and $\bar{1}\bar{1}\bar{1}$, each edge of the
contour producing one or other of these reflections. Thus the form of the
bright-field image of the contour is qualitatively described by a pair of curves
like figs. 9 and 10 arranged back to back, joining up in the region of negative
w (shown as x on these figures) where the bright field intensity is low. In thin
regions a trace across the contour shows intensity oscillations as predicted in
figs. 8 and 10. In thicker regions the intensity oscillations fade out as predicted in fig. 10b, so that in such regions the bend extinction contour looks
like a dark band. The regions on either side of this dark band show good trans-

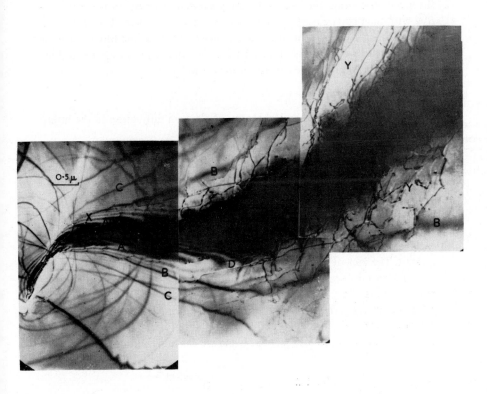

Fig. 12. Bright-field image of a bend extinction contour in a region of varying thickness of an aluminium foil. Note the reduced intensity inside the contour compared with the outside especially in thick regions. Note also the disappearance of subsidiary oscillations in thick regions.

mission corresponding to the maximum in the intensity profile for $w > 0$ in figs. 9 and 10.

We conclude by pointing out the physical reason for the asymmetry about $w = 0$ of bright-field images of bend extinction contours. We refer to eqs. (28) and (29) of sect. 1 which give the amplitudes $\psi^{(1)}$ and $\psi^{(2)}$ describing the excitation of the two Bloch waves on the two branches of the dispersion surface. We see from these equations that at $w = 0$ $(\beta = \pi/2)$, both Bloch waves are excited to the same extent. However for $w > 0$ $(\beta < \pi/2)$ $\psi^{(1)}$ is greater than $\psi^{(2)}$ and vice-versa for $w < 0$ $(\beta > \pi/2)$. Thus for $w > 0$ the Bloch wave $B^{(1)}$, with the lower absorption coefficient is mainly excited, whereas for $w < 0$ the wave $B^{(2)}$ with the higher absorption coefficient is mainly excited. The asymmetry is therefore a result both of the channelling properties of the Bloch waves and of the extent to which these are excited as the orientation varies, i.e. of the boundary conditions at the surface of the crystal.

3. Applications of the dynamical theory of electron diffraction to the interpretation of contrast effects at crystal defects

We saw in the previous two sections how the theory could be developed in a simple manner and we have applied it to explain the details of extinction contours in perfect crystals. We now intend to apply the theory to crystals containing defects such as dislocations, faults, etc. The application of the theory is based on the use of the so-called "column approximation", which enables us to calculate the diffracted intensities from continuously deformed crystals. The idea of the column approximation is illustrated in fig. 13. A defect such as a dislocation line is located at O and it is assumed that the atomic displacements in the foil due to the defect are known. It is required to calculate the direct and diffracted amplitudes ϕ_o and ϕ_g at a point B on the bottom surface. We consider a narrow column of crystal AB in which the atomic displacement function is $\mathbf{R}(z)$, and we calculate the amplitudes ϕ_o and

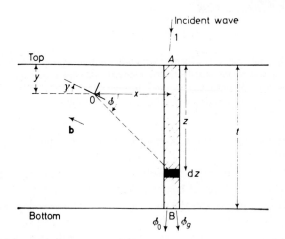

Fig. 13. Illustrating the coordinates used to describe a dislocation in a foil. r is a radial coordinate measured from O.

ϕ_g for this column as if it were of great lateral extent, i.e. we calculate for a crystal in which the displacement function $\mathbf{R}(z)$ is independent of the lateral coordinate. Such a crystal may be thought of as made up of a number of slabs, each perfect but displaced relative to each other according to $\mathbf{R}(z)$. The column approximation is a good approximation for electron diffraction, mainly because the Bragg angles are very small. Thus the fan included by direct and diffracted rays emanating from a point A on the top surface is very slender, and such rays essentially sample the strain field along a line in the crystal. For X-rays however the Bragg angle is much larger and the fan mentioned above may be quite wide. In this case account must also be taken of the variation of $\mathbf{R}$ with a lateral coordinate [15–17]. The significance of the column approximation is that it enables us to forget about the lateral dependence of displacements $\mathbf{R}$ when calculating contrast, and hence a system of coupled partial differential equations is reduced to a system of coupled ordinary differential equations. The contrast near the defect is obtained by varying the position x of the column, when, of course, the displacement field $\mathbf{R}(z)$ in the column will vary. The column approximation was first used in the treatment of contrast effects at stacking faults [18,19] where it was noted that the method led to the same result as a more detailed wave matching calculation at an inclined fault. Subsequently the approximation was used in the kinematical treatment of contrast at dislocations [20] and in the dynamical treatment [21,22]. A critical discussion of the column approximation has been given by Basinski and Howie [17].

3.1. Dynamical equations in a deformed crystal

If the displacement at depth z in the column is $\mathbf{R}(z)$, the equations corresponding to (5) of the first section are

$$\frac{d\phi_0}{dz} = i\frac{\pi}{\xi_0}\phi_0 + i\frac{\pi}{\xi_g}\phi_g \exp(2\pi isz + 2\pi i\mathbf{g}\cdot\mathbf{R})$$

$$\frac{d\phi_g}{dz} = i\frac{\pi}{\xi_g}\phi_0 \exp(-2\pi isz - 2\pi i\mathbf{g}\cdot\mathbf{R}) + i\frac{\pi}{\xi_g}\phi_g. \tag{67}$$

In this form the atomic displacements appear in the arguments of the exponentials in much the same way as they appear in the kinematical theory. We can see this by noting from eq. (2) of sect. 1 that ξ_g^{-1} is proportional to $f(\theta)$. If an atom is displaced by $\mathbf{R}$, the phase of the scattered wave is changed by $\exp(-2\pi i\mathbf{g}\cdot\mathbf{R})$. Thus in the first of eqs. (67) above a phase change of $\exp(+2\pi i\mathbf{g}\cdot\mathbf{R})$ should be introduced because the term describes scattering from the diffracted to the direct wave. Similarly in the second of eqs. (67) the phase change is $\exp(-2\pi i \mathbf{g} \cdot \mathbf{R})$ because the scattering is from the direct to the diffracted wave. If eqs. (67) are integrated down a column for a crystal of thickness t we obtain the amplitudes of direct and diffracted waves at the lower surface.

3.2. Stacking fault

The situation is illustrated in fig. 14. We have a stacking fault characterised by a displacement vector $\mathbf{R}$ at depth t_1. The displacement function is

$$R(z) = 0, \quad 0 \leqslant z \leqslant t_1; \quad R(z) = \mathbf{R}, \quad t_1 \leqslant z \leqslant t. \quad (68)$$

For the upper portion 1 of the crystal, the waves $\phi_0(t_1)$ and $\phi_g(t_1)$ incident on the fault are the same as for a perfect crystal of thickness t_1, the solution of which we have already obtained, (cf. eqs. (24), (27) and (30) of sect. 1). We may write this in matrix form

$$\begin{pmatrix} \phi_0(t_1) \\ \phi_g(t_1) \end{pmatrix} = \begin{pmatrix} \cos\frac{1}{2}\beta & \sin\frac{1}{2}\beta \\ -\sin\frac{1}{2}\beta & \cos\frac{1}{2}\beta \end{pmatrix} \begin{pmatrix} \exp(2\pi i\gamma^{(1)}t_1) & 0 \\ 0 & \exp(2\pi i\gamma^{(2)}t_1) \end{pmatrix}$$

$$\times \begin{pmatrix} \cos\frac{1}{2}\beta & -\sin\frac{1}{2}\beta \\ \sin\frac{1}{2}\beta & \cos\frac{1}{2}\beta \end{pmatrix} \begin{pmatrix} \phi_0(0) \\ \phi_g(0) \end{pmatrix}. \quad (69)$$

We have allowed for the possibility that $\phi_g(0)$ has a non-zero value at the top surface. In a similar manner eqs. (67) may be integrated in the lower crystal and obviously the solution must be like that of a perfect crystal of thickness t_2, except that we must now allow for the displacement $\mathbf{R}$. We put $\alpha = 2\pi\mathbf{g} \cdot \mathbf{R}$; α is called the phase angle of the fault. The constant displacement $\mathbf{R}$ causes the terms $C_g^{(i)}$ in eq. (30) of sect. 1 to become $C_g^{(i)} \exp(-i\alpha)$. Thus for the lower portion z of the crystal we have

$$\begin{pmatrix} \phi_0(t) \\ \phi_g(t) \end{pmatrix} = \begin{pmatrix} \cos\frac{1}{2}\beta & \sin\frac{1}{2}\beta \\ -\sin\frac{1}{2}\beta\exp(-i\alpha) & \cos\frac{1}{2}\beta\exp(-i\alpha) \end{pmatrix} \begin{pmatrix} \exp(2\pi i\gamma^{(1)}t_2) & 0 \\ 0 & \exp(2\pi i\gamma^{(2)}t_2 \end{pmatrix}$$

$$\times \begin{pmatrix} \cos\frac{1}{2}\beta & -\sin\frac{1}{2}\beta\exp(i\alpha) \\ \sin\frac{1}{2}\beta & \cos\frac{1}{2}\beta\exp(i\alpha) \end{pmatrix} \begin{pmatrix} \phi_0(t_1) \\ \phi_g(t_1) \end{pmatrix} \quad (70)$$

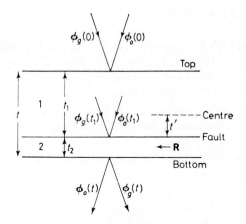

Fig. 14. Schematic diagram illustrating the parameters used to describe a stacking fault parallel to the surface. For an inclined fault t' varies across the fault.

For the column vector at the right of (70) we use the expression (69), and the solution for the faulted crystal becomes the products of several matrices. Putting $\phi_o(0) = 1$, $\phi_g(0) = 0$, corresponding to having only an incident wave at the top, we find after some algebra (omitting an unimportant phase term $\exp(\pi i(\gamma^{(1)} + \gamma^{(2)})t))$,

$$\phi_o(t) = \cos(\pi \Delta k t) - i \cos \beta \sin(\pi \Delta k t)$$

$$+ \tfrac{1}{2} \sin^2 \beta \, (\exp(i\alpha) - 1) \cos(\pi \Delta k t)$$

$$- \tfrac{1}{2} \sin^2 \beta \, (\exp(i\alpha) - 1) \cos(2\pi \Delta k t') \qquad (71)$$

$$\phi_g(t) = i \sin \beta \sin(\pi \Delta k t)$$

$$+ \tfrac{1}{2} \sin \beta \, (1 - \exp(-i\alpha)) \, [\cos \beta \cos(\pi \Delta k t) - i \sin(\pi \Delta k t)]$$

$$- \tfrac{1}{2} \sin \beta \, (1 - \exp(-i\alpha)) \, [\cos \beta \cos(2\pi \Delta k t') - i \sin(2\pi \Delta k t')]$$

$$(72)$$

where $t' = t_1 - \tfrac{1}{2}t$ is the distance of the fault from the centre of the crystal (fig. 14), and where

$$\Delta k = (1+w^2)^{\frac{1}{2}}/\xi_g \tag{73}$$

For an inclined fault running across the crystal, t' in (71) and (72) will vary. Thus there will be fringes due to the third terms in (71) and (72). The depth periodicity of the fringes will in general be $\xi_g/\sqrt{1 + w^2}$. If $\alpha = 0$, or $2n\pi$ we note that (71) and (72) reduce to the perfect crystal expression of the first section, as expected. Moreover, even when α is non zero, the solutions (71) and (72) join continuously to that of the perfect crystal at the top and bottom surfaces ($t'=-\frac{1}{2}t$ and $t'=+\frac{1}{2}t$).

We note also that (71) and (72) are applicable to the case of an absorbing crystal provided we put

$$\Delta k = \frac{\sqrt{1 + w^2}}{\xi_g} + \frac{i}{\xi_g' \sqrt{1 + w^2}} \tag{74}$$

and multiply ϕ_0 and ϕ_g by $\exp(-\pi t/\xi_0')$ to include mean absorption.

3.3. Dislocations, inclusions etc.

Each problem encountered under this heading usually has to be studied individually. The first step is to try to find a satisfactory model for describing the displacement field $\mathbf{R}$ around the defect. Usually simple models based on isotropic continuum elasticity theory are employed for want of more exact models. Effects such as the nature of relaxation of the strain field due to the free surface of a foil or to the presence of oxide films are usually neglected, or crudely approximated. We wish to stress, therefore, that there may be difficulties involved in expressing the displacement field $\mathbf{R}$ accurately, before proceeding with the computation of contrast from eq. (67).

It is useful to transform eqs. (67) by putting

$$\phi_0' = \phi_0 \exp(-i\pi z/\xi_0) \tag{75}$$

$$\phi_g' = \phi_g \exp\left(-i\pi \frac{z}{\xi_0} + 2\pi isz + 2\pi ig\cdot R\right). \tag{76}$$

Making the substitutions (54) and (55) of sect. 2, we obtain

$$\frac{d\phi'_0}{dz} = -\frac{\pi}{\xi'_0}\phi'_0 + \pi\left(\frac{i}{\xi_g} - \frac{1}{\xi'_g}\right)\phi'_g$$

$$\frac{d\phi'_g}{dz} = \pi\left(\frac{i}{\xi_g} - \frac{1}{\xi'_g}\right)\phi'_0 + \left(-\frac{\pi}{\xi'_0} + 2\pi i(s+\beta')\right)\phi'_g \tag{77}$$

where

$$\beta' = \frac{1}{2\pi}\frac{d\alpha}{dz} = \frac{d}{dz}(\mathbf{g}\cdot\mathbf{R}(z)) . \tag{78}$$

The transformations (75) and (76) do not affect intensities, and in practice the eqs. (77) are simpler to use than eqs. (67), since calculation of an exponential at every step of the integration by numerical methods is undesirable. Moreover, eqs. (77) now contain only the derivative of the displacement, β', and in some cases it is easier to calculate the derivative than the displacement itself. The eqs. (77) also demonstrate that strain contrast essentially arises from local bending of the lattice planes causing Bragg reflection. The tilting of these planes is proportional to β', and the equations show that this tilt simply increases the deviation parameter s locally.

3.4. *Examples of the application of the theory to contrast problems*
3.4.1. Stacking faults $|\alpha| = 2\pi/3$

The image of a stacking fault is characterised by the value of $\alpha = 2\pi\mathbf{g}\cdot\mathbf{R}$ in eqs. (71) and (72). In face centred cubic materials stacking faults may be produced on {111} planes by a shear of type $\frac{1}{6}\langle112\rangle$, or by removal or insertion of a plane of atoms as happens when vacancies or interstitial atoms condense on close packed planes. The nature of the faults produced by shear or by condensation of point defects is the same. The only difference lies in the type of partial dislocation bounding the fault. Faults formed by shear are bounded by glissile Shockley partials, whereas those formed by condensation of point defects are bounded by sessile Frank partials. Experimentally stacking faults may be produced in a variety of ways, by deformation (by movement of Shockley partial dislocations), by accidents during crystal growth (e.g. vapour deposition or electrodeposition of thin films) or by experiments involving condensation of point defects (e.g. in quenching or radiation damage). In face centred cubic materials faults are generally classified as intrinsic or extrinsic. An intrinsic fault is caused by motion of a single Shockley partial (involving shear on one plane only), or by condensation of vacancies (i.e. by removal of a plane of atoms). An extrinsic fault is caused by motion of a Shockley partial involving shear on two adjacent planes, or by condensation of interstitial atoms (i.e. by insertion of a close packed plane of atoms). The net shear of an extrinsic fault is opposite to that of an intrinsic fault. Therefore if an intrinsic fault is characterised by a certain value of α in a particular situation, an extrinsic fault in the same situation will be characterised by the negative of that value.

We may take an intrinsic fault on (111) in the fcc lattice with shear vector $\mathbf{R} = \frac{1}{6}[1\bar{2}1]$. For the reflection $\mathbf{g} = (h,k,l)$, $\alpha = 2\pi \mathbf{g} \cdot \mathbf{R}$ is then given by

$$\alpha = \frac{1}{3}\pi\,(h-2k+l)\,. \tag{79}$$

In the fcc lattice, h,k,l are either all odd or all even, thus α turns out to be $2n\pi/3$, where $n = 0, \pm1, \pm2$ etc., depending on the indices of the Bragg reflection. It is customary to refer to α modulo 2π $(-\pi<\alpha\leqslant+\pi)$. The possible values of α are $0, \pm2\pi/3$ modulo 2π. For $\alpha = 0$ the fault will be invisible. This vanishing criterion can be used to determine the direction of $\mathbf{R}$ by examining the visibility of a fault in a number of reflections. The method can be used to determine the phase angle of a fault, e.g. to distinguish between π-faults and $2\pi/3$-faults (Drum [23], Van Landuyt et al. [24]).

The contrast from $2\pi/3$-faults computed from eqs. (71) and (72) is shown in fig. 15 for the case of no absorption (Whelan and Hirsch [18]). The abscissa

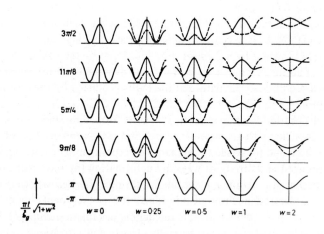

Fig. 15. Computed profiles of stacking fault fringes for the case of no absorption. Broken curves refer to negative values of w.

on each graph is $2\pi t' \sqrt{1 + w^2}/\xi_g$. It is seen that when $w = 0$ the fringes have a depth periodicity $\Delta t' = \frac{1}{2}\xi_g$, i.e. half that of the corresponding wedge fringes which would be observed if one half of the faulted crystal were removed. Away from the Bragg position, fringes are alternately strong and weak and the depth periodicity is $\Delta t' = \xi_g/\sqrt{1 + w^2}$. Without absorption the fringe profile across the fault is uniform. Fig. 16a and b illustrates schematically the appearance of fringes in a wedge crystal and in a bent crystal. It is seen that the fringes show a branching behaviour near where they cross extinction contours in the foil.

Fringes at stacking faults are well known experimentally. Figs. 17 and 18 show examples from a Cu + 7% Al alloy and fcc cobalt (due to Heidenreich). Fig. 17a is a bright-field image; fig. 17b is the corresponding dark-field image. We notice immediately a discrepancy between the theoretical profiles without absorption and the experimental images. While the image in fig. 17a is symmetrical about the centre of the foil, the fringe profile is not uniform across the fault. The visibility of the fringes is greater near the edges of the fault, i.e. near where the fault intersects top and bottom surfaces. Moreover, the dark-field image is asymmetrical about the centre. One edge has a dark fringe while the other has a light fringe. This behaviour which is not explained by the curves of fig. 15, is a result of absorption. Fig. 18 shows the branching of fringes near thickness extinction contours. It is clear from this picture that the branching occurs near the centre of the fault, the edge fringe being continuous. This

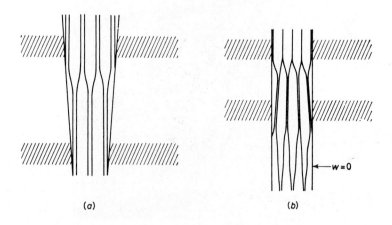

(a)   (b)

Fig. 16. Schematic diagram of branching of fringes at stacking fault images for no absorption. (a) fixed w, t varying; (b) fixed t, w varying.

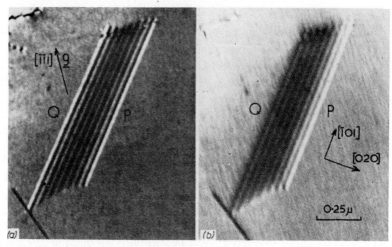

Fig. 17. Images of a +2π/3-fault in Cu + 7% Al alloy. Normal to foil is [101]. (a) Bright-field image; (b) dark-field image. Compare with fig. 19.

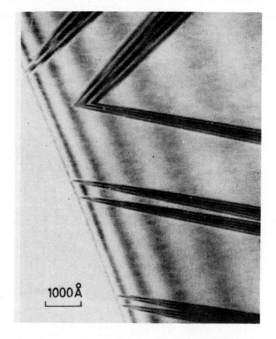

Fig. 18. The behaviour of fringes at stacking faults near thickness extinction contours in cobalt foil. Note that the branching of fringes occurs near the centre of the fault. The micrograph is due to R.D.Heidenreich.

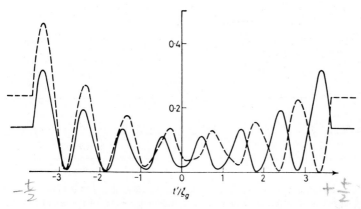

Fig. 19. Computed profile of stacking fault fringes in fig. 17. Full line is bright-field image; broken line is dark-field image. $a = +2\pi/3$; $t/\xi_g = 7.25$; $\xi'_0 = \xi'_g$; $\xi_g/\xi'_g = 0.075$; $w = -0.2$.

again is in disagreement with the theory without absorption, where branching should occur uniformly across the fault and in particular at the edges (fig. 16).

In fig. 19 we show a computed profile of stacking fault fringes calculated to match the images in fig. 17. Account has been taken of anomalous absorption by the method mentioned at the end of sect. 3.2. We notice that the bright-field image is symmetrical while the dark-field image is asymmetrical, as observed experimentally. Also the visibility of the fringes is lower near the centre of the foil. A detailed study of the fringes in wedge shaped or bent crystals also shows that the branching of the fringes occurs near the middle of the foil only, the edge fringes being continuous, as observed in fig. 18 [25,26]. Thus these special contrast effects at faults provide further evidence for the correctness of the theory of electron diffraction including absorption.

3.4.2. Determination of the type of stacking fault

Fig. 19 also illustrates a further important point from which interesting deductions can be made. The edge fringes in the bright-field image are seen to be bright for the chosen case $\alpha = +2\pi/3$. If α had been chosen to be $-2\pi/3$, the edge fringes would have been a dark fringe. Thus the sense of the edge fringe is determined simply by the sign of the phase angle α. The result holds for reasonably thick crystals in the presence of anomalous absorption. From fig. 19 we also see that bright-field and dark-field images are similar at the top surface ($t' = -\frac{1}{2}t$, where the electron beam enters) and are pseudo-complementary near the bottom surface ($t' = +\frac{1}{2}t$). We can therefore say that P is the top

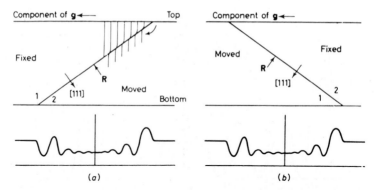

Fig. 20. Illustrating the two possible senses of inclination of a stacking fault. The bright field images would differ. In (a) $a = +2\pi/3$ and the edge fringe of the bright-field image would be light; in (b) $a = -2\pi/3$ and the edge fringe of the bright-field image would be dark. The dark field images of both cases are the same as illustrated.

surface and Q is the bottom surface for the fault in fig. 17a and b. Thus by taking bright-field and dark-field micrographs we can distinguish between the two possible senses of inclination of the fault, as shown in fig. 20. Since we know the sign of α from the edge fringe of the bright-field image, we have the information necessary to determine the sense of $\mathbf{R}$, the displacement of crystal 2 with respect to crystal 1 in fig. 14. The method was first given by Hashimoto et al. [27]. The sense of $\mathbf{R}$ enables us to say whether the fault is intrinsic or extrinsic.

The method has been elaborated by Gevers et al. [26], who pointed out that the type of the fault can be determined from the dark-field image alone, the sense of inclination not being required. This is understandable in terms of fig. 20, where we note that although (for the same type of fault) the sign of α will be different in the two situations illustrated, the dark-field image will be the same. Gevers et al. [26] have given a rule, illustrated in fig. 21, which enables the type of fault to be determined with little geometrical consideration. The diffraction vector $\mathbf{g}$ is drawn as an arrow with its origin at the centre of the dark-field image. $\mathbf{g}$ is arranged to point towards the right as in fig. 21. Fig. 21 then lists the sense of the edge fringes bordering the fault for two possible inclinations of the fault and the two possible types of fault. B denotes a a bright-fringe while D denotes a dark fringe. Full lines denote the top surface fringe; broken lines denote the bottom surface fringe. A and B denote two classes of Bragg reflections. A includes {200}, {222}, {440}; B includes {111}, {220}, {400}. For a given class (A or B), the dark-field image (with

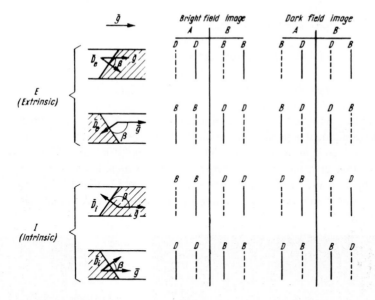

Fig. 21. Schematic diagram illustrating the nature of the edge fringes at $\pm 2\pi/3$-faults for various cases (after Gevers et al. [26]).

g inscribed as above) enables the type of fault to be determined by inspection of fig. 21. For example in fig. 17b, **g** points towards the dark fringe. The reflection is of class B (111), and therefore the fault is intrinsic by comparison with column B for intrinsic faults.

3.4.3. Stacking faults $|\alpha| = \pi$

In certain crystal structures stacking faults or anti-phase domain boundaries with phase angle π may occur. π-anti-phase boundaries in ordered alloys, produced by slip of imperfect dislocations or by thermal treatment are well known (Pashley and Presland [28]), Fisher and Marcinkowski [29]). More recently examples of π-faults in inorganic crystal structures such as hexagonal AlN (Drum and Whelan [30]) and tetragonal TiO_2 (rutile) (van Landuyt et al. [24]) have been studied. Eqs. (71) and (72) can be applied to the case $\alpha = \pi$ [30,24]. An exhaustive discussion is given by van Landuyt et al. [24]. Here we give only a brief survey of the main points of interest.

We consider the case of $\alpha = \pi$ with no absorption. At the reflecting position ($\beta=\pi/2$) the intensity derived from eq. (71) is

$$I_0(t',t) = \cos^2(2\pi t'/\xi_g) .$$ (80)

The corresponding equation for a $2\pi/3$-fault is

$$I_0(t',t) = \tfrac{1}{4}\cos^2(\pi t/\xi_g) + \tfrac{3}{4}\cos^2(2\pi t'/\xi_g) .$$ (81)

We notice immediately that the fringe profile across a π-fault with no absorption should be independent of the thickness fringes visible in a wedge crystal because (80) does not contain t. On the other hand, for a $2\pi/3$-fault eq. (81) shows that the fringe profile is dependent on t through the term $\cos^2(\pi t/\xi_g)$. Examples of this behaviour are given in figs. 22a and b. Fig. 22 refers to a $2\pi/3$-fault in AlN, while fig. 22b refers to a π-fault in the same material.

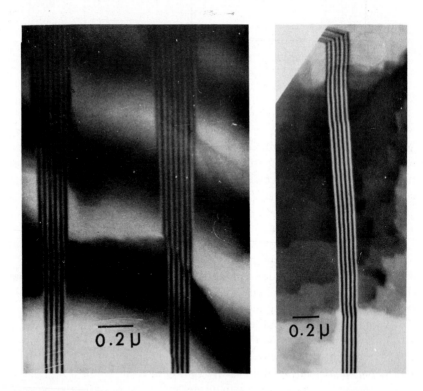

Fig. 22a, b. Illustrating the behaviour of fault fringes in AlN. (a) $a = 2\pi/3$, basal fault; (b) $a = \pi$, $(\bar{1}2\bar{1}0)$ fault.

Fig. 22b demonstrates the uniformity in the fringe profile, even though the thickness varies from about $3\xi_g$ to $2\xi_g$ along the fault. Figs. 23a and b illustrate another difference in the behaviour of $2\pi/3$-faults and π-faults for the case where stacking fault bends are observed. Fig. 23a refers to a triangular stacking fault defect in silicon (Booker and Stickler [31]) for which $\alpha = 2\pi/3$, while fig. 23b refers to bent and intersecting stacking faults in magnetite (Fe_3O_4 with a spinel structure). Fig. 23b is due to G.S.Baker (unpublished work) who has shown that these faults are on $\{110\}$planes with $\frac{1}{4}\langle 112\rangle$ shear vectors and that $|\alpha| = \pi$. In fig. 23a the operating Bragg reflection is $20\bar{2}$ and the fault parallel to $\mathbf{g}$ is "out of contrast". Thus only two faults of the triangular defect are visible, and for one of these $\alpha = +2\pi/3$, giving rise to bright edge fringes, while for the other $\alpha = -2\pi/3$ giving rise to dark edge fringes. As a result, at the stacking fault bend the fringes are discontinuous, bright fringes

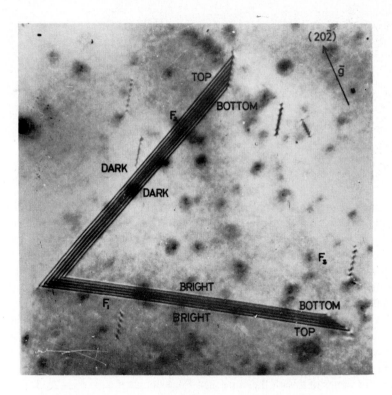

Fig. 23a. Illustrating the behaviour of fault bends. $\alpha = 2\pi/3$, faults at triangular defects in silicon.

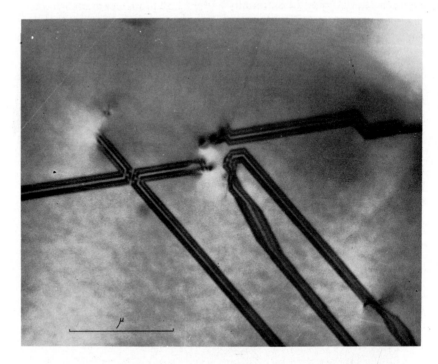

Fig. 23b. Illustrating the behaviour of fault bends. $\alpha = \pi$ faults in magnetite, Fe_3O_4. The faults are on $\{110\}$planes with shear vectors $\frac{1}{4}\langle 112 \rangle$. See text for discussion.

joining to dark fringes. This behaviour is commonly observed at bends in $2\pi/3$-faults. In the fcc structure it is also possible to have bent faults for which α has the same sign for both faults. In this case the fringes are continuous across the bend [24]. However when $\alpha = \pi$, there is no difference between these two situations, since a fault with phase angle π has the same profile as one with phase angles $-\pi$. Thus in fig. 23b the fringes are continuous across the fault bends in all cases.

Another interesting effect occurs at the intersection of faults. A column of crystal passing through the intersection will have a net phase angle equal to the sum of the phase angles of the individual faults. For $2\pi/3$-faults either the sum may be zero for values of α with opposite sign, or the sum may be non-zero for values of α with the same sign. For example if $\alpha_1 = \alpha_2 = 2\pi/3$, the sum is $4\pi/3$, which is equivalent modulo 2π to a value $-2\pi/3$. However, if $\alpha_1 = -\alpha_2 = 2\pi/3$, the sum is zero, and the contrast from a column through the point of intersection will be the same as that for a perfect crystal, i.e. there will be no contrast at the line of intersection of the faults. Thus for $2\pi/3$-faults there may either be contrast or no contrast at the intersection depending on the values of α_1 and α_2. However, for π-faults the intersection will always show no contrast. An example of this is visible in fig. 23b.

A further property of fringes at π-faults is that the bright-field and dark-field images are both symmetrical about the centre of the fault, and they are pseudo-complementary, even when absorption occurs [24]. This can be understood physically in terms of the offset of the Bragg reflecting planes. For a π-fault the offset of the planes above and below the fault is half the interplanar spacing. The fringes at faults are essentially due to interference between the two Bloch waves on each branch of the dispersion surface (fig. 3, sect. 1) after redistribution of amplitudes of the Bloch waves has occurred at the fault. A fuller discussion of this so-called interband and intraband scattering is given by Hirsch et al. [32]. Reference to fig. 8 of sect. 2 will make clear the fact that when the offset is half the interplanar spacing, the type 1 Bloch wave in the upper crystal propagates into the lower crystal as the type 2 Bloch wave, and similarly the type 2 Bloch wave propagates as the type 1 wave in the lower crystal. Thus the two Bloch waves switch branches of the dispersion surface on propagating through a π-fault, i.e. the scattering is entirely interband. It therefore makes no difference in which order the two crystals are encountered. The same waves emerge whether they encounter the crystal of thickness t_1 first and that of thickness t_2 second, or vice-versa. The bright-field and dark-field profiles are therefore symmetrical about the centre for π-faults even with absorption, contrary to the situation for $2\pi/3$-faults.

3.4.4. Overlapping stacking faults

Configurations of faults are often observed with consist of two or more stacking faults on closely spaced parallel planes. The fringe profile will depend on the separation and nature of the faults, and a particular situation can always be dealt with by the scattering matrix method outlined in sect. 3.2. We consider here the case where the faults are closely spaced so that propagation phase factors due to the separation of the faults can be ignored. Fig. 24 shows an example of overlapping faults in austenitic (fcc) stainless steel. Here we have a configuration of faults which might be produced by the twinning mechanism involving a spiral source of partial dislocation rotating round a pole dislocation. It is well known that this mechanism produces a thin lamellar region of twin by generating stacking faults on adjacent close-packed planes, the number of overlapping faults increasing from the edge of the lamella. If the phase angle α is $2\pi/3$ for a single fault, the net phase angle for n overlapping

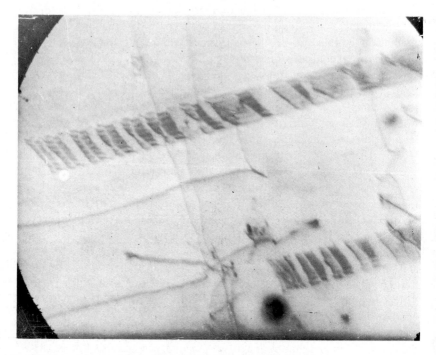

Fig. 24. Sequence of overlapping stacking faults in stainless steel. The number of overlapping faults increases from one at the leading fault. Every third overlap produces no contrast.

faults will be $2n\pi/3$. Thus for two intrinsic faults α is $4\pi/3$, or $-2\pi/3$ (modulo 2π). The sign of α changes, and as a result a reversal of fringe contrast occurs [19]. For three overlapping faults α is zero (modulo 2π). We therefore see a characteristic set of fringes where every third fault shows no contrast. Such a sequence of fault fringes is visible in fig. 24.

Defects resembling stacking faults in silicon are shown in fig. 25 (Booker and Howie [33]). The micrograph is a bright-field image, and we note that, contrary to the situation for single faults, the image is asymmetric about the centre, one edge of the faults having a bright fringe (B) while the other has a dark fringe (D). These contrast effects may be explained by assuming that the defects are intrinsic-extrinsic fault pairs separated by distances of about 50 to 100Å. For this separation phase factors corresponding to propagation between faults are not negligible, and therefore fringes are visible even though no fringes would be expected simply by adding the α values of each individual

'LINE' DEFECTS

BRIGHT   FIELD   IMAGE

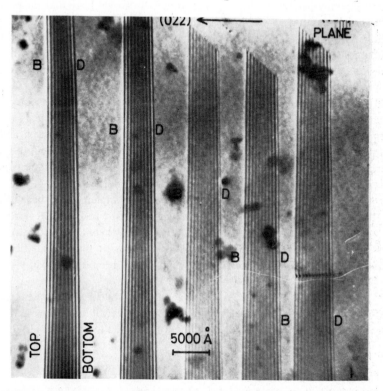

Fig. 25. Fringes at defects in silicon. The defects are believed to be pairs of intrinsic and extrinsic faults separated by small distances. Note that one edge fringe is bright and the other dark in the bright-field image.

fault. The asymmetric image can be explained by attributing one edge fringe to the intrinsic fault and the other to the extrinsic fault.

3.4.5. Moiré fringes; δ-fringes

In a number of papers [34–39] Gevers and his coworkers have considered contrast effects at more general planar defects. The theoretical basis of the investigations is again eqs. (67), but now we allow the possibility that $\mathbf{g}$ and s may be slightly different for two overlapping crystals.

The situation where $s_1 \cong s_2$, but $\mathbf{g}_1 \neq \mathbf{g}_2$, due to some small rotation or lattice parameter difference, gives rise to the case of moiré patterns. In this case $\mathbf{g}$ changes by $\Delta\mathbf{g}$ on passing through the interface between the crystals. $\Delta\mathbf{g}$ is generally parallel to the interface. It may be shown [34] that the profile of moiré fringes is given by the fault eqs. (71) and (72) provided $\alpha = -2\pi\Delta\mathbf{g}\cdot\mathbf{r}_s$, where $\mathbf{r}_s$ is a coordinate in the interface. α is therefore a linear function of $\mathbf{r}_s$ and is constant along lines perpendicular to $\Delta\mathbf{g}$. Thus we obtain fringes of constant α, i.e. moiré fringes, perpendicular to $\Delta\mathbf{g}$. The spacing of the fringes is given by $|\Delta\mathbf{g}|^{-1}$. These are well known properties of moiré fringes.

In a more general situation both $\mathbf{g}$ and s may change on passing through an interface, and the resulting situation has applications to contrast effects at domain boundaries [38]. The fringes have been referred to as δ-fringes, and they resemble stacking fault fringes but they are not regularly spaced. In the dark-field image the first fringe at the top and bottom of the foil is the same and is bright if $s_1 > s_2$, and is dark if $s_1 < s_2$. Bright-field and dark-field images are similar near the top surface and pseudo-complementary near the bottom surface. The theory is able to predict the nature of fringes at ferro-electric domain boundaries in barium titanate [38], where the crystal structure is actually tetragonal and the domain boundaries are twin boundaries. Similar domain boundaries formed by twinning have been observed in V_3Si at low temperatures (Goringe and Valdrè [40]).

More complicated boundaries having a fault component as well as a lattice misorientation may also be treated with the theory. Such boundaries are referred to as $\alpha-\delta$ boundaries and the student is referred to Gevers et al. [35] for a full discussion.

3.4.6. Images of dislocations

Consider first a screw dislocation parallel to the surface of a foil at depth y (fig. 13). The image of an inclined dislocation may be calculated by allowing y to vary and by including an inclination factor which affects the image width [20]. We will generally ignore inclination factors. The atomic displacements around the screw are given by isotropic elasticity theory,

$$\mathbf{R} = \frac{\mathbf{b}}{2\pi} \tan^{-1}\{(z-y)/x\}. \tag{82}$$

Thus α to be inserted in eqs. (78) is

$$\alpha = n \tan^{-1}\{(z-y)/x\} \tag{83}$$

where $n = \mathbf{g}\cdot\mathbf{b}$ is an integer which may take values $0, \pm 1, \pm 2$ etc. If $n = 0$, i.e. if the Burgers vector $\mathbf{b}$ lies in the Bragg reflecting planes, the dislocation will be invisible. The eqs. (77) may be integrated by numerical methods with a computer. Image profiles for $n = 1$ and 2 are shown in figs. 26 and 27. For $n = 1$ near $w = 0$ (fig. 26) the image profile consists of a single dark peak of similar shape for both the bright-field and the dark-field images. This is a result of anomalous absorption for thick crystals. For $n = 2$ the image profile consists of a pair of dark peaks, the region at the dislocation core having background intensity. The reason for this is that a column passing through the core will have a displacement function equal to a lattice vector below the core when $\mathbf{g}\cdot\mathbf{b} = 2$. When the dislocation is inclined, the image profile may vary as y varies (particularly for regions near the surfaces) giving rise to special contrast effects. Examples of such contrast effects at inclined dislocations are visible in fig. 1 of sect. 1. The dislocations may appear like a zig-zag line or as a string of dark blobs depending on the total thickness of the foil [22].

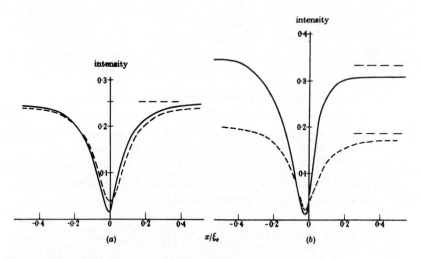

Fig. 26. Computed images of screw dislocation in the middle of a foil with $t = 8\xi_g$. $\mathbf{g}\cdot\mathbf{b} = 1$, $\xi_0' = \xi_g'$, $\xi_g/\xi_g' = 0.1$. In (a) $w = 0$; in (b) $w = 0.3$. Full curves are bright-field images; broken curves are dark-field images.

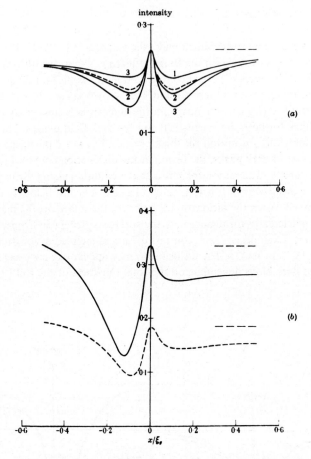

Fig. 27. Computed images of a screw dislocation for $\mathbf{g}\cdot\mathbf{b} = 2$, $t = 8\xi_g$. (a) $w = 0$, (b) $w = 0.3$. Curves (1), (2) and (3) in (a) refer to $y/\xi_g = 4$, 4.25 and 4.5 respectively.

For a general dislocation parallel to the surface in fig. 13 we may use the atomic displacements given by isotropic elasticity theory

$$\mathbf{R} = \frac{1}{2\pi}\left\{\mathbf{b}\Phi + \mathbf{b}_e\frac{\sin 2\Phi}{4(1-\nu)} + \mathbf{b}\times\mathbf{u}\left(\frac{(1-2\nu)}{2(1-\nu)}\ln|r| + \frac{\cos 2\Phi}{4(1-\nu)}\right)\right\} \quad (84)$$

where ν is Poisson's ratio, $\Phi = \phi - \gamma$, $\mathbf{b}$ is total Burgers vector, $\mathbf{b}_e$ is the edge component of $\mathbf{b}$, and $\mathbf{u}$ is a unit vector along the dislocation line. If $\mathbf{g}$ lies in the foil plane $\mathbf{g}\cdot(\mathbf{b}\times\mathbf{u}) = \mathbf{g}\cdot\mathbf{b}_e\tan\gamma$ and the expression for α becomes

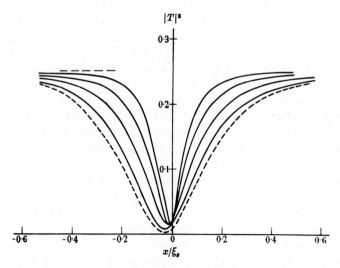

Fig. 28. Computed bright-field images of mixed dislocations shown as a function of p (see text). $\mathbf{g} \cdot \mathbf{b} = 1$, $t/\xi_g = 8$, $y/\xi_g = 4$, $w = 0$, $\xi_0' = \xi_g'$, $\xi_g/\xi_g' = 0.1$. In order of increasing width the images are for $p = -0.5$, 0, 0.5 and 1.0. The broken curve is for $p = 1$, $\tan \gamma = 1$.

$$\alpha = \mathbf{g} \cdot \mathbf{b}\phi + \mathbf{g} \cdot \mathbf{b}_e \ \{\tfrac{3}{8} \sin 2\phi + \tan \gamma \ (\tfrac{1}{4} \ln |r| - \tfrac{3}{8} \cos 2\phi)\} \qquad (85)$$

where we have put $\nu = \tfrac{1}{3}$. When $\mathbf{g} \cdot \mathbf{b}_e = 0$ the image of the mixed dislocation is the same as that of a pure screw dislocation. Images calculated for general dislocations in terms of the parameter $p = \mathbf{g} \cdot \mathbf{b}_e / \mathbf{g} \cdot \mathbf{b}$ are shown in fig. 28. The curve for $p = 0$ is that for a pure screw; $p = 1$ is that for a pure edge. All curves in fig. 28 except the broken curve refer to $\gamma = 0$. It is seen that the image of an edge dislocation is wider than that of a screw dislocation. The broken curve in fig. 28 shows the effect of tilting an edge dislocation so that $\gamma = 45°$.

3.4.7. Computer simulation of images

Recently [41] a very useful technique has been developed for displaying computed images of dislocations and stacking faults directly on computer output paper by arranging for the output printer to produce a "scale of grey" by over-printing type symbols. The numbers giving the intensities as solutions of eqs. (77) may then be displayed as a "dot" of a certain density, and the image may be constructed by a two-dimensional array of "dots". Head [42] has also shown that if surface relaxation effects are neglected, eqs. (77) need not be integrated every time the depth of the defect is changed. The equations are linear, and therefore only two independent solutions need be found to satisfy the initial boundary conditions for the defect at any depth. The equations are integrated for a column with the defect at the centre of a foil of thickness $2t$, and the solutions ϕ_0 and ϕ_g at 128 points spaced $t/64$ apart are found for the conditions $\phi_0(0) = 1$, $\phi_g(0) = 0$ and $\phi_0(0) = 0$, $\phi_g(0) = 1$. A linear combination of these solutions is easily found for which $\phi_0 = 1$, $\phi_g = 0$ at any of the chosen points. Thus the column of length $2t$ needs only two integrations to obtain the solutions for a foil of thickness t with the defect at 64 different depths. A considerable increase in the speed of the calculation is thereby obtained.

Fig. 29 is an example of the method applied to dislocations in ordered β-brass [41]. In this material elastic anisotropy is important. This leads to the result that screw dislocations for which $\mathbf{g} \cdot \mathbf{b} = 0$ are visible as a pair of closely spaced images with no contrast at the core (fig. 29a, b). Fig. 29 a–d show experimental images. Fig. 29 e–h are computer simulated images for $\mathbf{b} = [\bar{1}11]$, while fig. 29 i–l are computer simulated images for $\mathbf{b} = \frac{1}{2}[\bar{1}11]$. Direct comparison shows that the Burgers vector $\mathbf{b} = [\bar{1}11]$ provides the closest correspondence with the observed images. This example illustrates how it has become possible to determine not only the direction of the Burgers vector but also its magnitude by comparison with computer simulated images. Further applications of the method have been given by Head et al. [42], by Humble [43] and by Head [44].

The technique has been refined by Bullough, Maher and Perrin (unpublished work), who have used a cathode ray tube curve plotter to produce simulated images of dislocation loops, which are almost indistinguishable in quality from experimental images. Fig. 30 (due to Bullough et al.) shows the simulated image of a loop in the centre of a (001) foil of Nb of thickness $5\xi_{110}$. The loop lies on (111), has a radius ξ_{110}, and has Burgers vector $\mathbf{b} = \frac{1}{2}[\bar{1}\bar{1}1]$. The two pictures show the change in size of the image with n. In one picture $n = \mathbf{g} \cdot \mathbf{b} = +1$ while in the other $n = -1$. For comparison purposes we show experimental micrographs of loops in α-irradiated aluminium (Mazey et al. [45]). This demonstrates the change in size of the image with tilting. The simulated pictures and the micrographs are not directly comparable since the parameters are different. However, the simulated images do show how well the theory accounts for the details observed in experimental images.

Undoubtedly the computer simulation technique will be widely used in the future.

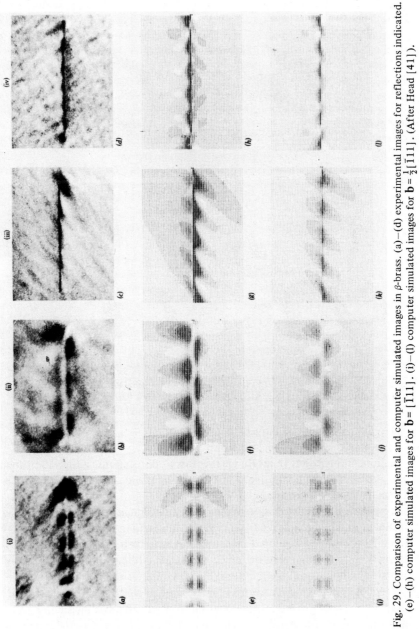

Fig. 29. Comparison of experimental and computer simulated images in β-brass. (a)–(d) experimental images for reflections indicated. (e)–(h) computer simulated images for $\mathbf{b} = [\bar{1}11]$. (i)–(l) computer simulated images for $\mathbf{b} = \frac{1}{2}[\bar{1}11]$. (After Head [41]).

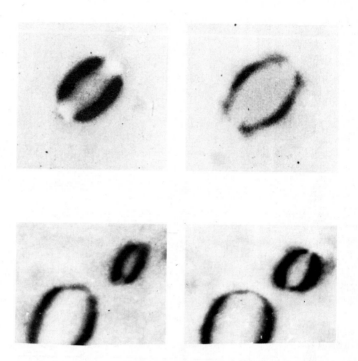

Fig. 30. Experimental images (lower pair) and computer simulated images (upper pair) of dislocation loops. Upper pair is due to Bullough, Maher and Perrin (unpublished). The lower pair is due to Mazey et al. [45]. (See text for discussion.)

3.4.8. Determination of Burgers vectors

Electron microscope image contrast provides a very useful technique for obtaining information about Burgers vectors of dislocations. Information about the direction of the Burgers vector, its magnitude, and also its sense can be obtained from suitable images.

The direction of the Burgers vector is usually obtained from tilting experiments in which one endeavours to make the dislocation vanish. We have seen (sect. 3.4.6) that a screw dislocation vanishes when $\mathbf{g} \cdot \mathbf{b} = 0$, i.e. when the Burgers vector is parallel to the reflecting planes. Although this criterion does not strictly hold for a mixed dislocation, very often it approximately holds (except in certain special cases), and weak residual contrast visible at a mixed dislocation when $\mathbf{g} \cdot \mathbf{b} = 0$ is often referred to as an "effective invisibility". The $\mathbf{g} \cdot \mathbf{b} = 0$ criterion for invisibility is illustrated in fig. 31. The material is quenched

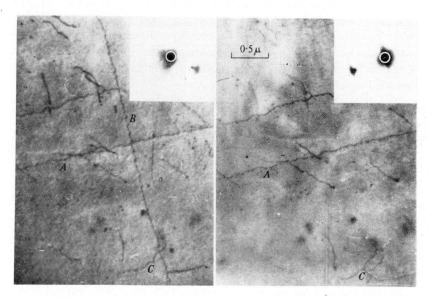

Fig. 31. Illustrating the vanishing of dislocations when $\mathbf{g} \cdot \mathbf{b} = 0$.

Al + 4% Cu alloy. It is known that this material contains long screw dislocation which have become helical by vacancy climb [46]. Thus the helical dislocations A and B in fig. 31 have Burgers vectors along the axes of the helices.
The diffraction patterns inset show the operating Bragg reflections. It is clear
that in fig. 31a with the 020 reflection $\mathbf{g} \cdot \mathbf{b} = 1$ for dislocations A and B and
both are visible. However, in fig. 31b the foil has been tilted to bring in the
$2\bar{2}0$ reflection. For this reflection the Burgers vector of B lies in the reflecting
planes and the dislocation B vanishes while A is still visible.

In using this method it is important to have available a specimen stage with
good goniometer facilities for tilting the specimen to various Bragg positions.
Kikuchi lines and bands are often used as an aid for tilting to a required reflection. If a dislocation can be made to vanish in two different reflections, the
direction of $\mathbf{b}$ is uniquely defined.

Care should be exercised in using the vanishing criterion to determine
Burgers vectors as evidenced by the experiences of Dingley and Hale [47], who
used large $\mathbf{g}$ vectors in dark-field to determine Burgers vectors in iron and steel.
Vanishing evidence suggested there were appreciable numbers of $\langle 100 \rangle$ and
$\langle 110 \rangle$ Burgers vectors in addition to the expected Burgers vector $\frac{1}{2}\langle 111 \rangle$. It
turns out, however, that "effective invisibility" may be obtained, even when

$\mathbf{g} \cdot \mathbf{b} \neq 0$, when dislocations are observed with large $\mathbf{g}$ vectors such as $321, 013$, and 222 in a deviated condition $s \neq 0$. For the large $\mathbf{g}$ vectors employed, $w = \xi_g s$ may be in the range 4 to 6 for small angular deviations from the Bragg position because of the large extinction distance for high order reflections. Under such conditions calculations show that "effective invisibility" may be obtained even though $\mathbf{g} \cdot \mathbf{b} \neq 0$ [48–50].

The magnitude of the Burgers vector can be obtained by comparison of the images observed with theoretically expected images. An example of this was given for β-brass in the previous section (fig. 29). Even in fig. 31 for which accurate comparisons have not been made, it is possible to surmise that $|\mathbf{g} \cdot \mathbf{b}| = 1$ in fig. 31a and that $|\mathbf{g} \cdot \mathbf{b}| = 2$ for A in fig. 31b from the appearance of the images, and hence that $b = \frac{1}{2}\langle 110\rangle$. Near the Bragg position the image for $|\mathbf{g} \cdot \mathbf{b}| = 2$ may be double while that for $|\mathbf{g} \cdot \mathbf{b}| = 1$ is always single (figs. 26,27). The image in fig. 31b is typical of a $|\mathbf{g} \cdot \mathbf{b}| = 2$ case in a deviated condition. Fig. 27b shows that the image in this case is characterised by a rather sharp edge on one side and a tail on the other, as is visible in fig. 31b.

The sense of the Burgers vector of a dislocation may be obtained by using the fact that even for $n = \mathbf{g} \cdot \mathbf{b} = 1$ the image of a dislocation observed in a deviated condition lies on one side of the core of the dislocation. This result may be obtained by the kinematical theory of contrast [20], and calculations also show that the result follows from dynamical theory [22,32]. The behaviour of the image as s varies in a bent foil is indicated schematically in fig. 32. The FS/RH-perfect crystal convention is used to define the Burgers

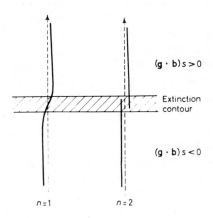

Fig. 32. Behaviour of a dislocation image at an extinction contour as seen by an observer looking from below the foil as in a normal positive photographic point.

vector. The side on which the image lies is determined by the sign of $(\mathbf{g} \cdot \mathbf{b})s$. It is clear that if $\mathbf{g}$ is known and the sign of s is known, the sense of the Burgers vector may be obtained from the image displacement. The sign of s can be obtained from the position of Kikuchi lines. Often when using low order reflections, the specimen is observed with w or s positive ($w \cong 1$) corresponding to the regions of good transmission in the perfect crystal rocking curve (figs. 9 and 12 of sect. 2). In this case the movement of the image may be observed by tilting the crystal so that the sign of $\mathbf{g}$ is changed. This is done by tilting so that a dark bend contour (as in fig. 12 of sect. 2) sweeps across the dislocation. In carrying out the analysis it is important to allow for an inversion of the diffraction vector $\mathbf{g}$ with respect to the image which occurs in the electron optical imaging process in electron microscopes employing three magnifying lenses [51].

Numerous determinations have been made of the sense of Burgers vectors of dislocation loops produced by various methods such as quenching, radiation damage or fatigue. It is important to find $\mathbf{b}$ in order to establish whether such loops are of the vacancy or interstitial type. The image of a loop will lie entirely inside or entirely outside the core of the dislocation depending on the sign of $(\mathbf{g} \cdot \mathbf{b})s$ (figs. 30 and 33). The formal analysis outlined above may of course be used, but the situation is made much clearer by a diagram like fig. 34 (Groves and Kelly [52]), where it can easily be seen on what side the image lies from the sense of bending of lattice planes. This diagram also shows that two loops of opposite sense inclined in different ways will give the same image contrast. Hence it is necessary to distinguish the sense of inclination of the loop. This may be done by tilting the specimen in a known sense through a large angle and noting the change in shape of the loop. Loops in MgO crystals have been studied by Groves and Kelly [52]. The loops were found to be vacancy type. Loops in α-irradiated aluminium have been studied by Mazey et al. [45] (see fig. 30) and were found to be of interstitial type. A simple method

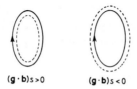

$(\mathbf{g} \cdot \mathbf{b})s > 0$ $(\mathbf{g} \cdot \mathbf{b})s < 0$

Fig. 33. Relative positions of a dislocation loop (continuous line) and its image (broken line) for $(\mathbf{g} \cdot \mathbf{b})s$ positive and negative as viewed from below the specimen.

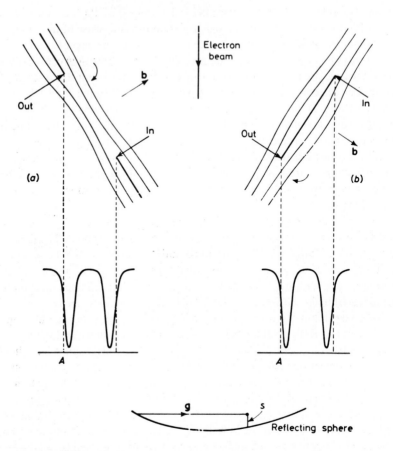

Fig. 34. Schematic diagram illustrating the influence of both the nature (i.e. interstitial or vacancy) of a loop and its sense of inclination in the foil on the size of the image. With a change in either of these quantities the loop image would lie outside the loop. s is assumed to be positive and the arrows indicate local lattice rotation.

of determining the nature of loops from the appearance of images on tilting through an extinction contour has been given by Edmondson and Williamson [53].

3.4.9. Partial dislocations

A partial dislocation has a Burgers vector which is not a lattice translation vector, and therefore the parameter $n = \mathbf{g} \cdot \mathbf{b}$ need not necessarily be an integer

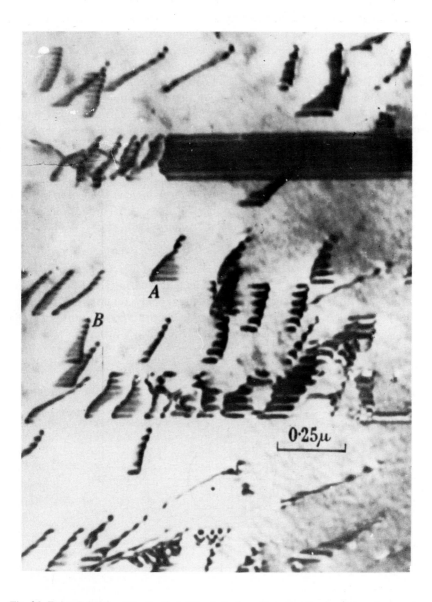

Fig. 35. Extended dislocations in Cu + 7% wt Al alloy. Note that for the dislocations A, B and others, one partial dislocation is visible as a dark line, while the other is invisible.

as for a whole dislocation. Also the partial dislocation must have a stacking fault on one side. For both Shockley and Frank partials in the fcc lattice n takes values 0, $\pm\frac{1}{3}$, $\pm\frac{2}{3}$, ±1 etc. Howie and Whelan [22] have considered the images of screw Shockley partials for various values of $\mathbf{g}\cdot\mathbf{b}$ and have shown that there is an effective invisibility when $\mathbf{g}\cdot\mathbf{b} = \pm\frac{1}{3}$, as well as the real invisibility when $\mathbf{g}\cdot\mathbf{b} = 0$. On the other hand partials for which $\mathbf{g}\cdot\mathbf{b} = \pm\frac{2}{3}$ are visible as dark lines. Fig. 35 shows an example of this behaviour where extended dislocations with stacking fault fringes are visible. Only one partial bounding the fault shows up as a dark line. Silcock and Tunstall [54] have studied the images of partials at precipitates of NbC in stainless steel. They were able to show that the precipitation occurred at extrinsic faults formed from a whole dislocation by dissociation into a sessile Frank partial and a Shockley partial. Further applications to faults and partial dislocations have been given by Booker and Tunstall [55], and to double faults and partial dislocations at loops in quenched aluminium by Tunstall and Goodhew [56].

3.4.10. Inclusions and vacancy clusters

The situation illustrated in fig. 36 refers to the case of a coherent precipitate or inclusion embedded in a matrix. The lattice parameter of the inclusion is different from that of the matrix and a strain field is set up in the matrix and precipitate which gives rise to diffraction contrast. The contrast was studied the Cu + Co system using kinematical diffraction theory by Phillips and

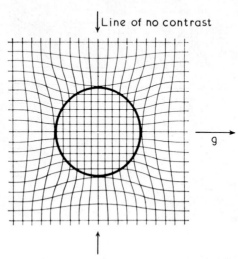

Fig. 36. Illustrating the strain field of a coherent spherical precipitate of Co in Cu + Co alloy.

Livingstone [57], and using dynamical theory by Ashby and Brown [58].
The displacement $\mathbf{R}$ to be inserted in eq. (78) for the dynamical calculation of
contrast is

$$\mathbf{R} = \frac{\epsilon r_0^3}{r^3}\,\mathbf{r}\,, \qquad |\mathbf{r}| \geqslant r_0$$

$$\mathbf{R} = \epsilon\mathbf{r}\,, \qquad |\mathbf{r}| \leqslant r_0 \tag{86}$$

where ϵ is a parameter called the "constrained strain". For isotropic elasticity
theory, where inclusion and matrix have the same elastic constants, $\epsilon = \frac{2}{3}\delta$,
where δ is the misfit parameter of inclusion and matrix lattices. For small precipitates of cobalt in copper the lattice distortion is as illustrated in fig. 36
and the misfit parameter δ is about -0.018.

In eq. (86), $\mathbf{r}$ is the radius vector from the centre of the inclusion; r_0 is the
radius of the inclusion. We see immediately that there will be a line of no

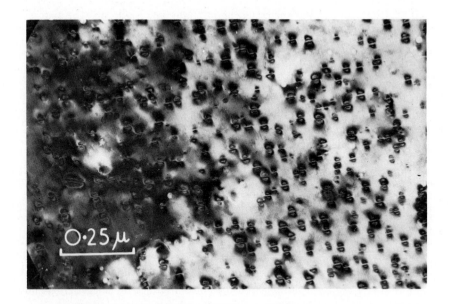

Fig. 37. Bright-field image of coherent Co precipitates in Cu + Co alloy. 311 reflection.
(After Ashby and Brown [58]).

Fig. 38. Dark-field image of coherent Co precipitates in Cu + Co alloy. 200 reflection.
(After Ashby and Brown [58].)

contrast on the image perpendicular to the **g** vector, since the displacements
are radial (fig. 36). Examples of this behaviour are shown in figs. 37 and 38,
due to Ashby and Brown. Fig. 37 is a bright field image taken with a 311 reflection, while fig. 38 is a dark field image taken with a 200 reflection. The
image of a spherical inclusion consists of a pair of lobes of strain contrast
separated by the line of no contrast. Ashby and Brown [58] have studied the
profiles and widths of the images and have given graphs from which it is possible to estimate ϵ from the observed width.

It is also possible to determine the nature of the inclusion from the appearance of the dark-field image, i.e. to determine the sign of ϵ. A rule similar to
that for the dark-field image of an intrinsic stacking fault with a class B reflection holds (sect. 3.4.2. and fig. 21). For inclusions near the top foil surface,
bright-field and dark-field images are similar for thick crystals with anomalous
absorption, while for inclusions near the bottom surface the images are pseudo-
complementary. Inclusions near either surface behave similarly for dark-field
images, and the contrast is in the form of a pair of lobes, one dark and the
other bright (fig. 38). For an interstitial type inclusion (ϵ positive) the **g** vector

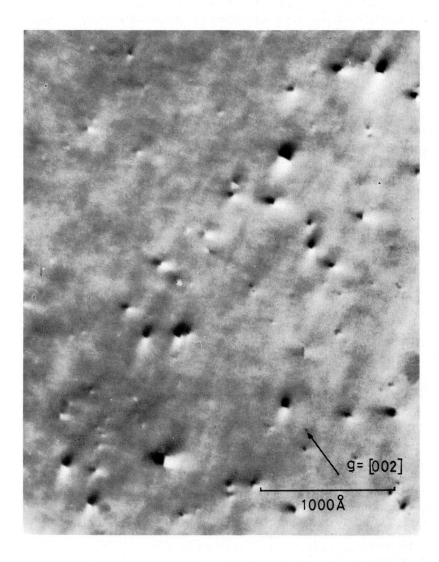

Fig. 39. Bright-field image of point defect clusters produced by irradiating thin copper foils with Cu⁺ ions of energy 30 keV. Analysis shows that the clusters are Frank vacancy type loops on {111} planes of diameter ≈50 A. (After Wilson [61].)

points towards the dark lobe, and vice-versa for a vacancy type inclusion (ϵ negative). For further discussion of precipitate contrast effects the student should refer to Hirsch et al. [32].

Finally, reference should be made to the problem of determining the nature of very small point defect clusters in irradiated metals (Rühle et al. [59], McIntyre [60].) Usually the observed defects are very small (≈ 70 Å diameter) so that a distinct loop of dislocation is not resolved. Instead the clusters often appear as very small regions of strain contrast, similar in appearance to the contrast of inclusions mentioned above. It is thought that the defects represent small dislocation loops. The plane of the loop may be inclined to the foil surface, and the line of no contrast is not always perpendicular to **g**. In attempting to determine the nature of these loops, a rule similar to the one outlined above for inclusions is expected to hold, at least for Frank sessile loops perpendicular to the surface, and very close to the surface, observed with a **g** vector perpendicular to the plane of the loop. Complications occur for very small loops since the contrast is found to reverse with increasing depth. Clusters in neutron irradiated metals will be distributed throughout the foil thickness, so that it becomes necessary to determine the depth of the clusters by stereo techniques. The work of Rühle et al. [59] suggests that loops in neutron irradiated copper are of vacancy type, while that of McIntyre [60] suggests that they are of interstitial type. Fig. 39 shows point defect clusters in copper foils which have been irradiated with copper ions of energy 30 keV. The penetration of the ions is small so that the clusters are located within about 100 Å from the surface. Analysis shows that the clusters are of vacancy type (Wilson [61]).

References

[1] C.G.Darwin, Phil. Mag. 27 (1914) 315, 675.
[2] P.B.Hirsch, A.Howie and M.J.Whelan, Phil. Trans. Roy. Soc. 252 (1960) 499.
[3] H.A.Bethe, Ann. Phys. Lpz. 87 (1928) 55.
[4] C.H.McGillavry, Physica 7 (1940) 329.
[5] J.Hillier and R.F.Baker, Phys. Rev. 61 (1942) 722.
[6] R.D.Heidenreich and L.Sturkey, J. Appl. Phys. 16 (1945) 97.
[7] H.Yoshioka, J. Phys. Soc. Japan 12 (1957) 628.
[8] K.Molière, Ann. Phys. Lpz. 34 (1939) 461.
[9] M.von Laue, Acta Cryst. 2 (1949) 106.
[10] G.Borrmann, Phys. Zeitschrift 42 (1941) 157.
[11] W.H.Zachariasen, Theory of X-ray diffraction in Crystals, 1945 (Dover, 1967).
[12] H.Hashimoto, J. Appl. Phys. 35 (1964) 277.
[13] A.J.F.Metherell and M.J.Whelan, Phil. Mag. 15 (1967) 755.

[14] C.J.Humphreys and P.B.Hirsch, Phil. Mag. 18 (1968) 115.
[15] S.Takagi, Acta Cryst. 15 (1962) 1311.
[16] B.Jouffrey and D.Taupin, Phil. Mag. 16 (1967) 703;
     D.Taupin, Acta Cryst. 23 (1967) 25.
[17] A.Howie and Z.S.Basinski, Phil. Mag. 17 (1968) 1039.
[18] M.J.Whelan and P.B.Hirsch, Phil. Mag. 2 (1957) 1121.
[19] M.J.Whelan and P.B.Hirsch, Phil. Mag. 2 (1957) 1303.
[20] P.B.Hirsch, A.Howie and M.J.Whelan, Phil. Trans. Roy. Soc. A252 (1960) 499.
[21] A.Howie and M.J.Whelan, Proc. Roy. Soc. A263 (1961) 217.
[22] A.Howie and M.J.Whelan, Proc. Roy. Soc. A267 (1962) 206.
[23] C.M.Drum, Phil. Mag. 11 (1965) 313.
[24] J.van Landuyt, R.Gevers and S.Amelinckx, Phys. Stat. Sol. 7 (1964) 519.
[25] H.Hashimoto and M.J.Whelan, J. Phys. Soc. Japan 18 (1963) 1706.
[26] R.Gevers, A.Art and S.Amelinckx, Phys. Stat. Sol. 3 (1963) 1563.
[27] H.Hashimoto, A.Howie and M.J.Whelan, Proc. Roy. Soc. A269 (1962) 80.
[28] D.W.Pashley and A.E.B.Presland, J.Inst. Metals 87 (1959) 419.
[29] R.M.Fisher and M.J.Marcinkowski, Phil. Mag. 6 (1961) 1385.
[30] C.M.Drum and M.J.Whelan, Phil. Mag. 11 (1965) 205.
[31] G.R.Booker and R.Stickler, Brit. J. Appl. Phys. 13 (1962) 446; 33 (1962) 3281.
[32] P.B.Hirsch, A.Howie, R.B.Nicholson, D.W.Pashley and M.J.Whelan, Electron Micro-
     scopy of Thin Crystals (Butterworths, 1965).
[33] G.R.Booker and A.Howie, Appl. Phys. Letters 3 (1963) 156;
     G.R.Booker, Disc. Faraday Soc. No. 38 (1964) 298.
[34] R.Gevers, Phil. Mag. 7 (1962) 1681.
[35] R.Gevers, P.Delavignette, H.Blank and S.Amelinckx, Phys. Stat. Sol. 4 (1964) 383.
[36] R.Gevers, Phys. Stat. Sol. 3 (1963) 1672.
[37] R.Gevers, J.Van Landuyt and S.Amelinckx, Phys. Stat. Sol. 11 (1965) 689.
[38] R.Gevers, P.Delavignette, H.Blank, J.Van Landuyt and S.Amelinckx, Phys. Stat.
     Sol. 5 (1964) 595.
[39] R.Gevers, J.Van Landuyt and S.Amelinckx, Phys. Stat. Sol. 18 (1966) 325.
[40] M.J.Goringe and U.Valdrè, Proc. Roy. Soc. A295 (1966) 192.
[41] A.K.Head, Australian J. of Phys. 20 (1967) 557.
[42] A.K.Head, M.H.Loretto and P.Humble, Phys. Stat. Sol. 20 (1967) 505.
[43] P.Humble, Australian J. of Phys. 21 (1968) 325.
[44] A.K.Head, Australian J. of Phys. 22 (1969) 43.
[45] D.J.Mazey, R.S.Barnes and A.Howie, Phil. Mag. 7 (1962) 1861.
[46] G.Thomas and M.J.Whelan, Phil. Mag. 4 (1959) 511.
[47] D.J.Dingley and K.F.Hale, Proc. Roy. Soc. A295 (1966) 55.
[48] K.F.Hale and M.Henderson Brown, Proc. Fourth Eur. Regional Conf. on Electron
     Microscopy, Rome Vol. 1 (1968) p. 409;
     K.F.Hale and M.Henderson Brown, Proc. Roy. Soc. A310 (1969) 479.
[49] L.K.France and M.H.Loretto, Proc. Fourth Eur. Regional Conf. on Electron Micro-
     scopy, Rome Vol. 1 (1968) p. 301.
[50] D.J.Dingley, Proc. Fourth Eur. Regional Conf. on Electron Microscopy, Rome Vol.
     1 (1968) p. 303.
[51] G.W.Groves and M.J.Whelan, Phil. Mag. 7 (1962) 1603.
[52] G.W.Groves and A.Kelly, Phil. Mag. 6 (1961) 1527; 7 (1962) 892.

[53] B.Edmondson and G.K.Williamson, Phil. Mag. 9 (1964) 277.

[54] J.M.Silcock and W.J.Tunstall, Phil. Mag. 10 (1964) 361.

[55] G.R.Booker and W.J.Tunstall, Phil. Mag. 13 (1966) 71.

[56] W.J.Tunstall and P.J.Goodhew, Phil. Mag. 13 (1966) 1259.

[57] V.A.Phillips and J.D.Livingston, Phil. Mag. 7 (1962) 969.

[58] M.F.Ashby and L.M.Brown, Phil. Mag. 8 (1963) 1083, 1649.

[59] M.Rühle, M.Wilkens and U.Essmann, Phys. Stat. Sol. 11 (1965) 819.

[60] K.G.McIntyre, Phil. Mag. 15 (1967) 205.

[61] M.M.Wilson, Proc. Fourth Eur. Regional Conf. on Electron Microscopy, Rome Vol.
      1 (1968) p. 365;
      M.M.Wilson, Radiation Effects 1 (1969) 207.

Diffraction and Imaging Techniques in Material Science,
eds. S. Amelinckx, R. Gevers and J. van Landuyt
© *North-Holland Publishing Company, 1978*

THE STUDY OF PLANAR INTERFACES
BY MEANS OF ELECTRON MICROSCOPY

S. AMELINCKX and J. Van LANDUYT

Studiecentrum voor Kernenergie, SCK/CEN, Mol
and Rijksuniversitair Centrum Antwerpen

1. Introduction

"Single crystals" in the common sense of the word are often fragmented into domains. The origin of the fragmentation is usually connected with the creation of order of some kind, accompanied by a decrease in symmetry.

One can distinguish domains due to: (i) chemical order, i.e. ordering of atoms according to their chemical nature; (ii) magnetic order, i.e. ordering of magnetic moments either in the ferromagnetic or in the anti-ferromagnetic mode; (iii) electric order, i.e. ordering of electric dipoles either according to the ferroelectric or to the anti-ferroelectric mode.

The structures within the different domains are of course identical; however, the structures within different domains can be geometrically related in various ways, giving rise to different types of interfaces. The type and number of variants of the ordered structure in the domains can be derived from group theoretical considerations [1]. The logical classification in *orientation* and *translation* variants leads to the distinction between three categories of interfaces:

(i) Translation interfaces between translation variants.

(ii) Twin interfaces separating orientation variants.

(iii) Inversion boundaries separate variants having the inversion relation with respect to each other.

We shall discuss briefly the geometrical characteristics of each of them.

2. Geometrical description of the interface

2.1. *Translation interfaces*

If the structure in one part of the crystal can be derived from that in the other part of the same crystal by means of a parallel translation, the interface can be characterized by a constant displacement vector $\mathbf{R}$, by convention representing the displacement of the crystal part last met by the electrons with respect to the front part; it is only determined modulus a lattice vector.

If $\mathbf{R}$ is a lattice vector for the disordered structure but not for the ordered one, the interface is called an *antiphase boundary* (APB) (fig. 1b). If on the other hand $\mathbf{R}$ is not a lattice vector for the disordered structure it is called a *stacking fault* (S.F.) (fig. 1a). The occurrence of stacking faults is common in structures consisting of close packed layers, because on such layers there are well defined positions which correspond to relative minima in stacking fault energy.

Whereas stacking faults are *geometrical* faults, APB's are rather *chemical* faults.

Antiphase boundaries are common in ordered alloys. In fig. 1b, a two-dimensional schematic view of an APB in an AB alloy is shown.

APB's are *conservative* if the displacement vector is in the boundary plane. If this is not the case a slab of material with thickness $t = \mathbf{R} \cdot \mathbf{n}$ ($\mathbf{n}$ is unit normal on boundary plane) is either removed or inserted. If this slab has a chemical composition, which is different from that of the crystal, the APB is termed *non-conservative* since its presence causes a change in chemical composition (figs. 2a, b). The name *crystallographic shear plane* is also given to such interfaces in non metallic compounds such as oxides. So called *non-stoichiometric* compounds often contain regular sequences of crystallographic shear planes. They are then called *shear structures* [2,3] (fig. 3). Similarly the periodic

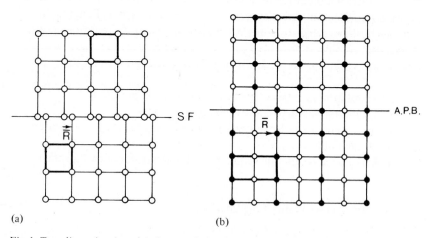

(a)   (b)

Fig. 1. Two-dimensional models for translation interfaces. (a) Stacking fault; (b) antiphase boundary.

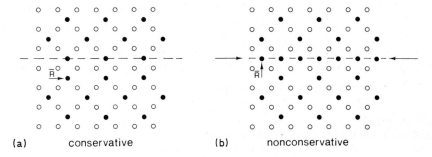

(a)   conservative   **(b)**   nonconservative

Fig. 2. Hypothetical planar defects illustrating the conservative (a) or the non conservative (b) character depending on the direction of the displacement vector **R**.

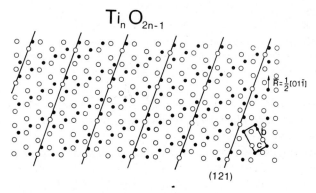

Fig. 3. Model for a *shear structure* in the rutile phase. Periodic arrays of non-conservative translation interfaces give rise to a new structure.

arrangement of APB's in alloys gives rise to *long period superstructures.*

In ordered alloys a planar interface may be simultaneously a SF and a APB, such interfaces are called *complex faults* [4].

APB's may be of thermal nature, i.e. result from ordering, either substitutional ordering or ordering of vacancies, or they may be generated by glide. Glide often generates *complex faults* i.e. interfaces which contain simultaneously a chemical and a geometrical fault.

2.2. *Twin interfaces*

From the electron microscopic point of view it is convenient to describe a twin boundary as resulting from the displacement field pictured in fig. 4. The displacement field now consists of a vector with constant direction and sense,

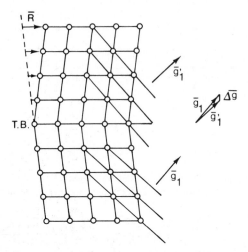

Fig. 4. Model for a twin- or orientation interface. The displacement field is indicated by
the **R**-vectors. At the interface (twin boundary: TB), the grating changes orientation into
its mirror image; corresponding **g**-vectors enclose an angle.

but with a magnitude which increases linearly with the distance to the contact
plane between the two crystal parts.

We shall consider two extreme situations, which are both of practical interest:

(i) the displacement per atom plane is a very small fraction of the interatomic distance, i.e. the "obliquity" of the twin is small [5] ;

(ii) the displacement per atom plane is a large fraction of the interatomic
distance.

In the second case the two crystal parts have to be considered as separate,
although related by a symmetry operation of the disordered crystal. From
the diffraction point of view they behave as two different crystals i.e. diffracting separately. In most of the diffraction situations only one of the two crystal parts is in reflecting position. The electron beam then only "sees" this one
member of the twin.

In the first case the crystal can still be considered as "single", the lattice of
the two crystal parts being only slightly different. The points in the reciprocal
lattice are then "practically" coincident in such a way that the two crystal
parts still diffract simultaneously, although with a different excitation error
(i.e. deviation from the Bragg position). Such interfaces will be termed *domain
boundaries*. These interfaces are characterized by a Δ**g** as indicated in fig. 4.

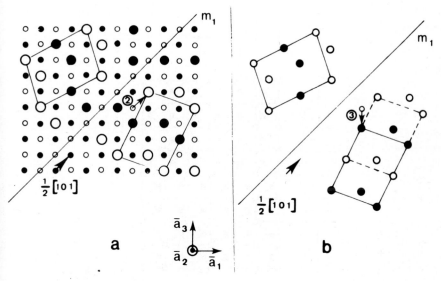

Fig. 5. Two examples of mixed interfaces combining a mirror m_1 and a translation resp. 2 and 3. Both yield the same configuration since the displacements differ by a lattice vector.

2.3. Mixed interfaces

Certain combinations of boundary operations for orientation variants with the translations that characterize antiphase boundaries lead to new types of interfaces. It is well known that the combination of a rotation with a translation perpendicular to the axis is equivalent to a rotation over the same angle and in the same sense about a parallel axis. Similarly the combination of a mirror operation with a translation perpendicular to the mirror plane is equivalent to a mirror operation with respect to a parallel plane. Such combinations are not considered as essentially new interface operations. However if the translation has a component parallel to the mirror plane or to the rotation axis, an essentially new boundary operation describes the interface. An example of a glide twin boundary in the ordered alloy Au_5Mn_2 is represented in fig. 5.

2.4. Inversion boundaries

On transforming from a centro-symmetrical into a non-centro-symmetrical structure, boundaries between domains in which the structures are related by an inversion operation are often formed. A schematic representation in two dimensions of such a boundary is shown in fig. 6. The lattice is now the same in both domains but the structure is *not*.

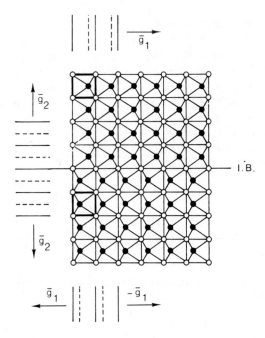

Fig. 6. Model for an inversion boundary (IB) in a non-centrosymmetrical crystal. It is clear from the model that the non-centrosymmetry is not revealed by reflections such as $\mathbf{g}_2$.

Such an inversion can sometimes be combined with a parallel translation (fig. 7). The structures in the two domains can of course again be deduced one from the other by means of a single inversion. Nevertheless it is meaningful to introduce the concept of a displacement vector $\mathbf{R}$ also in this case [6] because the presence of such a displacement can be revealed for reflections which are not affected by the centro-symmetrical nature of the structure. Boundaries of this nature have been found in the alloy δ-NiMo [7] in the χ-phase $Fe_{36}Cr_{12}Ti_5Mo_5$ [8] and in GeTe [9].

A related situation is observed in non centro-symmetrical crystals containing domains related by a 180° rotation about an axis which is not an axis of even order for the structure. For reflections belonging to the zone with its axis parallel to the rotation axis, the reflection $+\mathbf{g}$ is excited in one domain whereas the reflection $-\mathbf{g}$ is excited in the other, a structural relation which is akin to the inversion relation. Dauphine twins in quartz are a typical example of such a situation [10]. Observations of these boundaries and the particular contrast they produce will also be discussed.

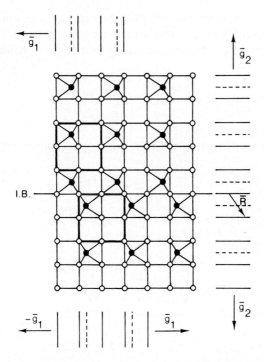

Fig. 7. Combination of an inversion boundary with an antiphase boundary. The displacement vector **R** is marked to the right of the figure.

3. Contrast theory

In order to interpret the images of these defects it will be necessary to analyse in detail the interaction between incident electrons and a crystal foil. In the first place the two-beam dynamical theory will be developed for a perfect crystal (3.1) afterwards the case of a faulted crystal will be treated.

3.1. *Basic equations for the perfect crystal*

We shall systematically make the following assumptions: (i) the dynamical theory for the symmetrical Laue case applies; (ii) a two-beam situation is realized; (iii) the column approximation applies; (iv) anomalous absorption is adequately taken into account by making the extinction distance complex; (v) normal absorption is systematically neglected unless otherwise stated.

The meaning and validity of these assumptions have been discussed in other lectures.

If the crystal is non-centrosymmetrical we shall moreover assume that the real and the imaginary parts of this lattice potential may have different phases for the same Fourier-coefficient. Let the complex lattice potential in that case be represented by:

$$V(\mathbf{r}) = v_0 + i w_0 + \sum_{\mathbf{g}} (v_{\mathbf{g}} + i w_{\mathbf{g}}) \, e^{2\pi i \mathbf{g} \cdot \mathbf{r}} , \tag{1}$$

where $\mathbf{g}$ is a reciprocal lattice vector.

The Fourier-coefficients $v_{\mathbf{g}}$ and $w_{\mathbf{g}}$ are in general complex and we shall write:

$$v_{\mathbf{g}} = |v_{\mathbf{g}}| \, e^{i\theta} \mathbf{g} ; \qquad v_{-\mathbf{g}} = |v_{-\mathbf{g}}| e^{-i\theta} \mathbf{g} ,$$

$$w_{\mathbf{g}} = |w_{\mathbf{g}}| \, e^{i\phi} \mathbf{g} ; \qquad w_{-\mathbf{g}} = |w_{-\mathbf{g}}| e^{-i\phi} \mathbf{g} . \tag{2}$$

We shall furthermore put:

$$(v_{\mathbf{g}} + i w_{\mathbf{g}})/k_{\mathbf{g}} = \frac{1}{\xi_{\mathbf{g}}} \, e^{i\theta} \mathbf{g} + \frac{i}{\xi'_{\mathbf{g}}} \, e^{i\phi} \mathbf{g} = \frac{1}{q_{\mathbf{g}}} \, e^{i\theta} \mathbf{g}$$

$$(v_{-\mathbf{g}} + i w_{-\mathbf{g}})/k_{\mathbf{g}} = \frac{1}{\xi_{\mathbf{g}}} \, e^{-i\theta} \mathbf{g} + \frac{i}{\xi'_{\mathbf{g}}} \, e^{-i\phi} \mathbf{g} = \frac{1}{q_{-\mathbf{g}}} \, e^{-i\theta} \mathbf{g} \tag{3}$$

where:

$$\frac{1}{q_{\mathbf{g}}} = \frac{1}{\xi_{\mathbf{g}}} + \frac{i}{\xi'_{\mathbf{g}}} e^{i\beta} \mathbf{g} , \qquad \frac{1}{q_{-\mathbf{g}}} = \frac{1}{\xi_{\mathbf{g}}} + \frac{i}{\xi'_{\mathbf{g}}} e^{-i\beta} \mathbf{g} , \tag{4}$$

with:

$$\beta_{\mathbf{g}} = \phi_{\mathbf{g}} - \theta_{\mathbf{g}} . \tag{5}$$

Also we have $w_0/k_0 = 1/\xi_0$; $k_0 \simeq k_{\mathbf{g}}$ is the wave vector of the incident and scattered electron.

With this notation the generalized Howie–Whelan system of coupled differential equations becomes [11]

$$\frac{d\psi_0}{dz} = \frac{\pi i}{q_{-\mathbf{g}}} e^{-i\theta} \mathbf{g} \, \psi_{\mathbf{g}} - \frac{\pi}{\xi'_0} \, \psi_0 ,$$

$$\frac{d\psi_{\mathbf{g}}}{dz} = \frac{\pi i}{q_{\mathbf{g}}} e^{i\theta} \mathbf{g} \, \psi_0 + 2\pi i s_{\mathbf{g}} \psi_{\mathbf{g}} - \frac{\pi}{\xi'_0} \, \psi_{\mathbf{g}} , \tag{6}$$

where s_g describes the deviation from the exact Bragg condition; ψ_0 and ψ_g are the amplitudes of transmitted (ψ_0) and scattered (ψ_g) beams respectively, z measures the depth in the crystal, the origin being in the entrance face. This system of equations describes the dynamical interplay between incident and diffracted beam.

The substitution:

$$\psi_0 = T_g\, e^{-\pi z/\xi_0'}\, e^{\pi i s z}, \quad \text{and} \quad \psi_g = S_g\, e^{-\pi z/\xi_0'}\, e^{i\theta_g}\, e^{\pi i s z}, \qquad (7)$$

transforms the system of eqs. (6) into:

$$\frac{dT_g}{dz} = \frac{\pi i}{q_{-g}} S_g - \pi i s_g T_g, \qquad \frac{dS_g}{dz} = \frac{\pi i}{q_g} T_g + \pi i s_g S_g. \qquad (8)$$

The normal absorption, described by the parameter ξ_0' is clearly accounted for by the decreasing exponential factor in the expressions (7). Since this factor is common for ψ_0 and ψ_g we shall ignore it in the rest of the discussion. The expression (7) also demonstrates that due to the presence of the factor $e^{i\theta_g}$ a phase difference is introduced between diffracted and transmitted beam. This phase difference is of opposite sign for the $+g$ and the $-g$ reflections operating; this will have direct consequences on the contrast behaviour of inversion boundaries.

In the centrosymmetrical case one can choose the origin in a centre of symmetry and then $V(\mathbf{r}) = V(-\mathbf{r})$ as a result $\beta_g = 0$ or π and $\theta_g = 0$. Assuming $\beta_g = 0$ and simplifying the notation, the set of eq. (8) reduces to:

$$\frac{dT}{dz} + \pi i s T = \frac{\pi i}{q_{-g}} S, \qquad \frac{dS}{dz} - \pi i s S = \frac{\pi i}{q_g} T, \qquad (9)$$

where $1/q_g = 1/\xi_g + i/\xi_g'$.

Putting $\sigma = (1/q_g)\sqrt{1 + (sq_g)^2}$ we obtain for the real and imaginary parts of σ:

$$\sigma = \sigma_r + i\sigma_i \quad \text{with} \quad \sigma_r \simeq \frac{1}{\xi_g}\sqrt{1 + (s\xi_g)^2} \; ;$$

$$\sigma_i \simeq \frac{1}{\xi_g'\sqrt{1 + (s\xi_g)^2}}, \qquad (10)$$

where higher order terms in ξ_g/ξ_g' have been neglected.

The solution of (9) with the initial values $T = 1, S = 0$ at $z = 0$ is now:

$$T(z, s) = \cos \pi \sigma z - i(s/\sigma_r) \sin \pi \sigma z$$

$$S(z, s) = [i/(\sigma_r \xi_g)] \sin \pi \sigma z , \qquad (11)$$

where as a further approximation, σ has been replaced by σ_r in the coefficients but not in the exponentials or goniometric expressions.

From (11) the diffracted intensity $I_S = SS^*$ is found:

$$I_S(s, z) = \frac{\sin^2 \pi \sigma_z}{(\sigma_r \xi_g)^2} . \qquad (12)$$

The solution of the same system of equations, but for the initial values $T = 0$ and $S = 1$ at $z = 0$, is on the other hand:

$$T = S(z, s) \equiv S^- , \qquad S = T(z, s) \equiv T^- . \qquad (13)$$

This follows by noting that the initial values $T = 1, S = 0$ reduce to the initial values $T = 0, S = 1$ if one interchanges T and S. Performing the same interchange in the set of eqs. (8) and (9) and simultaneously changing the sign of s leaves the set of equations unchanged. The solution is therefore obtained by performing this substitution in the expressions (11) which leads immediately to the proposed solution (13). In matrix notation we thus obtain:

$$\begin{pmatrix} T \\ S \end{pmatrix}_{out} = \begin{pmatrix} T & S^- \\ S & T^- \end{pmatrix} \begin{pmatrix} T \\ S \end{pmatrix}_{in} = M(z, s) \begin{pmatrix} T \\ S \end{pmatrix}_{in} , \qquad (14)$$

where the subscripts in and out refer respectively to the incoming and outgoing wave for the slab of perfect crystal.

The square matrix M is the *response matrix* of the crystal slab. Knowing the amplitudes of the wave incident on the crystal in the directions of the incident beam and of the Bragg scattered beam it allows to calculate the amplitudes of outgoing waves in the same directions. If the considered slab is the one first met by the electrons:

$$\begin{pmatrix} T \\ S \end{pmatrix} = M(s, z) \begin{pmatrix} 1 \\ 0 \end{pmatrix}. \qquad (15)$$

Evidently $M(s, z)$ must have the property:

$$M(z_1 + z_2 + ... + z_n, s) = M(z_n, s) ... M(z_2, s) M(z_1, s), \qquad (16)$$

which is easy to verify. Also the property is physically evident, it expresses the fact that it is immaterial whether or not the perfect crystal is thought to be divided into a number of lamellae by introducing interfaces parallel to the foil surfaces.

For the *non-centro symmetrical crystal* one cannot ignore the phase factor $e^{i\theta}\mathbf{g}$ in the scattered amplitude even when $\beta_\mathbf{g} = 0$. The response matrix must therefore be written as:

$$\begin{pmatrix} T_\mathbf{g} & S_\mathbf{g}^- e^{-i\theta\mathbf{g}} \\ S_\mathbf{g} e^{i\theta\mathbf{g}} & T_\mathbf{g}^- \end{pmatrix}. \qquad (17)$$

For a single perfect slab it leads to the correct expressions. This response matrix can be written as a product of matrices:

$$\begin{pmatrix} 1 & 0 \\ 0 & e^{i\theta\mathbf{g}} \end{pmatrix} \begin{pmatrix} T_\mathbf{g} & S_\mathbf{g}^- \\ S_\mathbf{g} & T_\mathbf{g}^- \end{pmatrix} \begin{pmatrix} 1 & 0 \\ 0 & e^{-i\theta\mathbf{g}} \end{pmatrix} \begin{pmatrix} 1 \\ 0 \end{pmatrix} \qquad (18)$$

$$\begin{pmatrix} T_\mathbf{g} \\ S_\mathbf{g} e^{i\theta\mathbf{g}} \end{pmatrix} = \delta(\theta_\mathbf{g}) M(z, s) \delta(-\theta_\mathbf{g}) \begin{pmatrix} 1 \\ 0 \end{pmatrix} \qquad (19)$$

where:

$$\delta(\alpha) = \begin{pmatrix} 1 & 0 \\ 0 & e^{i\alpha} \end{pmatrix}. \qquad (20)$$

Note that the δ-matrix has the property that:

$$\delta(\alpha_1)\delta(\alpha_2) = \delta(\alpha_2)\delta(\alpha_1) = \delta(\alpha_1 + \alpha_2),$$

and further that $\delta^{-1}(\alpha) = \delta(-\alpha)$.

Crystal parts which are far from any reflecting position behave with respect to scattering as a *vacuum layer*. We therefore need the response matrix for a layer of non-scattering crystal. We can express this by noting that the extinction distance for that layer becomes infinite. For an infinite extinction distance the set of eq. (9) reduces to:

$$\frac{dT}{dz} + \pi i s T = 0 \; ; \qquad \frac{dS}{dz} - \pi i s S = 0 \; . \tag{21}$$

The solution then clearly is:

$$T = T_0 e^{-i\pi s z} \; ; \qquad S = S_0 e^{\pi i s z} \; , \tag{22}$$

where T_0 and S_0 are the amplitudes of the beam incident on the vacuum layer respectively in the incident and in the scattered directions. We can write:

$$\begin{pmatrix} T \\ S \end{pmatrix} = \begin{pmatrix} e^{-\pi i s z} & 0 \\ 0 & e^{\pi i s z} \end{pmatrix} \begin{pmatrix} T_0 \\ S_0 \end{pmatrix} \equiv V(z, s) \begin{pmatrix} T_0 \\ S_0 \end{pmatrix} \; , \tag{23}$$

where V is the *vacuum matrix*, which depends on the s-value of the crystal part that *preceeds* the vacuum layer, whereas z is the thickness of the layer.

3.2. Equations for a crystal containing defects
3.2.1. General deformation

The deformation of the crystal is characterized by means of the displacement field $\mathbf{R}(\mathbf{r})$. The atom which would be at $\mathbf{r}$ in the perfect crystal is now to be found at $\mathbf{r} + \mathbf{R}(\mathbf{r})$ in the faulted crystal. Since the crystal is described by its lattice potential one can write:

$$V_F(\mathbf{r}) = V_P(\mathbf{r} - \mathbf{R}) \; , \tag{24}$$

where F and P refer to faulted and perfect crystal respectively. The lattice potential of the faulted crystal then becomes:

$$V_F(\mathbf{r}) = \sum_{\mathbf{g}} v_{\mathbf{g}} e^{2\pi i \mathbf{g} \cdot (\mathbf{r} - \mathbf{R})} = \sum_{\mathbf{g}} (v_{\mathbf{g}} e^{-i\alpha_{\mathbf{g}}}) e^{2\pi i \mathbf{g} \cdot \mathbf{r}} \; , \tag{25}$$

where $\alpha = 2\pi \mathbf{g} \cdot \mathbf{R}$ (26). The deformation is thus taken into account by replacing the Fouriercoefficient $v_{\mathbf{g}}$ of the perfect crystal by $v_{\mathbf{g}} e^{-i\alpha_{\mathbf{g}}}$. In view of the inverse proportionality between the extinction distance $\xi_{\mathbf{g}}$ and the Fouriercoefficient $v_{\mathbf{g}}$ (3) one concludes that the following substitution must be performed in the system of equations:

$$\frac{1}{q_g} \rightarrow \frac{1}{q_g} e^{-i\alpha_g} ,$$

and since moreover $\alpha_{-g} = -\alpha_g$, we also have:

$$\frac{1}{q_{-g}} \rightarrow \frac{1}{q_{-g}} e^{i\alpha_g} .$$

The system of eqs. (9) therefore becomes:

$$\begin{cases} \dfrac{dT}{dz} + \pi i s T = \dfrac{\pi i}{q_{-g}} e^{i\alpha_g} S , \\[3mm] \dfrac{dS}{dz} - \pi i s S = \dfrac{\pi i}{q_g} e^{-i\alpha_g} T . \end{cases} \tag{27}$$

The substitution: .

$$T = T' e^{\pi i \alpha'} , \qquad S = S' e^{-\pi i \alpha'} , \tag{28}$$

with $\alpha' = \alpha/2\pi$ reduces the set of equations to the following one:

$$\frac{dT'}{dz} + \pi i \left(s + \frac{d\alpha'}{dz} \right) T' = \frac{\pi i}{q_{-g}} S' ,$$

$$\frac{dS'}{dz} - \pi i \left(s + \frac{d\alpha'}{dz} \right) S' = \frac{\pi i}{q_g} T' . \tag{29}$$

The deformation is clearly described by the variation of the effective s value; where α' varies with z the effective s-value:

$$s_{eff} = s + \frac{d\alpha'}{dz} \tag{30}$$

is in general also a function of z.

For a stacking fault $\alpha' =$ constant and $d\alpha'/dz = 0$; the system of equations then reduces to that for a perfect crystal. This expresses the physically evident fact that a parallel displacement of the crystal does not affect the amplitudes of transmitted or scattered beam.

For a domain boundary α' is a linear function of z and therefore $d\alpha'/dz = k$ = constant.

The presence of the domain boundary causes the second part of the crystal to have an s-value: $s_2 = s_1 + k$, differing by a constant from that of the first part (s_1).

3.2.2. Planar defect: application of the response matrix concept

The transmitted and scattered beams which emerge from the first crystal part are now incident on the second part. For a crystal containing a planar interface both crystal parts are of course perfect, but related one to the other in some definite way, depending on the type of interface.

(i) Twin or grain boundary: only one of the crystal parts is in reflecting orientation.

(ii) Domain boundary (twin): the s-value in the second part (s_2) is constant and different from that in the first part (s_1).

(iii) Inversion boundary: whereas $+\mathbf{g}$ is active in the first part $-\mathbf{g}$ is active in the second part. The deviation from the Bragg position is the same in both parts.

(iv) Translation boundary: α = constant, $s_1 = s_2$, i.e. the orientation is again the same in both parts.

Transmission through the crystal must now be described by the product of a succession of response matrices, one related to each part. A parallel displacement, such as that caused by the presence of a translation interface, has to be taken into account by the introduction of an appropriate matrix, as we shall see further.

1. Twin boundary. In the case of a large obliquity twin or grain boundary usually one of the crystal parts is in reflecting position ($\xi_{\mathbf{g}_2} = \infty$). The electrons then only see a wedge shaped crystal (apart from the normal absorption in the non-diffracting crystal part).

The response matrix, since there is only one crystal part reduces to $M(z_1, s)$

$$\begin{pmatrix} T \\ S \end{pmatrix} = M(z_1, s) \begin{pmatrix} 1 \\ 0 \end{pmatrix}. \tag{31}$$

2. Inversion boundary. The response matrix of the crystal is now described by the product of response matrices:

$$\mathcal{S}(-\theta_{\mathbf{g}}) M(z_2, s) \mathcal{S}(\theta_{\mathbf{g}}) \mathcal{S}(\theta_{\mathbf{g}}) M(z_1, s) \mathcal{S}(-\theta_{\mathbf{g}}) ,$$

$$\underbrace{\phantom{\mathcal{S}(-\theta_{\mathbf{g}}) M(z_2, s) \mathcal{S}(\theta_{\mathbf{g}})}}_{\text{part II}} \underbrace{\phantom{\mathcal{S}(\theta_{\mathbf{g}}) M(z_1, s) \mathcal{S}(-\theta_{\mathbf{g}})}}_{\text{part I}}$$

where the phase angle for reflection $\mathbf{g}$ is $\theta_{\mathbf{g}}$ in the first part, it is $-\theta_{\mathbf{g}}$ in the second part, referred to the same origin.

Making use of the properties of the δ matrices one finds, apart from irrelevant phase factors,

$$\binom{T}{S} = M(z_2, s)\, \delta\, (2\theta_{\mathbf{g}})\, M(z_1, s) \binom{1}{0} . \tag{32}$$

We shall see further below that this is equivalent to the response of a crystal containing a pure translation interface with $\alpha = 2\theta_{\mathbf{g}}$.

3. Domain boundary. The response of the crystal is given by the product of the response matrices of the two crystal parts, which have now a slightly different orientation:

$$\binom{T}{S} = M(z_2, s_2)\, M(z_1, s_1) \binom{1}{0} . \tag{33}$$

Note that the s values are different for the two matrices.

4. Translation boundary. We shall now consider for generality an interface which is simultaneously a translation interface and a domain boundary i.e. $\alpha \neq 0$ and also $s_1 \neq s_2$ (fig. 5).

The response matrix for the first part is clearly $M(z_1, s_1)$. The transmitted and scattered beams of the first part are now incident on the second part.

Let the response matrix of the second part be represented by:

$$\begin{pmatrix} A & B \\ C & D \end{pmatrix} .$$

The amplitudes of scattered and transmitted beam for part II are solutions of the set of eq. (27). The substitution:

$$\binom{T''}{S''} = \begin{pmatrix} 1 & 0 \\ 0 & e^{i\alpha} \end{pmatrix} \binom{T}{S} , \tag{34}$$

transforms eq. (27) into the set for a perfect crystal. It does not affect the initial values. For the initial values:

$$\begin{pmatrix} T'' \\ S'' \end{pmatrix}_{in} = \begin{pmatrix} 1 \\ 0 \end{pmatrix},$$

the solution is:

$$T'' = T(z_2, s_2), \qquad S'' = S(z_2, s_2). \tag{35}$$

For the original system (27) the solution is therefore:

$$T = T(z_2, s_2), \qquad S = S(z_2, s_2) e^{-i\alpha}, \tag{36}$$

i.e. the elements A and C are:

$$A = T(z_2, s_2) \equiv T_2 \quad \text{and} \quad C = S(z_2, s_2) e^{-i\alpha} \equiv S_2 e^{-i\alpha}.$$

In order to determine B and D we write the solution of the set (27) for the initial values:

$$\begin{pmatrix} T \\ S \end{pmatrix}_{z=0} = \begin{pmatrix} 0 \\ 1 \end{pmatrix}.$$

Interchanging T and S clearly reduces these initial values to the previous ones. The following substitution leaves the system of eq. (27) invariant:

$$T \rightleftarrows S ; \qquad \alpha \to -\alpha ; \qquad s \to -s ,$$

The solution thus becomes:

$$B = S(z_2, -s_2) e^{i\alpha} \equiv S_2^- e^{i\alpha} ; \qquad D = T(z_2, -s_2) \equiv T_2^- ,$$

and the complete matrix therefore is:

$$\begin{pmatrix} T_2 & S_2^- e^{i\alpha} \\ S_2 e^{-i\alpha} & T_2^- \end{pmatrix}. \tag{37}$$

By analogy with (17) this can be written as a product of matrices:

$$\begin{pmatrix} 1 & 0 \\ 0 & e^{-i\alpha} \end{pmatrix} \begin{pmatrix} T_2 & S_2^{(-)} \\ S_2 & T_2^{(-)} \end{pmatrix} \begin{pmatrix} 1 & 0 \\ 0 & e^{i\alpha} \end{pmatrix},$$

(38)

or finally for the faulted crystal:

$$\begin{pmatrix} T \\ S \end{pmatrix} = \delta(-\alpha) M_2 \delta(\alpha) M_1 \begin{pmatrix} 1 \\ 0 \end{pmatrix}.$$

(39)

This expression can readily be generalised for overlapping interfaces. Let the phase angles of the interfaces be α_j', when referred to the front part of the crystal and let the s values be s_j, we then obtain:

$$\begin{pmatrix} T \\ S \end{pmatrix} = \dots \delta(-\alpha_2') M_3 \delta(\alpha_2') \delta(-\alpha_1') M_2 \delta(\alpha_1') M_1 \begin{pmatrix} 1 \\ 0 \end{pmatrix}.$$

(40)

Introducing the angles $\alpha_j = \alpha_j' - \alpha_{j-1}'$ and putting $\alpha_0' = 0$, we can rewrite this:

$$\begin{pmatrix} T \\ S \end{pmatrix} = \dots M_3 \delta(\alpha_2) M_2 \delta(\alpha_1) M_1 \begin{pmatrix} 1 \\ 0 \end{pmatrix}.$$

(41)

Where now the α_j represent the phase angles resulting from the relative displacement of two successive lamellae, each lamella always being displaced with respect to the previous one.

Note that the expression (39) is the same as that for an inversion boundary, provided $s_1 = s_2$ and $\alpha = 2\theta_g$ and ignoring an irrelevant phase factor which does not affect the intensities.

For a single interface the explicit expressions for T and S can easily be written down, they are:

$$T = T_1 T_2 + S_1 S_2^{(-)} e^{i\alpha}, \qquad S = T_1 S_2 e^{-i\alpha} + S_1 T_2^{(-)}.$$

(42)

The amplitude of the transmitted beam thus results from the interference between the doubly transmitted $(T_1 T_2)$ and the doubly scattered beams $(S_1 S_2^{(-)} e^{i\alpha})$ (fig. 8).

One has to remember that for the double scattering event the beam is incident on part II in the direction of the primary scattered beam; this is accounted

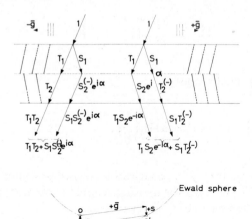

Fig. 8. Illustration of eq. (42) representing the different contributions to the transmitted and scattered amplitudes for a crystal containing an interface.

for by the use of $-s$ for the deviation parameter. Furthermore the wave scattered by the second part suffers a phase change α as a result of the stacking fault; this introduces the phase factor $e^{i\alpha}$.

The amplitude of the scattered beam similarly results from the interference between the beam scattered by part I and subsequently transmitted by part II in the scattered direction $(S_1 T_2^{(-)})$ and the beam transmitted by part I and subsequently scattered by part II suffering a phase change $-\alpha$ because scattering by part II now occurs from the other side as compared to the term $S_1 S_2^{(-)} e^{i\alpha}$ in T.

This type of analysis is also valid in the case of overlapping interfaces. However the number of terms becomes rapidly large.

3.3. Fringe pattern contrast types

The relation (42) yields expressions for the amplitudes T and S. The intensities are obtained from:

$$I_T = TT^* \quad \text{and} \quad I_S = SS^* \tag{43}$$

where the asterisk means complex conjugate.

From the periodic character of the expressions (11) for the T_1 and S_1 it can however be guessed that the images for inclined planar defects, where z_1 and z_2 vary continuously, will also have a periodic character and give rise to a kind of fringe pattern with the "fringes" parallel with the intersection lines of the defect with the foil surfaces. The explicit analytical expressions cannot easily be discussed in the general case; such a discussion can be found in [12,13]. We shall limit ourselves to two special cases

(1) s_2 large , $\xi_{2,g} = \infty$ (wedge fringes)

(2) $\alpha \neq 0$, $s_1 = s_2 = 0\ (\delta = 0)$ (α-fringes)

(3) $\alpha = 0$, $s_1 \xi_{1,g} - s_2 \xi_{2,g} = \delta \neq 0$ (δ-fringes)

where $\xi_{1,g}$ and $\xi_{2,g}$ are the extinction distances in the crystal parts on either side of the boundary.

3.3.1. Wedge fringes

If s_2 is large the second crystal part can be considered as non diffracting. The amplitudes (apart from normal absorption) are then given by expression (1) and the intensity I_S from (43) is:

$$I_S = \frac{\sin^2 \pi \sigma_1 z_1}{(\sigma_1 \xi_{1,g})^2} \tag{44}$$

This is a with z_1 periodically varying intensity that will give rise to a fringe pattern parallel with the foil plane–interface plane intersection. A typical example is observed at the single twin boundary in fig. 17.

3.3.2. α-fringes

The symmetry properties can be derived directly from the expression (43) and (42); one has:

$$I_T(z_1, z_2, s, \alpha) = I_T(z_2, z_1, s, \alpha) ,$$

$$I_S(z_1, z_2, s, \alpha) = I_S(z_2, z_1, -s, -\alpha) ,$$

which means that the bright field fringe pattern will be symmetrical with respect to the centre of the foil; the dark field image on the other hand will be asymmetrical. In particular the nature of the outer fringe will be the same in the BF image, whereas their nature will be different in the DF image.

Explicitely one can write this expression as the sum of three terms:

$$I_{T,S} = I_{T,S}^{(1)} + I_{T,S}^{(2)} + I_{T,S}^{(3)} , \tag{45}$$

with:

$$I_{T,S}^{(1)} = \tfrac{1}{2} \cos^2(\alpha/2) \left[\cosh 2\pi\sigma_i z_0 \pm \cos 2\pi\sigma_r z_0\right] ,$$

$$I_{T,S}^{(2)} = \tfrac{1}{2} \sin^2(\alpha/2) \left[\cosh 4\pi\sigma_i u \pm \cos 4\pi\sigma_r u\right] , \tag{46}$$

$$I_{T,S}^{(3)} = \tfrac{1}{2} \sin \alpha \left[\sin 2\pi\sigma_r z_1 \sinh 2\pi\sigma_i z_2 \pm \sin 2\pi\sigma_r z_2 \sinh 2\pi\sigma_i z_1\right] .$$

The upper sign applies to I_T, whereas the lower sign applies to I_S; z_0 is the total thickness ($z_0 = z_1 + z_2$) whereas, $2u = z_1 - z_2$. In fact u is the distance of the interface from the foil centre.

Fig. 9 illustrates the various terms that have to be summed up in order to obtain the resulting intensity distribution in the case $\sin\alpha > 0$. For $\alpha = 0$ or a multiple of 2π the first term is the only non-vanishing one; this means that this term represents the contribution from the perfect crystal; it cannot represent fault fringes.

In sufficiently thick foils, i.e. for:

$$2 \sinh 2\pi\sigma_i z_0 \gg \mathrm{tg}\,\alpha/2 ,$$

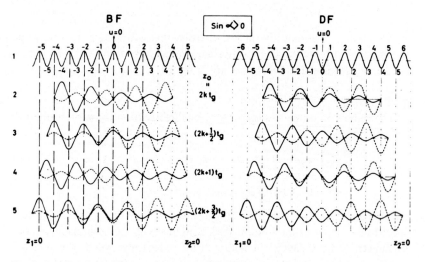

Fig. 9. Graphic representation of the contributions to the intensity distributions given by $I_{T,S}^{(2)}$ and $I_{T,S}^{(3)}$ in expression (46). Curve 1 is term $I_{T,S}^{(2)}$; curves 2, 3, 4 and 5 are the terms $I_{T,S}^{(3)}$ for the different foil thicknesses z_0 as indicated.

and for $\alpha \neq \pi$ the general behaviour of the fringe pattern is described by the third term, which consists itself of two terms.

The first term is large at the entrance face since $\sinh 2\pi\sigma_i z_2$ is larger there ($z_2 \cong z_0$). It represents a damped sinusoid which dissappears at the back surface where $z_2 \simeq 0$. The first extremum will be a maximum for $\sin \alpha > 0$ i.e. the first fringe will then be bright.

The second term is similarly large at the exit face since there $\sinh 2\pi\sigma_i z_1$ is large because $z_1 \simeq z_0$, it disappears at the front face since then $z_2 \simeq 0$. This term also represents a damped sinusoid; the first extremum, which now corresponds to the last fringe, is a maximum or a minimum for $\sin \alpha > 0$, depending on whether we consider I_T or I_S. If $\sin \alpha < 0$ the maxima become minima and vice versa.

In conclusion we find the result summarized in table 1 for the nature of the outer fringes.

It should be noted that these results are only valid for *thick* foils. For thin foils, as well as for a discussion of the detailed behaviour in the central part of the fringe pattern one has to use the complete expression.

Fig. 10 shows a number of computed fringe profiles for $\alpha = 2\pi/3$, $s = 0$, $\xi_g/\xi_g' = 0.035$ with varying thickness.

For $\alpha = \pm 2\pi/3$ and in sufficiently thick foils the fringes have the following properties.

(i) New fringes are created in the centre of the foil with increasing thickness.

(ii) The fringes are parallel to the closest surface.

(iii) The BF fringe pattern is symmetrical with respect to the foil centre, whereas the DF image is similar to the BF image close to the front surface, but pseudo-complementary close to the back surface.

These properties can be verified in fig. 11.

The singular case $\alpha = \pi$ gives rise to an extremely simple pattern if $s = 0$. The profile is now described completely by the second term:

Table 1
α-Fringes.

	BF		DF	
	F	L	F	L
$\sin \alpha > 0$	B	B	B	D
$\sin \alpha < 0$	D	D	D	B

B: bright; D: dark; F: first fringe; L: last fringe.

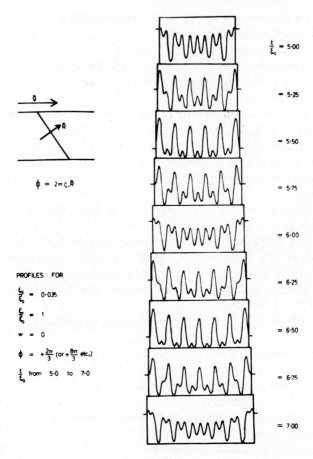

Fig. 10. Fringe profiles for stacking faults with $\alpha = \pm 2\pi/3$ for various thicknesses and $s = 0$. (After Booker.)

$$I_{T,S} = \tfrac{1}{2}(\cosh 4\pi\sigma_i u \pm \cos 4\pi\sigma_r u) \tag{47}$$

where $\sigma_r = 1/\xi_g$. The following properties of the fringe pattern are immediately apparent from this formula:

(i) Bright and dark field image are complementary with respect to the background given by:

$$\tfrac{1}{2}\cosh 4\pi\sigma_i u$$

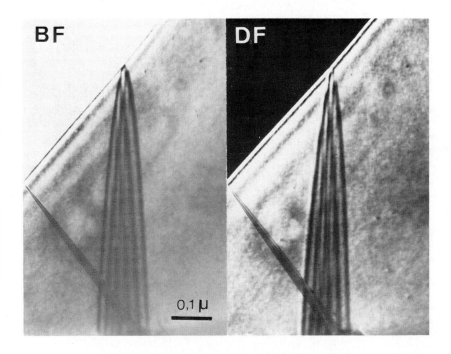

Fig. 11. Bright field and dark field image of a stacking fault $\alpha = 2\pi/3$ in stainless steel in a foil of continuously varying thickness.

(ii) The central fringe ($u \simeq 0$) is bright in the BF image and dark in the DF image.

(iii) The fringes are parallel to the foil centre i.e. determined by u rather than to the closest surface (i.e. determined respectively by z_1 or z_2); their depth period is $\frac{1}{2}\xi_g$.

(iv) With increasing foil thickness new fringes are created at the surface rather than in the centre.

Examples of π-fringes are visible in figs. 12 and 13.

3.3.3. δ-fringes

We shall limit ourselves to the discussion of the simplest case $s_1 = -s_2 = s$ i.e. the *symmetrical* case. For a general discussion we refer to [12]. Assuming that the foil is sufficiently thick one finds that the profile is adequately described by the third term

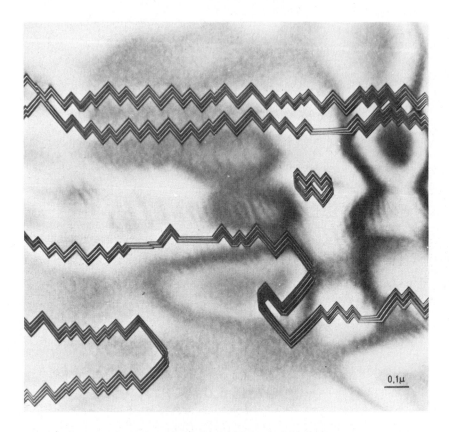

Fig. 12. Isolated shear planes in TiO_2 imaged by fringe patterns of the π-type; since s is slightly different from zero, coupled fringes are observed.

$$w^4 I^{(3)}_{T,S} = -(\tfrac{1}{2})\, \delta\, \{\cos 2\pi\sigma_{1r}z_1 \, \sinh[2(\pi\sigma_{2i}z_2 \pm \phi_2)]$$

$$\mp \cos 2\pi\sigma_{2r}z_2 \, \sinh[2(\pi\sigma_{1i}z_1 + \phi_1]\}\,, \tag{48}$$

with

$$w^2 = 1 + (s\xi_\mathbf{g})^2 \; ; \quad \delta = s_1\xi_{\mathbf{g},1} - s_2\xi_{\mathbf{g},2} \; ; \quad 2\phi_j = \mathrm{argsinh}(s\xi_\mathbf{g})_j \,, \tag{49}$$

where now $\xi_{\mathbf{g},1}$ and $\xi_{\mathbf{g},2}$ are the extinction distances in the first and second part respectively. The upper sign applies to I_T and the lower to I_S. Close to

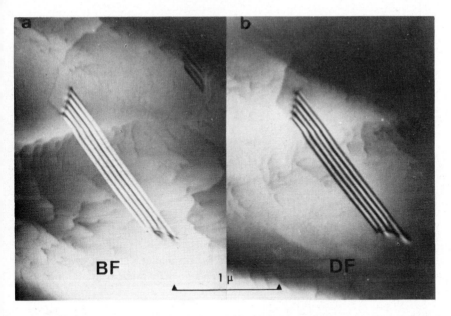

Fig. 13. Bright and dark field image of a stacking fault in SiC illustrating the typical π-fringe characteristics i.e. BF and DF symmetrical and complementary for $s = 0$.

front surface the first term again dominates, whereas close to the back surface the second term is the dominating one. One concludes that close to the front surface BF and DF are similar, whereas they are pseudo-complementary close to the back surface. This is in fact a general property of two-beam defect images in thick foils; it is a result of anomalous absorption.

The fringes have furthermore the following properties:

(i) The depth period may be different close to front and back surface if $\xi_{g,1}$ is significantly different from $\xi_{g,2}$.

(ii) The pattern is symmetrical in the DF as far as $\xi_{g,1}$ is equal to $\xi_{g,2}$.

(iii) Fringes are parallel to the closest surface and therefore new fringes are added in the central part.

(iv) The nature of the outer fringes depends on the sign of δ in the manner shown in table 2; they have the same nature in the DF, but opposite nature in the BF.

(v) Extinction occurs for $\delta = 0$.

(vi) The domains on either side of the boundary have a different contrast in the BF image, whereas it may be the same in the DF images (symmetrical position).

Table 2
δ-Fringes.

	BF		DF	
	F	L	F	L
δ > 0	B	D	B	B
δ < 0	D	B	D	D

These properties can be verified in fig. 14.

Also from fig. 14 it is evident that in the BF image the contrast of the fringes is best at the end of the pattern which is close to the bright fringe. This behaviour follows from expression (48).

A striking effect in the DF image is the difference in average intensity of the fringe pattern for both interfaces. This difference can only be explained by taking into account the other terms of the complete expression given in ref. [12]. It results mainly from the difference in magnitude of the term $I_S^{(1)}$

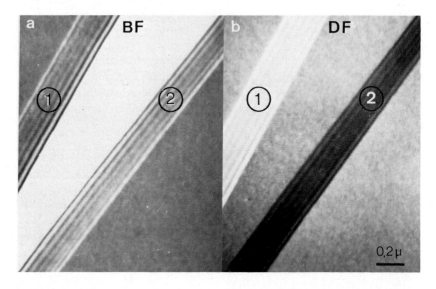

Fig. 14. Bright and dark field image of a δ-type interface. The example is taken from work by Delavignette and Nandedkar on the Zr_3Al_4 compound. (a) Bright field image. The interfaces are marked (1) and (2). They have opposite asymmetric fringe profiles. (b) Dark field image where the symmetric character of the patterns is observed.

for both interfaces. In particular the term:

$$\tfrac{1}{2}A^2C^2 \cosh 2[(\pi\sigma_{1i}z_1 + \pi\sigma_{2i}z_2) + (\phi_1 - \phi_2)]$$

determines the general level of intensity. For interface (1) $\phi_1 - \phi_2$ is negative whereas it is positive for interface (2). As a result the hyperbolic cosine will be much larger for interface (2) than for interface (1) i.e. the background intensity will be larger than for (2).

In the BF image the average intensity level is slightly higher for interface (1) than for interface (2). Also this is consistent since now the term which determines the average intensity level is given by the first part of $I_T^{(1)}$ i.e.

$$\tfrac{1}{2}A^2C^2 \cosh[2(\pi\sigma_{1i}z_1 + \pi\sigma_{2i}z_2) + (\phi_1 + \phi_2)] \,,$$

where for interface (1) $\phi_1 + \phi_2$ is slightly positive if $|s_2| > |s_1|$ and slightly negative for interface (2). The average intensity level should be the same if $|s_1| = |s_2|$.

3.3.4. Mixed fringes

It is possible that for certain interfaces as well α as δ are different from zero. Such interfaces produce fringes which have properties which are intermediate between those of α and δ-fringes [12].

Mixed interfaces such as the ones described in the introduction 2.3 will usually not give rise to mixed fringes since the orientation of the two crystal parts is significantly different. Only one variant is diffracting and a contrast of the wedge fringe type will be observed even if a translation component is present. If a common reflection is active then only the translation interface shows up as an α-fringe pattern. This procedure can be used to determine the displacement vector of the translation component of the interface (see sect. 4).

3.4. Contrast for a combination of interfaces

Using the response matrix formalism it is a simple matter to describe, at least formally, the contrast effect for a number of situations. We shall only give a few examples; voids, microtwins, overlapping translation and overlapping domain boundaries.

1. Voids. The contrast at a cavity can be treated in a straightforward manner. Let the geometry be as presented in fig. 15. The transmitted and scattered amplitudes are then given by:

$$\begin{pmatrix} T \\ S \end{pmatrix} = \mathcal{M}_3 V(z_2, s_1) \mathcal{M}_1 \begin{pmatrix} 1 \\ 0 \end{pmatrix} \tag{50}$$

S.AMELINCKX and J.Van LANDUYT

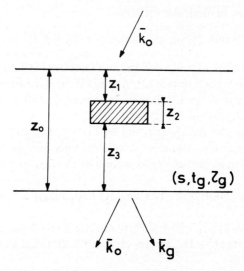

Fig. 15. Cavity in a crystal; the hatched part is considered as non diffracting

Since a cavity causes no normal absorption it is clear that the influence of normal absorption on the contrast must now be taken into account also. A detailed discussion is given in ref. [14]. Fig. 16 demonstrates clearly that the contrast cannot be normal absorption contrast only. This figure shows the same area for two different s-values; certain cavities show up brighter than the background in one photograph and darker in the other, which must obviously be due to diffraction contrast.

2. Microtwin in a face centered cubic crystal. We assume that the matrix is in a reflecting position, whereas the thin twin is far from any reflecting position and therefore behaves as a vacuum layer.

Depending on the exact thickness of the twin lamella, the displacement between the two crystal parts on either side of the micro-twin gives rise to a phase shift: $\alpha = 0$, or $\pm 2\pi/3$. The amplitudes of transmitted and scattered beams can therefore be found from the following relation:

$$\begin{pmatrix} T \\ Se^{i\alpha} \end{pmatrix} = M_2 V(z_2, s) \, \delta(\alpha) M_1 \begin{pmatrix} 1 \\ 0 \end{pmatrix} \tag{51}$$

where the succession of V and δ is immaterial since it is not determined unambigeously by the physical situation; this is reflected by the fact that the

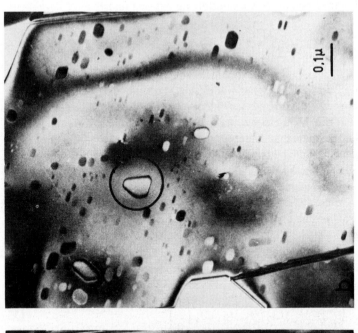

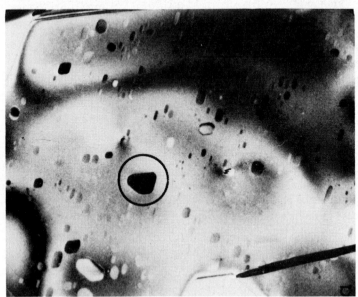

Fig. 16. Two slightly different orientations of a rutile foil containing cavities. Notice the pronounced contrast differences in particular at the encircled one.

matrices V and $\mathcal{S}$ commute. On multiplying out one finds:

$$\begin{pmatrix} T \\ Se^{i\alpha} \end{pmatrix} = M_2 \begin{pmatrix} 1 & 0 \\ 0 & e^{i\beta} \end{pmatrix} M_1 \begin{pmatrix} 1 \\ 0 \end{pmatrix}, \tag{52}$$

with $\beta = \alpha + 2\pi s z_2$. The contrast will thus be the same as that due to a pure translation interface with an s-dependent phase angle β. Furthermore it should be noted that the thickness that matters for anomalous absorption is $z_1 + z_3$, whereas the thickness that causes normal absorption is $z_1 + z_2 + z_3 = z_0$ ($z_0 =$ total thickness). Similar contrast effects occur in cases where a thin lamella of a second phase is included within a crystal in such a way that the matrix only is reflecting. The regions of overlap exhibit stacking fault like fringes, whereas the edge parts produce wedge fringes. This is clearly evidenced in fig. 17 where where microtwins are observed together with a single twin interface showing only wedge fringes.

3. Overlapping translation interfaces. The matrix expression giving transmitted and scattered amplitudes for a crystal containing overlapping interfaces with phase angles α_1 and α_2 is:

$$\begin{pmatrix} T \\ S \end{pmatrix} = M_3 \mathcal{S}(\alpha_2) M_2 \mathcal{S}(\alpha_1) M_1 \begin{pmatrix} 1 \\ 0 \end{pmatrix}. \tag{53}$$

For very small separations between the faults

$$M_2 \simeq \begin{pmatrix} 1 & 0 \\ 0 & 1 \end{pmatrix}$$

and one has:

$$\mathcal{S}(\alpha_2) M_2 \mathcal{S}(\alpha_1) \simeq \mathcal{S}(\alpha_1 + \alpha_2),$$

which means that the phase angles add.

In the case of faults with phase angles $\alpha_1 = \alpha_2 = \pi$ one obtains for $s = 0$:

$$\begin{pmatrix} T \\ S \end{pmatrix} = M_3(z_3, 0) \mathcal{S}(\pi) M_2(z_2, 0) \mathcal{S}(\pi) M_1(z_1, 0) \begin{pmatrix} 1 \\ 0 \end{pmatrix}. \tag{54}$$

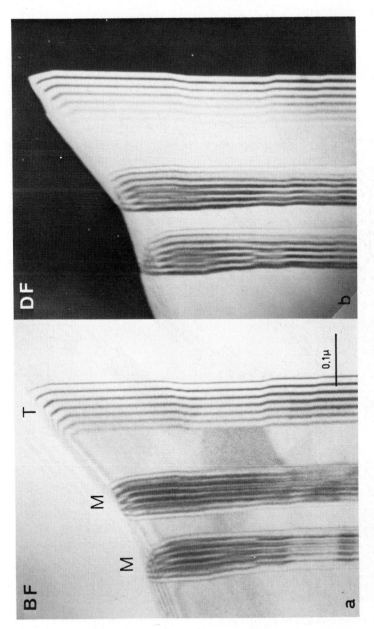

Fig. 17. Two microtwins (*M*) and a single twin boundary (*T*). Notice the stacking fault like contrast at the microtwins and the wedge fringe pattern at the single twin boundary in the same orientation. Bright field (BF) and dark field (DF) are shown.

Working out leads to:

$$\binom{T}{S} = M_3(z_3, 0)M(-z_2, 0)M(z_1, 0)\binom{1}{0}$$

$$= M(z_1 + z_3 - z_2, 0)\binom{1}{0}. \tag{55}$$

The crystal then behaves as a perfect crystal with a thickness $z_1 + z_3 - z_2$; the contrast is uniform in the overlap region (an example is given in fig. 18), where

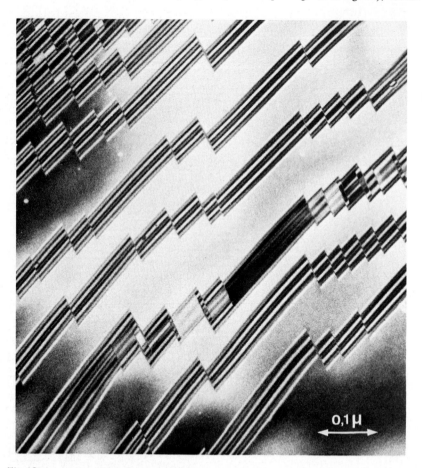

Fig. 18. Array of antiphase boundaries with $\alpha = \pi$ in rutile. Pronounced contrast changes are observed at the overlapping boundaries.

the contrast has not completely disappeared since s is slightly different from zero.

4. Overlapping domain boundaries. We consider in particular the case where a thin wedge shaped domain is formed within a large domain. This situation occurs frequently on the formation of twins with a small twin vector, such as in ferroeletrics and antiferromagnetics. The s-values in the three crystal parts are now such that $s_1 = s_3 \neq s_2$. In the overlap region the fringe pattern is then described by:

$$\begin{pmatrix} T \\ S \end{pmatrix} = M_3(z_3, s_1) \, M_2(z_2, s_2) M_1(z_1, s_1) \begin{pmatrix} 1 \\ 0 \end{pmatrix}. \tag{56}$$

One can deduce symmetry properties of the fringe pattern from this relation. It is for instance easy to show that interchanging z_1 and z_3, does not change T but changes S; one has in particular:

$$T(z_1, z_2, z_3, s_1, s_2, s_3) = T(z_3, z_2, z_1, s_3, s_2, s_1) \,,$$

and

$$S(z_1, z_2, z_3, s_1, s_2, s_3) = S(z_3, z_2, z_1, -s_1, -s_2, -s_3) \,. \tag{57}$$

This means that in the overlap region the bright field image will exhibit a symmetrical fringe pattern, whereas the dark field image will not, in accord with the observation.

3.5. Inversion contrast

Contrast at inversion boundaries requires a separate discussion since it implies the violation of Friedel's law.

In the framework of two-beam theory for non-centrosymmetrical crystals, contrast at inversion boundaries will only be found if the corresponding Fourier coefficient of the real and the imaginary parts of the lattice potential have different phase factors. Even then a contrast difference in the domain will only be found in the DF and never in the BF image [15]. In any case the contrast will be weak unless the absorption distance would be very small.

The boundaries themselves are imaged by α-like fringes i.e. fringes which are symmetrical in the BF and asymmetrical in the DF (fig. 19). The phase angle α for *pure* inversion boundaries is $\alpha = 2\theta_g$ when θ_g is the phase angle of the Fourier coefficient of the real part of the lattice potential corresponding to the active reflection g. This result is only true if there is *no* phase difference between real and imaginary part of the potential but it remains approximately true in other cases.

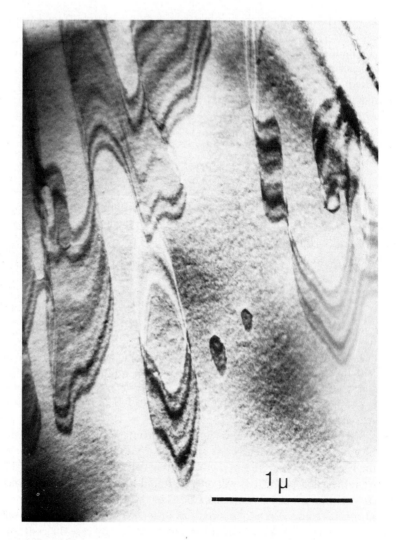

Fig. 19. Inversion boundaries in a ferro-electric crystal BaNa(NbO$_3$)$_5$. Notice the typical α-type fringes in this bright field image.

However the largest intensity differences between inversion domains are found in multiple beam situations (fig. 20) [15, 16]. Multiple beam theory does predict in fact that Friedel's law will be violated in the DF image but will still hold in the BF image. Of course if only reflections operate which belong

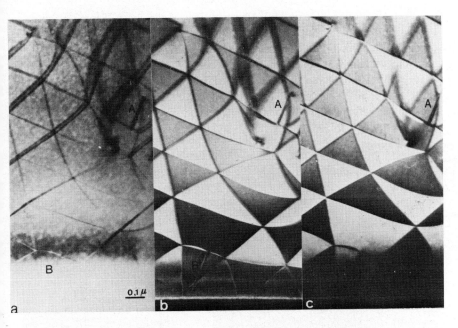

Fig. 20. Bright and two dark field images of inversion boundaries in the χ-phase. In the DF
image a contrast is observed between the domains.

to a zone along which the projection is centrosymmetrical the crystal behaves
as if it was centrosymmetrical, and the contrast between domains disappears.

The absence of contrast in the BF image under all circumstance against the
presence of contrast in the DF image under certain conditions, is the most
typical characteristic of inversion domains. The diffraction pattern is clearly
not affected since the lattice is the same in the two domains.

As mentioned in the introduction inversion contrast is also expected at
rotation twins in non-centrosymmetrical crystals for reflecting planes parallel
to the rotation axis; Dauphiné twins in quartz were cited as an example. These
twins are however also and for carefully chosen reflections more clearly
visualized by a different contrast mechanism: structure factor contrast.

3.6. Structure factor contrast

If for any structural reason the structure factor of simultaneously excited
reflections in two crystal parts are significantly different, expressions (11)
learn us that the background intensity will be different since ξ_g and σ are different. This is e.g. the case at Dauphiné twins in quartz where the simultaneously

excited reflections $30\bar{3}1$ and $03\bar{3}1$ have extinction distances of respectively 6049 Å and 1437 Å. A pronounced contrast is observed in dark field images using these reflections an example of which is illustrated in fig. 21 [17].

Another example of structure factor contrast between domains are "permutation twins" in δ-NiMo [7]. These boundaries are interfaces between domains where the a and b parameters are interchanged. Since the lattice is tetragonal, but the structure orthorhombic, simultaneously excited reflections have different structure factors.

3.7. Line images

Apart from the usual imaging conditions whereby the planar defect is inclined with respect to the incident electron beam, discussed in the previous pages and giving rise to fringe contrast, it is also possible to image defects which are exactly parallel with the electron beam.

In the case of single defects the image is a fine line as one could expect from the crude extrapolation of a fringe pattern. The theoretical analysis of

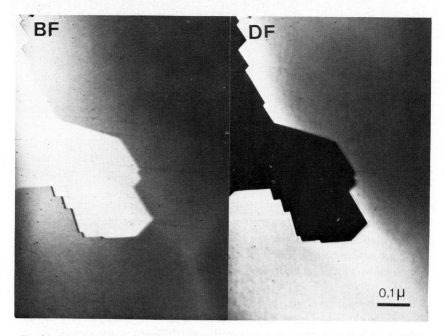

Fig. 21. Bright and dark field image of Dauphiné twins in quartz for a $(30\bar{3}1)$ reflection which has a significantly different ξ_g between domains. The *structure factor contrast* is pronounced.

this situation is quite complicated and is not the subject of this contribution. Experimentally usually a fine dark line is observed as evidenced in fig. 22 which shows both types of imaging conditions in one picture for shear planes in rutile.

The planar defects (stacking faults, shearplanes, antiphase boundaries, twins) sometimes occur in periodic arrays thus giving rise to respectively polytypes, mixed layer compounds, shear structures, superlattices and polysynthetic twin structures (fig. 23). If the period of these defects is sufficiently large the diffraction spots associated with it are necessarily included in the objective aperture.

Fig. 22. Individual shear planes in rutile. One family of boundaries is nearly parallel with the beam and is visible as a fine dark line.

Fig. 23. Periodic array of shear planes giving rise to a shear structure, cf. fig. 3.

For the interpretation of the images of these structures multiple beam calculations have to be performed in the appropriate theoretical approaches such as multislice methods [18] and other lattice imaging calculations [19].

As will be discussed in the next paragraph, valuable information can be deduced from observations in the "lattice imaging"-mode.

4. The use of the contrast features at defects and particular diffraction data

The information contents of electron micrographs and of the corresponding diffraction patterns can be exploited in the following way:

4.1. *Translation interfaces*
Such interfaces produce fringe patterns of the α-type or line images if parallel with the electron beam.

4.1.1. Determination of the **R**-vector
One can look for a number of reflections g_i for which the extinction condi-

tion $g_i \cdot R$ = integer is satisfied. For each such reflection one obtains an equation of the type $g_i \cdot R = n$. The solution for R is not always unambigeous; because of the ambiguity on n. Examples are given in refs. [20, 21]. In any case the vector R is only defined modulus a lattice vector.

If R is not a simple fraction of a lattice vector e.g. $R = R_0 + \varepsilon$, extinction, even in two-beam conditions, will in general not be perfect; a so called *residual fringe pattern* is left for certain reflections for which $g \cdot R_0$ = integer due to $g \cdot \varepsilon \neq 0$ (fig. 24). Such residual contrast can be used to determine the deviation ε from a simple vector R_0. In this case one knows that $g_i \cdot \varepsilon$ is smaller than

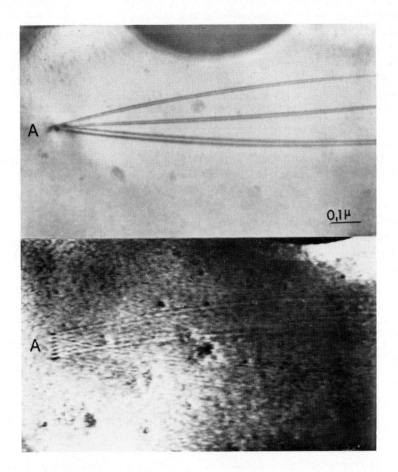

Fig. 24. Fringe pattern and residual contrast image at antiphase boundaries in Ni_3Mo.

1 since ε is small, and a determination of ε is possible; examples can be found in [22,23].

For periodic arrays of translation interfaces, giving rise to diffraction effects due to the superperiod, one can also use the diffraction pattern to determine R in the following way [24,25].

The diffraction pattern due to the periodic arrangement of translation interfaces with a displacement vector R and a spacing d, is described by the relation $g = H + (1/d)(m - H \cdot R)e_u$ where e_u is the unit vector perpendicular to the interfaces; g and H are the diffraction vectors, respectively of the superlattice and of the lattice; m is an integer (fig. 25). The diffraction pattern thus consists of linear arrays of superlattice spots g, grouped around each of the basic spots H, and shifted with respect to the basic spots by a fraction $H \cdot R$ of the interspot distance (fig. 26). A diffraction pattern from a selected area containing as well faulted as unfaulted structure thus allows to determine the projection of R on different H vectors (i.e. $H \cdot R$). Two independent sections of reciprocal space are then sufficient to determine R. This method was applied to TiO_2[24], Ni_3Mo[26], Al_5Mo[27] and γ-brass[28].

4.1.2. Nature of the interface

One can distinguish stacking faults from antiphase boundaries by noting that stacking faults produce fringe contrast for certain fundamental reflections, but are out of contrast for *all* superlattice reflections. On the other hand antiphase boundaries produce fringe patterns for certain superlattice reflections and are out of contrast for all fundamental reflections.

One can also determine the *sense* of R from the nature of the outer fringes. For faults in the F.C.C. structure the knowledge of the sense of R allows to

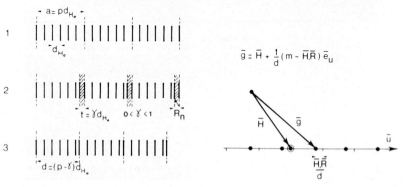

Fig. 25. Graphic representation of the reasoning used to determine the displacement vector of periodic interfaces from the diffraction pattern.

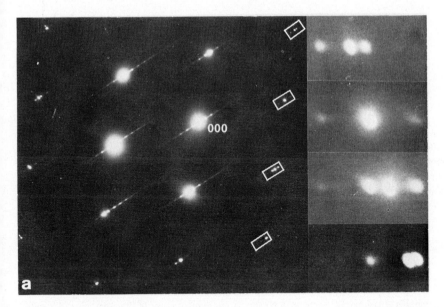

Fig. 26. Example of the spot shifts as observed in a diffraction pattern from the periodic array of defects in fig. 23.

conclude whether a fault is *intrinsic or extrinsic* [20,21]. The simple rule, which was demonstrated in [21] is outlined in the contribution of M.J. Whelan. In hexagonally closed packed structures one can similarly determine whether a fault is single or double [29].

The non conservative character of the interface can be deduced from the diffraction effects discussed in the previous paragraph.

4.1.3. Chemical composition of periodically faulted structures

From the data on the **R** vector in the case of periodic non conservative defects a structural model can be proposed from which the local compositional difference from that of the basic compound can be predicted. X-ray micro-analysis in the electron microscope also allows to compare the composition of the areas with periodic faults with that of perfect material by measuring the ratios of the characteristic X-ray peaks in both areas [30]. A typical applica-tion is illustrated in fig. 27 where a region of Ni_3Mo is observed together with a quasi periodically faulted area. Whereas from the structural model a composi-tion of $Ni_{17}Mo_5$ was predicted the microanalysis yielded a value of $Ni_{3.35}Mo$; the two values are apparently in very good agreement.

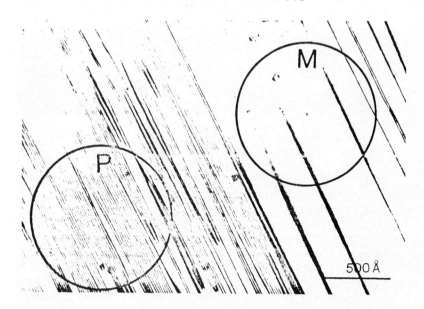

Fig. 27. Quasi periodic defects in Ni$_3$Mo. X-ray microanalysis of the areas marked P and M can be compared to evaluate the difference in composition.

4.2. *Twin interfaces and orientation variants*

Combined use of the fringe pattern which is now of the δ-type and of the diffraction pattern allows to deduce detailed information on twin interfaces.

4.2.1. Determination of the twinning vector and of the twin plane [13,31]

We shall consider in particular the case of a reflection twin (fig. 4). Let the twin vector be τ such that $\mathbf{R} = \tau z$. The vector $\Delta g = \mathbf{g}_1 - \mathbf{g}_2$ is then perpendicular to the coherent twin interface. The condition for the disappearence of contrast is then $\mathbf{g} \cdot \mathbf{R} = 0$ or $\mathbf{g} \cdot \tau = 0$, which allows to determine the direction of τ. The magnitude of τ can be deduced from the diffraction pattern. The simplest orientation is such that the twin plane is parallel to the electron beam. One can then deduce directly the plane of the interface since the twin plane is perpendicular to the row of unsplit spots, whereas the magnitude of the spot doubling is determined by the twinning vector.

4.2.2. Domain contrast: analysis of domain structures and their diffraction patterns

If for certain diffraction conditions the background intensity in bright and dark field images is different in the domain on either side of the boundary one concludes that the interface has twin character. Also spot splitting is usually apparent, especially for the spots far from the centre.

Orientation variants resulting from ordering reactions usually give rise to diffraction patterns which are a superposition of the patterns corresponding to the two variants, as it is the case for a regular twin. These patterns contain common spots which in the case of ordering domains coincide with the matrix spots. Making dark field images in one of these spots no contrast is revealed between the domains or twins; however in dark field images in one of the spots of the subpattern the corresponding variant lights up above the dark background resulting in a pronounced domain contrast. This procedure provides an excellent means to unravel the domain structure and its usually complex diffraction pattern.

4.2.3. Fringe contrast: twin geometry

If the two crystals always diffract simultaneously because the twin vector is small the interface gives rise to δ-fringes. The δ-fringes disappear for $\delta = 0$ i.e. reflections are used for which $\mathbf{g} \cdot \mathbf{\tau} = 0$. The sense of sloping of the interface can be deduced from the nature of the outer fringes, using table 2. This table also allows to deduce the sign of δ which is a useful piece of information for studying the twin geometry. For large twin vectors only one crystal part reflects at a time and the interface produces wedge fringes for the reflecting part.

4.2.4. Line contrast and domain contrast: structural information

The alternation of background intensity in the lattice images of periodic structures yields direct evidence on the presence of twins in these structures and their relation with the structure.

A typical investigation where this type of information was used to derive an alternative description of the structure is devoted to the hexagonal barium ferrites [32]. A "line"-lattice image is compared with a "line-band"-image, revealing the twinned nature of this ferrite (fig. 28).

4.3. *Mixed interfaces: analysis of displacement vector*

Such interfaces can be identified by a combination of the methods used for twin, and for antiphase boundaries. In order to determine the translation components one has to image the interface using reflections which do not reveal the twin i.e. using planes common to both components of the twin. For such planes the interface will exhibit a fringe pattern if a translation component is present. Unfortunately it is not always possible to have a sufficient number of reflections to allow a determination of the displacement vector [33].

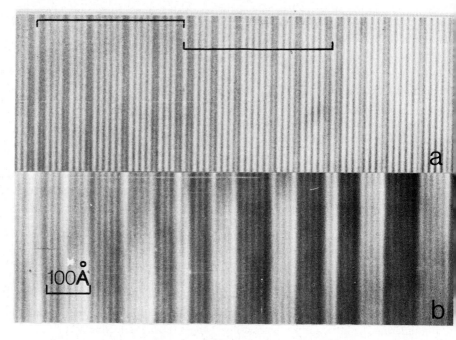

Fig. 28. Line image (a) and corresponding band image (b) of a hexagonal barium ferrite. The banded image is obtained by including twin spots in the objective aperture. The twin bands are revealed in different shades.

References

[1] G.Van Tendeloo and S.Amelinckx, Acta Cryst. A30 (1974) 431.

[2] A.Magneli, Acta Cryst. 6 (1953) 495.

[3] A.D.Wadsley, in: Non stoichiometric compounds, ed. L.Mandelcorn (Academic Press, New York, 1964) p. 98.

[4] B.H.Kear, A.F.Giamei, G.R.Laverant and J.M.Oblak, Scripta Met. 3 (1969) 123.

[5] J.W.Cahn, Phil. Mag. 3 (1954) 363.

[6] R.Serneels, M.Snykers, P.Delavignette, R.Gevers and S.Amelinckx, Phys. Stat. Sol. (b) 58 (1973) 277.

[7] G.Van Tendeloo and S.Amelinckx, Mat. Res. Bull. 8 (1973) 721.

[8] M.Meulemans, P.Delavignette, F.Garcia-Gonzales and S.Amelinckx, Mat. Res. Bull. 5 (1970) 1025;
    M.Snykers, P.Delavignette and S.Amelinckx, Phys. Stat. Sol. (b) 48 (1971) K1.

[9] M.Snykers, E.Serneels, P.Delavignette, R.Gevers and S.Amelinckx, Crystal Lattice Defects 3 (1972) 99.

[10] J.J.Comer, J. Cryst. Growth 15 (1972) 179.

[11] A.Howie and M.J.Whelan, Proc. Roy. Soc. A263 (1961) 217.

[12] R.Gevers, J.Van Landuyt and S.Amelinckx, Phys. Stat. Sol. 11 (1965) 689.

[13] R.Gevers, P.Delavignette, H.Blank and S.Amelinckx, Phys. Stat. Sol. 4 (1964) 383.

[14] J.Van Landuyt, R.Gevers and S.Amelinckx, Phys. Stat. Sol. 10 (1965) 319.

[15] R.Serneels, M.Snykers, P.Delavignette, R.Gevers and S.Amelinckx, Phys. Stat. Sol. (b) 58 (1973) 277.

[16] M.Snykers, R.Serneels, P.Delavignette, R.Gevers and S.Amelinckx, Crystal Lattice Defects, 3 (1972) 99.

[17] G.Van Tendeloo, J.Van Landuyt and S.Amelinckx, Phys. Stat. Sol. (a) 33 (1976) 723.

[18] J.M.Cowley and A.F.Moodie, Acta Cryst. 10 (1957) 609.

[19] P.Goodman and A.F.Moodie, Acta Cryst. A30 (1974) 280.

[20] R.Gevers, A.Art and S.Amelinckx, Phys. Stat. Sol. 3 (1963) 1563.

[21] A.Art, R.Gevers and S.Amelinckx, Phys. Stat. Sol. 3 (1963) 697; J.Van Landuyt, R.Gevers and S.Amelinckx, Phys. Stat. Sol. 18 (1966) 167.

[22] G.Van Tendeloo and S.Amelinckx, Phys. Stat. Sol. (a) 22 (1974) 621.

[23] G.Van Tendeloo and S.Amelinckx, Phys. Stat. Sol. (a) 27 (1975) 94.

[24] J.Van Landuyt, R.De Ridder, R.Gevers and S.Amelinckx, Mat. Res. Bul. 5 (1970) 353.

[25] R.De Ridder, J.Van Landuyt and S.Amelinckx, Phys. Stat. Sol. (a) 9 (1972) 551.

[26] G.Van Tendeloo, J.Van Landuyt, P.Delavignette and S.Amelinckx, Phys. Stat. Sol. (a) 25 (1974) 697.

[27] G.Van Tendeloo, J.Van Landuyt and S.Amelinckx, Mat. Res. Bull. 10 (1974) 941.

[28] H.J.Morton, Phys. Stat. Sol. (a) 23 (1974) 275.

[29] H.Blank, P.Delavignette, R.Gevers and S.Amelinckx, Phys. Stat. Sol. 7 (1964) 747.

[30] G.Van Tendeloo, P.Delavignette, J.Van Landuyt and S.Amelinckx, Phys. Stat. Sol. (a) 26 (1974) 359.

[31] R.Gevers, P.Delavignette, H.Blank, J.Van Landuyt and S.Amelinckx, Phys. Stat. Sol. 5 (1964) 595.

[32] J.Van Landuyt, S.Amelinckx, J.Kohn and D.W.Eckart, J. Sol. Stat. Chem. 9 (1974) 103.

[33] G.Van Tendeloo and S.Amelinckx, Phys. Stat. Sol. (a) 40 (1977).

Diffraction and Imaging Techniques in Material Science,
eds. S. Amelinckx, R. Gevers and J. van Landuyt
© *North-Holland Publishing Company, 1978*

THE WEAK-BEAM METHOD OF ELECTRON MICROSCOPY

D.J.H.COCKAYNE

Electron Microscopy Unit, Univ. of Sydney, NSW 2006, Australia

1. Introduction

When this volume was first published (1970), electron microscope studies of lattice defects using diffraction contrast were generally carried out by forming dark- or bright-field images with the lattice oriented near to the Bragg condition for the particular dark-field reflection (referred to as strong-beam images). However, this method has a serious drawback for high resolution studies of defects (i.e. studies of defect detail below ≈ 10 nm) in that many of the image features are not related in any obvious way to the defect geometry. For example, it is not at all obvious how the various intensity variations in fig. 1a should be interpreted in terms of a defect geometry. This difficulty can be overcome to some extent by using computer simulated images calculated for the various postulated defect models (see Humble, this volume). However, in many high resolution studies, no defect model is known a priori; and furthermore, the defect geometry may be complicated (e.g. constricted dislocations observed in silicon (fig. 1b); pinned and jogged dislocations observed in copper alloys [1]), making it difficult to obtain the displacement field necessary for image computation.

For these more detailed studies of defects, it would therefore be advantageous if the image were related to the defect geometry in a more obvious way. Since 1969, the weak-beam method [2] has been developed to meet this requirement. In fig. 1b, images taken using this method reveal that the particular dislocation has segments which are dissociated into two partial dislocations and segments where no dissociation is observed. By choosing appropriate Bragg reflections to form the weak-beam image, the areas of stacking fault can be revealed (fig. 1c) or the individual partials can be imaged separately (fig. 1d). From such images the electron microscope can be used to study properties of lattice defects at a higher resolution than was previously possible. For example,

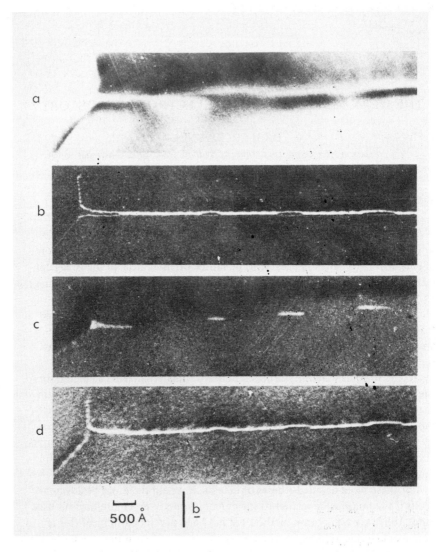

Fig. 1. A constricted dislocation in silicon imaged under various diffracting conditions: (a) A strong-beam $2\bar{2}0$ dark-field image, in which the constricted segments and node extension are masked. (b) A weak-beam $2\bar{2}0$ dark-field image showing both partial dislocations. (c) A weak-beam $11\bar{1}$ dark-field image, giving $\mathbf{g}\cdot\mathbf{b} = 0$ for the total Burgers vector, showing the stacking faults imaged at the extended node and at the 'bowed' dislocation segments. (d) A weak-beam $0\bar{2}2$ dark-field image, in which the partial dislocation with Burgers vector a/6 $[2\bar{1}\bar{1}]$ is out of contrast [30].

the separations of partial dislocations in pure face-centred cubic metals have been measured [3–5] and determinations of the stacking-fault energies of these materials obtained; the twofold and fourfold dissociation of superlattice dislocations in iron-aluminium alloys have been studied [6–8] and the antiphase boundary energies determined; studies of the motion of jogs have been made (1); geometries of dislocation loops [9,10] and point-defect clusters (11) have been determined. These investigations represent applications of the weak-beam method in what might be called an intermediate range of resolution. That is, it is a range of resolution of defect detail not attainable with normal strong-beam methods of microscopy, but one in which the interpretation of weak-beam images is relatively straight-forward. The measurement of the separation of dislocations $\gtrsim 2.5$ nm apart falls into this category, as do studies of point-defect clusters of dimension $\gtrsim 5$ nm.

There is also much interest in the possibility of using the weak-beam method at even higher resolution e.g. for the study of partial dislocation separations $\lesssim 2.5$ nm, for the investigation of small ($\lesssim 5$ nm dimension) point-defect clusters, and for the analysis of closely spaced dislocations in various networks such as grain boundaries. There is experimental evidence to show that sufficiently fine image detail is present in weak-beam images for such analyses (e.g. [12,13]) but the methods of image interpretation have yet to be considered in detail.

In this chapter, the principles of the weak-beam method, and the experimental procedures for obtaining weak-beam images, are discussed. The experimental diffraction conditions which must be satisfied to obtain quantitative results in the intermediate range of resolution, referred to above, are explained, and the present limitations of straight-forward image interpretation at the highest level of resolution are outlined.

2. Principles

The seeds of the weak-beam method can be found in several places in the literature. Thus it is observed that in many-beam computations of lattice defects [14,15], the weakly excited reflections show a narrow intensity peak close to dislocation cores. A similar effect is also to be expected from kinematical calculations of dislocation images [16,34]. The proposal of a method for using this effect for detailed quantitative studies of defect properties was made by Cockayne et al. [2] who also suggested a simple approach to the understanding of weak-beam images in terms of Bragg scattering from distorted lattice planes. This approach is of interest because it provides a physical picture of how weak-beam images arise, and enables us to understand, at least to a first approximation, how to interpret them.

2.1. *Pendellösung for a perfect lattice*

We consider an electron beam incident on a perfect parallel-sided foil from which there emerges an undiffracted beam and a diffracted beam g. The diffracted intenstiy, $|\phi_g|^2$, is shown in fig. 2 as a function of foil thickness z. These are the well-known Pendellösung curves (discussed by Gevers and by Whelan in this volume), so-called by analogy with the energy transfer between two coupled pendula as a function of time [17]. In fig. 2a the lattice is at the Bragg angle for the reflection g, and the intensity oscillates with a periodicity denoted by ξ_g, the extinction distance. This situation can be characterised by the statement that $s_g = 0$, where s_g is the distance of the Ewald sphere from the reciprocal lattice point g. In fig. 2c the lattice is far from the Bragg angle for a particular direction of beam incidence ($|s_g| \gg 0$), and again the intensity oscillates with foil thickness, but with a much shorter periodicity and a much smaller amplitude than in fig. 2a. This is the situation in which the diffracted intensity is given to a good approximation by the kinematical theory, and is represented in the coupled pendula analogue by having pendula of different length.

2.2. *Pendellösung for a lattice defect*

We can use fig. 2 to deduce the qualitative features of the scattered intensity from the idealised lattice planes shown in fig. 3a. The lattice has three sec-

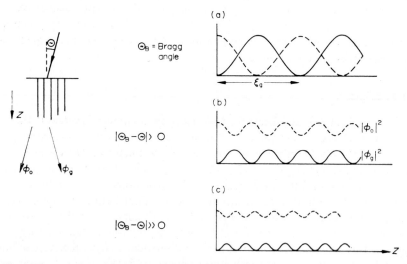

Fig. 2. The variation of incident and diffracted beam intensities in the two-beam situation without absorption, as a function of foil thickness for different incident beam directions [52].

tions; in the first and third sections $|s_g| \gg 0$, and in the second section $s_g = 0$
i.e. the second section is at the Bragg angle with respect to the incident beam
direction OO'. In the first section (AB) the beam is incident on the lattice at
an angle far from the Bragg condition, and consequently in our model the diffracted intensity follows the curve of fig. 2c. But in the second section, the
lattice is at the Bragg angle, and the diffracted intensity follows the Pendellösung
curve of fig. 2a. The diffracted intensity rises above its maximum value of the
first region, and would continue to oscillate with depth as in fig. 2a; but below
level C the lattice is again oriented into a condition such that $|s_g| \gg 0$. The dif-
fracted intensity therefore oscillates with a periodicity identical to its periodicity in region 1, but with a much increased mean value (fig. 3b). The diffracted
intensity (D) at the bottom of the foil is then greatly increased over the diffracted intensity from the undistorted lattice AA' (as indicated in fig. 3b). This
argument can be expressed mathematically (18) or demonstrated by means of
the familiar coupled pendulum analogue in which time is analogous to depth
in the foil, and total energy (kinetic plus potential) to beam amplitude. (By
giving one pendulum a variable length, the analogue of variable $|s_g|$ is obtained.)

We can now extend this argument to the case of a dislocation. For the idealized model of fig. 4a we can expect that the diffracted intensity from column 3,
in which BC is at the Bragg angle, will be greater than the diffracted intensity
from any other column. How much greater it will be is not obvious and, in this

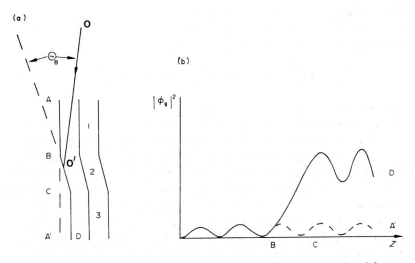

Fig. 3. Idealized lattice planes, and the resultant diffracted intensity deduced from
fig. 2 [52].

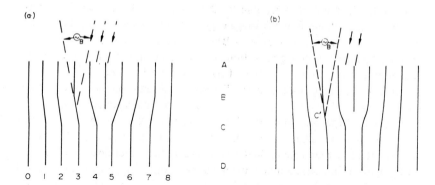

Fig. 4. An idealized lattice defect and a more realistic displacement field, showing the positions where the lattice, oriented at the Bragg angle with respect to the incident beam direction, is expected to give a weak-beam peak [52].

model, will depend critically on the distance BC. Moreover it is not evident how accurate the prediction of this position (column 3) for the maximum of the diffracted intensity will be when we replace the model of the dislocation in fig. 4a by a more realistic model such as that shown in fig. 4b. For this latter model, we might expect that, to a first approximation, the maximum diffracted intensity will occur for those columns in which the lattice is rotated into the Bragg condition by the local strain (i.e. at point C' in fig. 4b). This prediction can be expressed mathematically as follows (2): the image peak is predicted to occur for those columns in which

$$s_g + \mathbf{g} \cdot \frac{d\mathbf{R}}{dz} = 0 \quad \text{at a turning point of} \quad \mathbf{g} \cdot \frac{d\mathbf{R}}{dz} \tag{1}$$

where $\mathbf{R}$ is the local lattice displacement.

These considerations give us reason to expect that images taken with large $|s_g|$ will show an image peak to one side of each dislocation core. This is in agreement with images calculated using the kinematical theory of scattering ([16]; and see Gevers, this volume) and has been verified with many-beam calculations [2, 18–20]. A typical example is shown in fig. 5 for an undissociated edge dislocation in copper. The images are calculated for dislocations in foils of two thicknesses, and with the diffraction geometry indicated in the figure caption. The principal features of this image which differentiate it from dislocation images taken with $s_g \approx 0$ (such as those illustrated by Whelan, figs. 26 to 29, this volume) are its high contrast and the narrowness of the image peak (≈ 1.5 nm half width for $|s_g| = 0.2$ nm^{-1} and $\mathbf{g} \cdot \mathbf{b} \leqslant 2$). Experimental

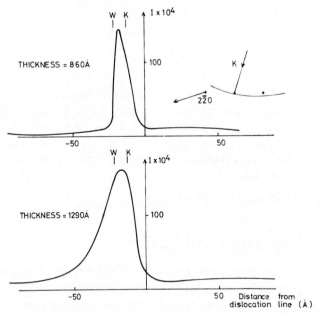

Fig. 5. Computed weak-beam images of an undissociated edge dislocation in copper at depth ξ_g in foils of thickness indicated. Parameters: $\mathbf{g} \cdot \mathbf{b} = 2$; $\mathbf{g} = 2\bar{2}0$; 6-beam calculation; 100 kV electrons; isotropic elasticity; $s_g = -0.25$ nm^{-1}. K is the image peak position predicted by eq. (4) and W by eq. (3).

examples showing both of these features are seen in fig. 1 where the weak-beam and strong-beam images from the same region of silicon crystal are compared.

2.3. Bloch wave description of weak-beam images

The occurrence of weak-beam image peaks has been discussed above in terms of a geometrical model of Bragg scattering from distorted lattice planes. It is important to appreciate that this model is an approximation in many respects, and that there are various features of weak-beam images which the model does not explain. The usefulness of the model lies in the physical insight it gives into the origin of the images, which leads to the ability to devise experiments for analysing defects.

There are other approaches to the analysis of weak-beam images, and in particular those involving Bloch wave scattering are important. Following the nomenclature of Howie (this volume), the amplitude $\phi_g(z)$ of a diffracted beam g at depth z in a foil can be expressed as

$$\phi_g(z) = \sum_{j=1}^{N} \psi^{(j)}(z) \exp(2\pi i \gamma^{(j)} z) \tag{2}$$

where $\psi^{(j)}(z)$ is the excitation amplitude of the jth Bloch wave and $C_g^{(j)}$ is the gth element of the jth eigen vector of the matrix A, (for details, see Howie, this volume, sect. 2.2.3). The weak-beam condition for the reflection g requires that in the perfect lattice $|\phi_g(z)| \ll 1$ for all z. Since in the absence of strain $\psi^{(j)}(z) = C_0^{(j)}$, eq. (2) then implies that $|C_0^{(j)} C_g^{(j)}| \ll 1$ for all j.

In the two-beam case

$$\psi^{(1)}(0) = C_0^{(1)} = C_g^{(2)} = \cos \beta/2$$

and

$$\psi^{(2)}(0) = C_0^{(2)} = -C_g^{(1)} = \sin \beta/2$$

with $\cot \beta = w = s\xi_g$. For $|s| \to \infty$, $\beta = \epsilon \approx 0$, $\psi^{(1)}(0) \approx 1$ and $\psi^{(2)}(0) \approx \epsilon$. Thus, in perfect crystal both terms in the (two-beam) summation of eq. (2) have magnitude $\cos \beta/2 \sin \beta/2 \approx \epsilon/2$. At a defect, interband transitions from branch 1 to branch 2 of the dispersion surface may occur, giving rise to an increase in $|\psi^{(2)}(z)|$ and consequently to an increase in $|\phi_g(z)|$ (19). Consequently, for $|s|$ large, those conditions which give appreciable interband scattering from the most strongly excited branch of the dispersion surface onto the branch j with the largest $C_g^{(j)}$ will produce appreciable contrast in the weak-beam image.

In fig. 6, the particular case where an image is formed using the reflection g with the reflection $-g$ almost Bragg-satisfied is shown (cf. fig. 7 of Howie, this volume). In this case $C_g^{(4)}$ is the largest of the $C_g^{(j)}$ and the most strongly excited branch of the dispersion surface is branch 1 (because branches 4 and 1 lie close to the spheres centred on the reciprocal lattice points g and 0 respectively). Consequently the interband transition $\overrightarrow{BD}$ is the most important in determining the properties of weak-beam images. For an alternative weak-beam image (see fig. 11) taken with the reflection g with the reflection $+3g$ almost Bragg satisfied, it can be shown that the most important transition is $\overrightarrow{DB}$. It can also be seen from fig. 6 that if one interband transition is to predominate, then it is preferable to avoid having any reflection exactly Bragg satisfied (see sect. 3.3).

Bloch wave analyses of images have particular advantages in the weak-beam case because the interband transitions can often be considered to be localised. Under these circumstances the mathematics can be simplified as in the perturbation treatment of Howie and Basinski ([15]; see Howie, this volume, sect. 3.5)

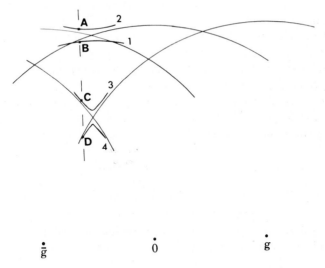

Fig. 6. Dispersion surface in the two-beam case (not to scale).

and in the modified Bloch wave scattering approach of Wilkens ([43] ; see Wilkens, this volume, sect. 4).

3. Analysis of weak-beam images

3.1. *Peak position*

An image such as fig. 1b would be experimentally ideal for determining the position of the dislocation core provided that the distance of the image peak from the core was a function of only those parameters which could be determined experimentally (e.g. s_g, $\mathbf{b}$, but not foil thickness or defect depth). Some attention has been given to this point since for simple interpretation of weak-beam images it may represent the limit of quantitative accuracy for determining core positions. The argument used to obtain eq. (1) is very simple, and it is not difficult to show that to derive it mathematically, several important approximations are necessary. It is therefore a valuable surprise to find that, for dislocations imaged with first-order reflections, and provided that certain conditions relating to $|s_g|$ are satisfied (see sect. 3.5), the image peak positions calculated using many-beam dynamical theory are in agreement with eq. (1) to better than 1 nm.

Of course, for any particular defect and set of diffraction conditions, we expect that images calculated using the many-beam dynamical theory will give the peak position more accurately than eq. (1). But the value of this equation is that it provides a simple means for determining the core position from an experimental image peak position to an accuracy of 1 nm if the form of the strain field is known. Consequently it can be used to interpret weak-beam images without necessitating dynamical calculations. On the other hand there is no a priori reason to expect this prediction of the peak position to be more accurate than, for example, the position predicted using the kinematical theory, and this point is discussed below. It is to be emphasized, however, that when detail $\approx$ 1 nm is being considered, these criteria for determining core positions from image peak positions should be used with caution.

Equation 1 implies that, except for the possible relaxation of the strain field for defects near the surface, the peak position is not a function of foil thickness or defect depth, but only a function of s_g and the form of the strain field. For a dislocation line lying parallel to the foil plane with a strain field described by isotropic elasticity, eq. (1) predicts that the peak position should occur at

$$X_W = -\frac{\mathbf{g} \cdot \mathbf{b}}{2\pi s} \left(1 + \frac{\kappa}{2(1-\nu)}\right) \tag{3}$$

where κ = 1 for an edge dislocation and 0 for a screw dislocation. This position is marked W in fig. 5. On the other hand it can be argued that for the conditions which are used in obtaining weak-beam images, the kinematical theory should be a good approximation for predicting the image peak position. If we use the approach of Hirsch et al. [16] to describe the average kinematical image (i.e. the distance between the centres of the initial and final circles on the amplitude-phase diagram), then the image peak position (for the case $\mathbf{g} \cdot \mathbf{b} = 2$) is given by

$$X_K = -\frac{2 \cdot 1}{2\pi s} \quad \text{(edge);} \qquad X_K = -\frac{1 \cdot 0}{2\pi s} \quad \text{(screw)} \tag{4}$$

This position is marked K in fig. 5. (If the exact kinematical image rather than the average kinematical image is used, the peak position given by the kinematical theory may depend upon dislocation depth and foil thickness.) Thus we have eqs. (3) or (4) which, with a knowledge of $|s_g|$ available from the Kikuchi pattern, we can apply to a particular weak-beam image to determine the positions of the dislocation cores from the image peaks. To determine which, if either, of these equations gives a satisfactory description of the distance of the image peak from the dislocation line, the positions predicted by eqs. (3) and (4) were compared with images computed using many-beam dynamical theory, in-

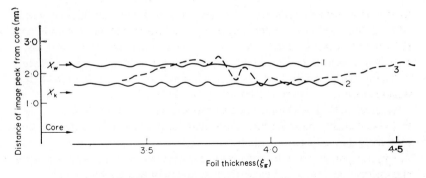

Fig. 7. A plot of the weak-beam image peak position as a function of foil thickness for an undissociated edge dislocation in copper. It is seen that the peak position lies between the positions predicted by eq. (2) (X_w) and eq. (3) (X_k). Parameters: $|\mathbf{g}\cdot\mathbf{b}| = 2$; 6-beam calculations; 100 kV electrons; isotropic elasticity. Curve 1, dislocation depth = $2.20\xi_g$; $\mathbf{g} = \overline{2}20$; $s_g = -0.24$ nm^{-1}; Curve 2, dislocation depth = $1.56\xi_g$; $\mathbf{g} = \overline{2}\overline{2}0$; $s_g = -0.25$ nm^{-1}; Curve 3, dislocation depth = $2.2\xi_g$; $\mathbf{g} = 220$; $s_g = +0.24$ nm^{-1} [52].

cluding absorption [2]. It was found that, for first-order reflections with $|s_g| \gtrsim 0.2$ nm^{-1} and $\mathbf{g}\cdot\mathbf{b} \leqslant 2$,

(i) the calculated image peak positions lay between the two positions given by eqs. (3) and (4), the exact position of the peak depending on foil thickness and dislocation depth;

(ii) for this value of $|s_g|$ the difference between X_W (eq. 3) and X_K (eq. 4) is about 1 nm so that either equation can be used to deduce the position of the dislocation core to an accuracy of ≈ 1 nm (for $|s_g| \gtrsim 0.2$ nm^{-1}).

These conclusions are supported by fig. 7 (D. Saldin unpublished), where the computed peak positions for an undissociated edge dislocation in copper are plotted as a function of foil thickness. X_W and X_K are the peak positions predicted by eqs. (3) and (4) respectively. (The relationship between these equations, and the approximations involved in their derivation from the dynamical theory, have been discussed by De Ridder and Amelinckx [21] and Cockayne [19].) In fig. 7, images have been calculated for two diffraction geometries (see caption) and the image peak positions plotted as a function of foil thickness. For both diffraction geometries, the image peak position lies (effectively) between X_W and X_K and is seen to vary periodically with foil thickness (period = $0.095\xi_{220} \approx 1/|s_g|$). This periodicity can be compared with the beat frequency between Bloch waves on branches 2 and 4 of the dispersion surface (numbering from the top of the dispersion surface) which have a difference in z components of their wave vectors of $\approx |s_g|$ (and hence a beat periodicity of $\approx 1/|s_g|$) for the large value of w (≈ 10.4) used. (It is of interest to note that for the diffraction geometry of curve 3, the high frequency oscillation discussed above is superimposed upon a lower frequency oscillation of periodicity $\approx 0.8\xi_{220}$. This periodicity can be compared with the beat frequency between Bloch waves on branches 1 and 2 of the dispersion surface.)

These considerations lead to the conclusion that for $|s_g| \gtrsim 0.2$ nm^{-1} the weak-beam image peak of a dislocation with $\mathbf{g} \cdot \mathbf{b} \leqslant 2$

(i) close to ($\lesssim 2$ nm from) the dislocation core

(ii) sufficiently narrow (≈ 1.5 nm at half height) to enable its position to be accurately defined experimentally

(iii) at a position which is relatively insensitive (to ≈ 1 nm) to foil thickness and dislocation depth, and given to an accuracy of $\leqslant 1$ nm by eq. (1).

The insensitivity of the image peak position mentioned in (iii) above is governed by the relative excitations of the Bloch waves and consequently by a restriction on w ($= s_g\xi_g$). The criterion $|w| = |s_g\xi_g| \gtrsim 5$ [19] appears to be a minimum requirement in this regard (see sect. 3.5). In summary, it can be stated that, for dislocations, the use of eq. (3) for analysis of first-order weak-beam images will give an accuracy of 1 nm for the dislocation core positions provided $|s_g| > 0.2$ nm^{-1} and, simultaneously, $|w| = |s_g\xi_g| \gtrsim 5$, for $\mathbf{g} \cdot \mathbf{b} \leqslant 2$.

In some investigations, this high accuracy in determining the dislocation core positions is not necessary. Then, provided that the condition $|w| = |s_g\xi_g| \gtrsim 5$ is not violated, values of $|s_g|$ smaller than 0.2 nm^{-1} can be used to increase image intensity. Thus to some extent decreased defect resolution can be traded against increased image intensity, enabling the weak-beam image to be more easily observed and focussed. Such a case may arise for example in regions of high dislocation density, where the dislocation images taken with $s_g \approx 0$ overlap. As an example, weak-beam images of dislocations in silicon formed with a $\langle 220 \rangle$ reflection ($\xi_{220} \approx 76$ nm) appear as bright narrow peaks for $|s_g| \gtrsim 0.1$ nm^{-1} ($w \gtrsim 7.6$), and Bicknell [9,22] has used this condition for obtaining the approximate shape of planar loops in silicon. Similar conditions have been used by Madden [23] for investigating defects in silicon. An example is seen in fig. 8 where a comparison with a normal ($s \approx 0$) bright-field image is shown.

3.2. *Image peak intensity*

It is important to realise that while the intensity of the weak-beam image peak is in general much larger than background, its absolute value is sensitive to the position of the defect in the foil and to the foil thickness. This is illustrated in fig. 9 which shows the computed weak-beam image peak intensity for an undissociated dislocation in copper. In fig. 9a, the image has been calculated for the dislocation lying at depth $1.5\xi_{220}$ in foils of varying thickness (wedge-shaped foil). It is seen that as the thickness increases, the peak intensity oscil-

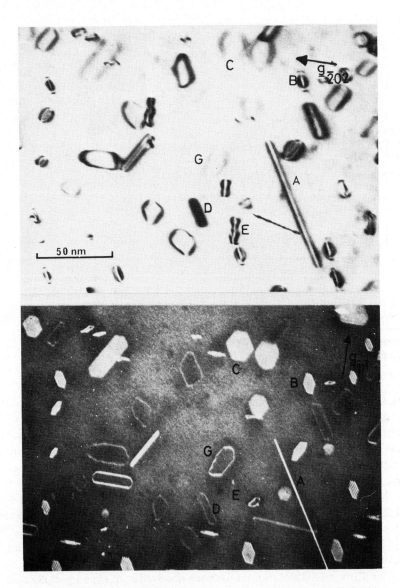

Fig. 8. A comparison of bright-field ($\mathbf{g} = \overline{2}02$) and weak-beam dark-field ($\mathbf{g} = \overline{1}1\overline{1}$) images of defects in silicon irradiated with 40 keV B[+] ions. The defect geometry and faulted nature of the loops is clearly seen in the weak-beam image e.g. Frank faulted loops (BC), prismatic loops (G) [23].

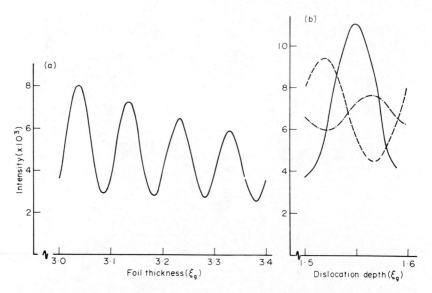

Fig. 9. (a) The variation of weak-beam image peak intensity with foil thickness for an un-dissociated edge dislocation at depth $1.5\xi_g$ in a copper foil. Parameters: $|\mathbf{g} \cdot \mathbf{b}| = 2$; $\mathbf{g} = 2\bar{2}0$; $s_g \simeq -0.2$ nm^{-1}; 100 kV electrons; isotropic elasticity. (b) The variation of weak-beam image peak intensity with dislocation depth for a dislocation with parameters similar to those above. Foil thickness = $3.00\xi_g$ (——), $3.02\xi_g$ (—·—·—·) and $3.04\xi_g$(———)[52].

lates with a thickness periodicity of $0.095\xi_{220}$. A similar effect results for dislocations at different depths, the amplitude of oscillation being a function of the depth. In fig. 9b, the curves show the variation in peak intensity as a function of dislocation depth for foils of several thicknesses (inclined dislocations). Each case shows an intensity oscillation of depth periodicity $0.095\xi_{220}$, the amplitude of the oscillation depending upon the thickness of the foil.

The observed periodicity of oscillation ($0.095\xi_{220}$ for both thickness and depth dependence) was compared in sect. 3.1 with the beat frequency between Bloch waves on branches 2 and 4 of the dispersion surface. In the case of fig. 9a, this beating is seen explicitly, and the oscillations in the intensity correspond to those shown schematically in fig. 3.

For dissociated dislocations it has been observed both experimentally and theoretically that this oscillation in peak height can be of such a magnitude as to produce a disappearance of image peaks for particular defect depths. An example is shown in fig. 10 for dissociated dislocations in silicon where the intensity of the image peak associated with each of the two partials is seen to vary

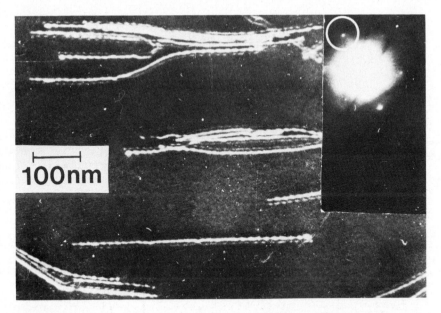

Fig. 10. Weak-beam images of dissociated dislocations in silicon, showing the variation of image peak intensity as a function of the depth of the dislocation in the foil [52].

as in fig. 9. These intensity variations can be suppressed if the incident electron beam is not parallel [24,25]. However, care should be taken when interpreting the absence of an image peak as meaning the absence of a defect core. If such image disappearance causes difficulties, a second image with a slightly different value of s_g can be used to overcome the difficulty.

3.3. Effect of other reflections

Strongly excited reflections can have an important influence upon weak-beam images [19,21,26,27]. The influence of strongly excited systematic reflections is illustrated in fig. 11 which shows computed six-beam images for a dissociated edge dislocation in copper with $\mathbf{b} = \mathbf{b}^1 + \mathbf{b}^2 = a/6\ [1\bar{2}1] +$ $a/6\ [2\bar{1}\bar{1}]$ lying at depth ξ_g in the plane of a (111) foil. The images, for $g = 20\bar{2}$, have $\mathbf{g} \cdot \mathbf{b}^1 \wedge \mathbf{u} = 0$ so that one of the partials is out of contrast (isotropic elasticity). A range of foil thicknesses has been chosen, and the images plotted for three diffracting conditions. In each case $|s_g| \approx 0.2$ nm^{-1} with the diffracting conditions being shown at the head of each column. In figs. 11b and 11c $|s_g^-| \neq 0$. The image peaks have narrow half widths (≈ 1.5 nm) and the peak positions are relatively thickness independent and lie within 1 nm of the posi-

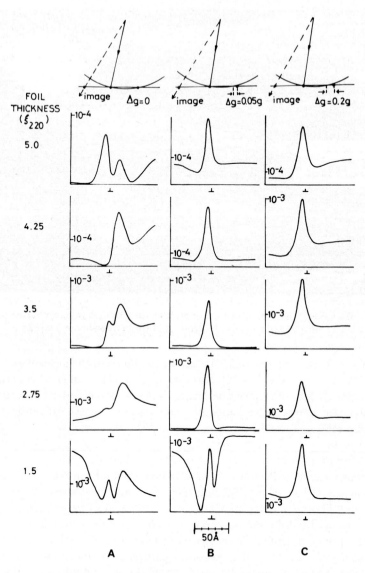

Fig. 11. Computed weak-beam images of a dissociated edge dislocation in copper lying at depth ξ_{220} in (111) foils of various thicknesses (as indicated). The images are for $\mathbf{g} = 20\bar{2}$ and $\mathbf{b} = \mathbf{b}^1 + \mathbf{b}^2 = a/6[1\bar{2}1] + a/6[2\bar{1}\bar{1}]$ so that $\mathbf{g} \cdot \mathbf{b}^1 = \mathbf{g} \cdot \mathbf{b}^1 \wedge \mathbf{u} = 0$. In each case $|s_g| \simeq 0.2$ nm^{-1} but the deviation from satisfying the Bragg condition for the reciprocal lattice point $\bar{2}02$ varies, as indicated at the top of each column [19].

tion predicted by eq. (3). On the other hand, $|s_g^-| = 0$ for fig. 11a, and the images show perturbations in which the peak position is depth dependent and varies in width. Nevertheless it is clear that even these disparities will only be detectable under conditions where experimental detail ≈ 1.5 nm can be measured.

The sensitivity of the weak-beam image to diffraction geometry, as illustrated above, has been considered in terms of the relative excitation of Bloch waves [19]. By considering the variation of these excitations as a function of diffraction geometry, the optimum conditions for avoiding such effects can be determined. However, in general, in order to avoid effects such as those observed in fig. 11a, it is sufficient to ensure that the Ewald sphere passes between, rather than intersecting, reciprocal lattice points. For this reason, and for the necessity of having a knowledge of $|s_g|$, it is advisable to use the Kikuchi pattern as reference. For example appropriate conditions for taking weak-beam images in copper and in silicon at 100 kV are shown in fig. 12, and such situations can be immediately recognised using the Kikuchi pattern.

3.4. Column approximation

The scattering theory used to compute the images for testing the accuracy of eq. (1) contains several approximations. The most important of these is the "column approximation", and this approximation may be under severe strain

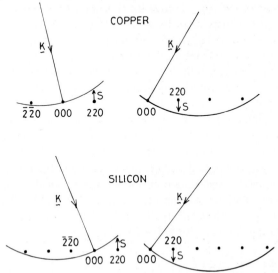

Fig. 12. The diffracting conditions in copper and silicon necessary to obtain $|s_{220}| \simeq 0.2$ nm^{-1} for 100 kV electrons [19].

for weak-beam images since the part of the image which is of most interest arises from regions close to the dislocation core. Howie and Sworn [20] have shown that images computed without the column approximation have certain features which do not appear in images computed with the column approximation. It is generally assumed that calculations performed without the column approximation will more accurately describe the experimental situation (but see [28]) and consequently the use of images calculated with the column approximation for interpreting these particular features will lead to difficulties. However, at the level of resolution of experiments performed to date (e.g. partial separations $\gtrsim 2$ nm) the calculations of Howie and Sworn [20] suggest that no important errors are introduced by this approximation (for a detailed discussion, see Howie, this volume).

3.5. Restrictions on the parameters w and s

An analysis of the dynamical scattering equations in their Bloch wave form has enabled the conditions for obtaining weak-beam images to be placed on a more quantitative basis, and the approximations involved in the use of either eq. (1) or the kinematical theory for interpreting weak-beam images to be investigated [19,29]. In essence, the analysis shows that the optimum conditions are for there to be one Bloch wave in the perfect crystal relatively strongly excited compared with the other Bloch waves. In a two-beam analysis, the condition to obtain one strongly excited Bloch wave is to have $|w| = |s_g \xi_g|$ as large as possible. But the image intensity is then decreased. A reasonable compromise [19] appears to be $|w| = |s_g \xi_g| \geqslant 5$. This relation can be compared with that given by Gevers (this volume) for the diffracted intensity in a perfect crystal to be negligible compared with the incident beam viz. $|w| = |s_g \xi_g| > \sim 3$. There is the further condition from many-beam considerations, discussed previously, that no reflection should have $s = 0$.

The two conditions given above are those which must be fulfilled for the weak-beam image for an isolated dislocation to appear as an intensity peak of high contrast. However, this does not ensure that the peak is narrow, nor that the image peak lies close to the projection of the core, and both of these features are desirable for high resolution studies. It is reasonable to assume that to a first approximation the image half-width Δx (i.e. width at half-height) of weak-beam images can be estimated from the kinematical theory. For dislocations, an approximate value for $\mathbf{g} \cdot \mathbf{b} = 2$ is [21]

$$\Delta x \approx \frac{0.28}{|s_g|} \left\{ 1 + \frac{\kappa}{2(1 - \nu)} \right\}$$

where ν is Poisson's ratio and $\kappa = 0$ and 1 for screw and edge dislocations respectively. Using $\nu = \frac{1}{3}$ and $|s_g| = 0.2$ nm^{-1}, this formula gives $\Delta x \approx 2.5$ nm for an edge dislocation, which is in reasonable agreement with computed images [19]. To ensure that the image peak position lies sufficiently close to the core for a particular investigation, eq. (1) can be used. The accuracy of this equation increases with $|s_g|$, but ultimately further gain in accuracy is not possible because of experimental difficulties of decreasing image intensity. It is important to note that for increasing values of $g \cdot b$, the peak position is predicted to lie further from the core, in agreement with the kinematical theory [16]. Therefore to obtain the same resolution of defect detail, larger values of $|s_g|$ are required for larger values of $g \cdot b$. This point has not been made sufficiently clearly in earlier papers on the subject.

4. Experimental conditions

To obtain weak-beam images the experimental precautions relevant to all high resolution studies are necessary i.e. the dark-field reflection must be aligned axially in the objective lens to minimise the effects of aberrations, and the image must be free from astigmatism and movement. In practice, weak-beam images require exposure times in excess of 8 (and often ≈ 30) seconds, and this imposes severe requirements on image and specimen stability. It also means that the image intensity is extremely weak, making focussing difficult. This difficulty can be overcome to some extent if a beam deflecting system with two or more channels is available. By arranging one channel to carry the weak-beam image and one to carry the bright-field image, the focal conditions can be set using the bright-field image. If the bright-field and weak-beam channels have both been accurately aligned, it is found experimentally that the weak-beam image is in good focus for these same focal conditions. (Of course the diffracting conditions for the two images are not the same, but this does not affect the focus.)

The general restrictions on the diffraction conditions have been discussed in sect. 3, primarily for the case of dislocations. It has been pointed out that the diffraction conditions chosen depend upon the accuracy required in the analysis. But the optimum conditions of the microscope capabilities are met with:

(i) $|s_g| \gtrsim 0.2$ nm^{-1} (for $g \cdot b \leqslant 2$)

(ii) $|w| = |s_g \xi_g| \gtrsim 5$

(iii) no other reflections (systematic or non-systematic) strongly excited.

The experimental procedure is then as follows:-

(a) Decide which reflection g is to be used to form the weak-beam image.

(b) Determine what the Kikuchi pattern will look like when the conditions (i) and (ii) above are satisfied for the reflection g.

(c) Align the microscope for high resolution microscopy for the reflection g; e.g. rotation centre, astigmatism.

(d) Tilt the specimen to obtain the correct diffraction conditions as determined in (b) above, with the reflection g on the optic axis.

(e) Make small adjustments to the specimen orientation so that no reflections are strongly excited.

(f) Attempt to focus the (weak-beam) dark-field image. If this is too difficult, use the bright-field image as discussed above.

(g) Expose the plate. Do not underestimate the exposure time required; a trial image which gives an over-exposure will at least show whether there is anything to be seen, and whether resolution is limited by drift etc. Exposure times of 30 seconds are not uncommon, although 8 to 15 seconds are usually sufficient.

5. Applications

5.1. Dislocation dissociation

The use of the weak-beam method for determining the separation of closely spaced Shockley partial dislocations, and from this stacking-fault energies γ, is now well established. For example studies of the separation of Shockley partials in pure f.c.c. metals have been made by Cockayne et al. [3] ($\gamma_{silver} = 16.3 \pm 1.7$ mJ mm^{-2}; $\gamma_{copper} = 41 \pm 9$ mJ mm^{-2}), Stobbs and Sworn [27] ($\gamma_{copper} = 41$ mJ mm^{-2}) and Jenkins [5] ($\gamma_{gold} = 32 \pm 5$ mJ mm^{-2}), and in diamond cubic materials by Ray and Cockayne [30,31] ($\gamma_{silicon} = 51 \pm 5$ mJ mm^{-2}, $\gamma_{germanium} = 60 \pm 8$ mJ mm^{-2}) and Haüsserman and Schaumberg [32]. Such measurements are not possible using normal strong-beam images, since images taken with $s_g \approx 0$ have half widths $\approx \xi_g/3$, limiting measurements to separations $\gtrsim \xi_g/3$. Comparison of micrographs with computer simulated images can overcome this difficulty to some extent (see Humble, this volume), but nevertheless partial separations $\leqslant 6$ nm as observed in weak-beam images in silicon, germanium and the pure f.c.c. metals have not been measured using strong-beam images even with such refinements. Other more complicated geometrical configurations of partial dislocations (e.g. nodes [33]) have been used for determining γ when the image widths in strong-beam images prevent the use of dissociated linear dislocations, but the determination of γ form such geometries is complicated, and in any case benefits from imaging under weak-beam conditions.

To illustrate the use of the weak-beam method for determining partial separa-

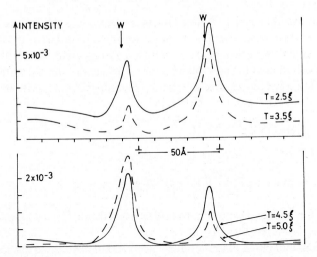

Fig. 13. Computed weak-beam images of a dissociated edge dislocation in copper lying at depth ξ_{220} in (111) foils of various thickness, T, as indicated. W are the image peak positions predicted using eq. (1). The images are for $\mathbf{g} = 2\overline{2}0$, $\mathbf{b} = a/2\ [1\overline{1}0] \rightarrow a/6\ [1\overline{2}1] + a/6\ [2\overline{1}\overline{1}]$, $\mathbf{u} = 1/\sqrt{6}\ [11\overline{2}]$, $|s_g| = 0.2$ nm^{-1} and unit incident beam intensity [19].

tions, we consider the dislocation reaction in an f.c.c. material

$$\mathbf{b} = a/2\ [1\overline{1}0] \rightarrow a/6\ [1\overline{2}1] + a/6\ [2\overline{1}\overline{1}]$$

for an edge dislocation parallel to $[11\overline{2}]$ in a foil with normal $[111]$. We have $\mathbf{g} \cdot \mathbf{b}_1^p = \mathbf{g} \cdot \mathbf{b}_2^p = 1$ for both partials if $\mathbf{g} = 2\overline{2}0$, where $\mathbf{b}_1^p$ and $\mathbf{b}_2^p$ are the Burgers vectors of the partial dislocations. There is then no stacking-fault contrast. As in the case of an undissociated dislocation, we can predict that there will be two image peaks, one close to each of the partials, and this is in accord with the earlier kinematical calculations of Wilkens and Hornbogen [34]. The prediction is verified by computed many-beam images (examples of which are shown in fig. 13). In general one partial shows a higher intensity peak than the other, because of the asymmetry of the strain field between and outside the partials, the relative intensities of the two changing with the sign of the g-vector. From fig. 13 and similar images, it is evident that the partial separation Δ can be equated with the image peak separation Δ_{obs} to an accuracy of better than ≈ 1.0 nm. However, there are two effects which cause Δ_{obs} and Δ to differ: (i) the image peak positions, and Δ_{obs}, vary about mean values with dislocation depth and foil thickness; (ii) there is a difference between Δ and the mean value of Δ_{obs} due to the fact that the mean positions of the image peaks are not equidistant from the respective dislocation cores. A method for allowing for the second of these effects is to make the assumption discussed in sect. 3.1, that the image peaks occur for those positions of the lattice where the strain field orients the lattice into the Bragg condition for the particular reflection used to form the weak-beam image. For the dislocation geometry discussed above, this criterion gives predicted peak positions (marked W in fig. 13) whose separation is given by

$$\Delta_{obs} = \sqrt{(\Delta^2 + 4/C^2)} \tag{5}$$

where

$$C = -s_g \left(\frac{\mathbf{g} \cdot \mathbf{b}^p}{2\pi} \left(1 + \frac{\kappa}{2(1-\nu)} \right) \right)$$

and $\kappa = 1$ for an edge dislocation. In typical cases the difference between Δ_{obs} and Δ in eq. (5) is less than 0.5 nm.

Numerous computed images of dissociated and undissociated dislocations in copper and silicon in orientations from screw to edge, and at various depths in foils from thickness ξ_g to $6\xi_g$ verify that the peak positions of images taken in $g = \langle 220 \rangle$ do not deviate by more than 1 nm from the position W given by the above criterion provided that $|s_g| > 0.2$ nm^{-1} and that no other reflections are strongly excited and that, for individual images, the value of Δ obtained using eq. (5) is accurate to ± 0.7 nm. This error, which arises largely through the dependence of the image on dislocation depth and foil thickness, can be reduced by suitable experimental sampling. The same approach for determining the predicted distance of the image peaks from the dislocation cores can be used for other defect geometries (e.g. dipoles [32]). In particular, for the above dislocation with $\mathbf{b} = a/2\ [1\bar{1}0]$ but in screw orientation, eq. [5] applies with $\kappa = 0$.

There are various other sources of error in determining partial separations from weak-beam images, most of which become increasingly important with decreasing Δ. In particular eq. (5) is derived from eq. (1) using isotropic elasticity, and for anisotropic materials should more properly be derived and examined using an expression for the anisotropic strain field. However, by comparing the above relationship with computed images based on both anisotropic and isotropic elasticity theory, Stobbs and Sworn [4] concluded that, at least for copper, the relationship between Δ_{obs} and Δ given by eq. (5) is accurate to better than 10%.

The usefulness of the weak-beam method for determining partial separations was demonstrated initially with Cu + 10 at % Al [2] where the partial separation (≈ 12 nm) for the dislocation line in edge orientation is sufficiently large to enable a comparison to be made with measurements from nodes taken

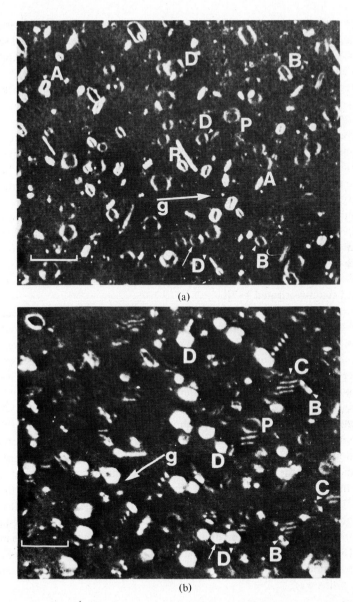

(a)

(b)

Fig. 14. An area of P$^+$ irradiated silicon imaged under different diffraction conditions.
(a) Weak-beam image in $\mathbf{g} = 2\bar{2}0$, with $s_g \approx 0.2$ nm^{-1}. Loops marked D show 'm' contrast.
(b) Weak-beam image in $\mathbf{g} = \bar{1}11$, with $s_g \approx -0.2$ nm^{-1}. Loops marked D show stacking-fault contrast, and lie parallel to foil plane. Loops marked C show stacking-fault contrast, and are inclined to foil plane. Scale mark = 50 nm [10].

with $s \approx 0$. To obtain values of γ from the partial separations, accuracy is gained by fitting the experimental separations with theoretical curves of partial separations as a function of dislocation line orientation for different γ. The experimental curve of partial separation as a function of dislocation line orientation proves of particular interest for copper, because in this material the Shockley partials have a separation of approximately 2 nm near screw orientation. At such a separation, there is the possibility that overlap of the dislocation cores may produce deviations from separations predicted by continuum elasticity theory using unextended cores. Indeed the experimental results led to the observation that the value of γ deduced from the partial separations could be sensitive to the dislocation core model used [3]. The deviations from continuum elasticity theory should be most appreciable for dislocations near screw orientation, and suggestions of a deviation of the experimental values near screw orientation from those predicted by anisotropic elastic continuum theory have been detected [4]. The possibility of interpreting these experimental results in terms of particular core models has been discussed [35–37], and the influence of core models on the value of γ obtained from a particular partial separation has been investigated [37].

5.2. Imaging small regions of stacking fault

The conditions for obtaining stacking-fault contrast using large $|s_g|$ are, of course, the same as for using $s_g \approx 0$, viz $\mathbf{g} \cdot \mathbf{R} \neq$ integer where $\mathbf{R}$ is the displacement vector of the fault. However, for inclined faults the depth periodicity of stacking-fault fringes for large $|s_g|$ is approximately $|s_g|^{-1}$. Consequently inclined faults can appear as narrow closely spaced fringes (figs. 8 and 14), while faults lying parallel to the foil surface show contrast which is sensitive to the fault depth (figs. 8 and 14). For a small region of fault bounded by a partial dislocation line, the image when $s \approx 0$ is often dominated by the influence of the strain field of the partial. The use of large $|s_g|$ can provide a means of observing the fault image because of the diminished width of the image of the partial dislocation [26], and in some cases the partial image and the fault image can be observed separately. Studies which have used weak-beam stacking-fault images include the investigation of geometries of dissociated dislocations in silicon [30] and the construction of a detailed model of point-defect clusters in ion irradiated copper and silver [11]. Regions of fault ≈ 5 nm in size can be imaged in this way.

5.3. Studies of point-defect clusters

The study of densities, sizes and geometries of small point-defect clusters by electron microscopy has been severely restricted by lack of image detail and by insensitivity of the image to details of the defect properties. Such detail as is available is often related to the defect geometry in a very complicated manner, although some advances in image interpretation have been made recently [38] by use of computer simulated images. As a consequence most studies have been restricted to the variations of gross features of images (e.g. black-white symmetry) as a function of diffraction geometry and defect depth (see Wilkens, this volume). These difficulties can be alleviated at two levels by studies using weak-beam images. The first of these concerns the identification of defect geometries of an intermediate size ($\gtrsim 5$ nm dimension) while the second concerns those of size $\lesssim 5$ nm dimension.

5.3.1. Clusters $\gtrsim 5$ nm in dimension

For many clusters of dimension $\gtrsim \xi_g$, bright- and dark-field images taken with $s_g \approx 0$ can be interpreted as if each part of the image arises from a dislocation line lying in the appropriate orientation. In this way, images of, for example, large loops and tetrahedra can be interpreted in a straight forward manner. For clusters of smaller dimension ($\lesssim \xi_g$) the strain fields of the various segments interact to a degree which makes such interpretations unsatisfactory. Because weak-beam images of strain fields only show appreciable contrast where the strain field is high, the image peak lies close to the cores of the various segments and consequently is less affected by the strain field of other segments of the defect. This means that even for defects too small to be investigated with strong-beam images, the weak-beam images of certain types of defect can be interpreted in a straight forward manner. The minimum size of defect which can be investigated in this way depends upon the nature of the defect; for example weak-beam images of small stacking-fault tetrahedra ($\lesssim 3$ nm side length) have been studied by Cockayne et al. [13] in quenched gold and by Bourret (private communication) in neutron-irradiated nickel. Recently Jenkins [11] has been able to identify certain of the defects produced in ion-irradiated copper and silver as stacking-fault tetrahedra.

A case of particular interest is the imaging of small planar edge loops viewed normal to their plane. By imaging in a reflection lying in the loop plane, $\mathbf{g} \cdot \mathbf{b} = 0$ and the loops are imaged in 'm' contrast ($\mathbf{g} \cdot \mathbf{b} \wedge \mathbf{u}$ contrast). With $|s_g| \gtrsim 0.2$ nm^{-1} the geometry of loops of diameter $\gtrsim 5$ nm can be determined in this way. The vacancy or interstitial nature of the loops can then be determined using two weak-beam images with the opposite sign of $(\mathbf{g} \cdot \mathbf{b})s_g$ [10,22,39]. Whether or not the defect is faulted can then be ascertained by forming weak-beam stacking- fault images, as discussed in sect. 5.2. An example of such an analysis of small loops in silicon irradiated with P$^+$ ions is shown in fig. 14. The images taken with both 'm' contrast and stacking-fault contrast reveal the hexagonal nature of the loops. As in the case of dislocation lines, the conditions on $|s_g|$ can be relaxed somewhat if less accurate studies of defect geometry, or larger defects, are involved, and in this way Bicknell [9], Madden and Davidson [40] and Guyot [41] have studied loops of diameter ≈ 20 nm in various materials.

5.3.2. Clusters $\lesssim 5$ nm in dimension

Similar difficulties to those experienced with strong-beam images of clusters of dimension $\lesssim \xi_g$ arise with weak-beam images of clusters of dimension $\lesssim 5$ nm. These images show detail at the level of 1 nm, but criteria such as eq. (1) are unlikely to be sufficiently accurate for image interpretation. At the same time the sensitivity of the image peak intensities to defect depth can result in the same defect placed at different depths having quite different image appearance [42]. It appears likely, however, that this effect will be suppressed by use of slightly convergent illumination [24].

It is possible that theories of kinematical Bloch wave scattering (e.g. [15, 43,44]) may be of use in image interpretation since the region of the strain

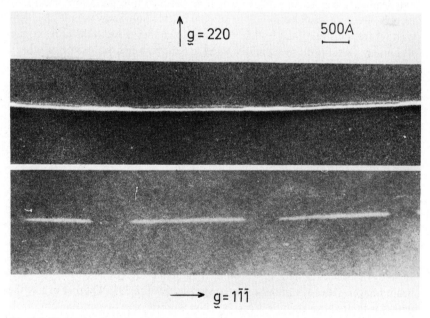

Fig. 15. Weak-beam images of a dissociated edge dislocation in silicon with constricted segments. For the weak-beam image with $g = 11\bar{1}$, $g \cdot b = g \cdot b \wedge u = 0$ for the total dislocation, and the stacking fault of width approx. 8 nm is observed.

field which is effective in producing peaks in the weak-beam image is very localised.

For defect clusters in both the categories of size mentioned above, the narrow extent of weak-beam images enables them to be used to give an indication of the size of the defect to a better accuracy than is possible with other methods available in electron microscopy, even though it may not be possible to determine the details of their geometries.

6. Closely spaced dislocations

Because of the narrowness of the image peaks, and the fact that the presence of each peak is primarily related to a particular dislocation core, weak-beam images find a wide variety of applications in the study of closely spaced disloca-

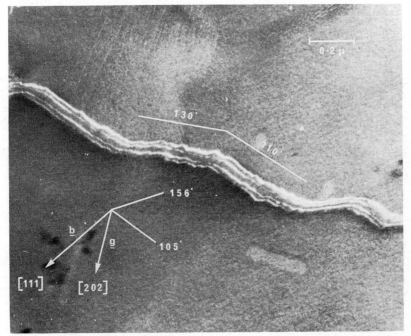

Fig. 16. Weak-beam image showing fourfold dissociation of superlattice dislocations in a DO_3-ordered Fe + 26 at% Al alloy. The average orientations of the dislocation lines (as indicated by straight lines) are unstable for a material of this anisotropy, but are seen to be composed of very fine zig-zags [8].

tions. The determination of their individual Burgers vectors can be carried out
using the normal $\mathbf{g} \cdot \mathbf{b} = 0$ invisibility criteria as for example in the determination
of the Burgers vectors of each partial in dissociated dislocations in silicon [30].
Examples are seen in figs. 1 and 15 which show sets of images in which the individual partials and the stacking faults between them are in contrast separately. By
reference to the Kikuchi pattern and by determination of the sense of the Burgers
vector (see Whelan, this volume), the nature of the fault (extrinsic or intrinsic)
can then be determined. Many other arrangements of interacting dislocations
suggest themselves as amenable to a more detailed investigation than has been
possible previously. A further example is seen in fig. 16 which shows a weak-beam
image of the fourfold dissociation of a superlattice dislocation in a DO_3-
ordered Fe + 26 at % Al alloy [8]. In this material, the dislocation line directions shown by the straight lines are unstable, due to the anisotropy of the
material, and the weak-beam image reveals that the partial dislocations avoid
these directions by zig-zagging between them. The ability to analyse Burgers
vectors of closely spaced dislocations has particular relevance to the study of
component dislocations in complex networks (such as are observed in grain
boundaries) where if imaged under strong-beam conditions the dislocations
appear as Moiré fringes [45–47].

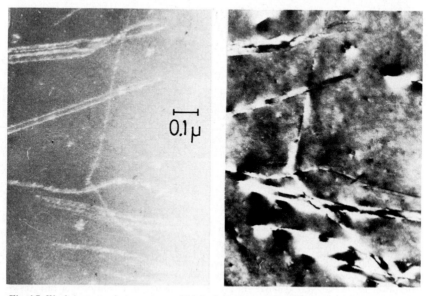

Fig. 17. Weak-beam and strong-beam 220 dark-field images of dislocations in silicon for
1 MV electrons, showing the decreased image width obtained in the weak-beam image [52].

In high voltage electron microscopy, calculations show that weak-beam images, and the conditions for obtaining them, are very similar to those at 100 kV [48,49]. The diffraction conditions are experimentally more difficult to obtain at 1 MV than at 100 kV, but an example of the improvement in image clarity obtained at 1 MV under these conditions is shown in fig. 17 for dislocations in silicon. The spotted nature of the image is a result of electron irradiation damage at this voltage. Such micrographs are clearly advantageous for overcoming difficulties due to overlapping images, but unless high resolution detail is required, they may not have advantages at 1 MV over bright-field images taken with a high index reflection satisfied [50].

7. Conclusion

There are many possibilities for applying weak-beam microscopy yet to be explored, and various theoretical aspects to be investigated. For example there is the possibility of obtaining more reliable size-density distributions of point-defect clusters, but in that field certain difficulties concerning defect visibility are yet to be resolved [42]. For this highest resolution, the importance of the contribution of inelastic scattering to the images [51] requires further investigation, as do considerations of the column approximation. Nevertheless, the principles of the method are now well understood, and provide a foundation upon which to base experiments. The optimum conditions for obtaining weak-beam images have been established but these conditions can be relaxed if less quantitative results are acceptable. The "optimum" conditions referred to are of course determined by a balance between the necessity to have sufficient intensity for recording purposes and the desirability of having image detail close to the resolution capabilities of the microscope. With advances in either of these fields, it may be possible to use appreciably higher values of $|s_g|$ and possibly higher order reflection with, as yet, undetermined advantages.

Acknowledgements

I am grateful to many colleagues in the Department of Metallurgy, University of Oxford, for their contributions to the subject matter discussed in this chapter and for permission to give examples from their unpublished work. I am particularly indebted to Professor P.B. Hirsch, F.R.S., and Drs. M.J. Whelan, I.L.F. Ray, M.L. Jenkins and J.M. Titchmarsh for their continued interest and helpful comments.

References

[1] C.B. Carter and I.L.F. Ray, Phil. Mag. 29 (1974) 1231.

[2] D.J.H. Cockayne, I.L.F. Ray and M.J. Whelan, Phil. Mag. 20 (1969) 1265.

[3] D.J.H. Cockayne, M.L. Jenkins and I.L.F. Ray, Phil. Mag. 24 (1971) 1383.

[4] W.M. Stobbs and C.H. Sworn, Phil. Mag. 24 (1971) 1365.

[5] M.L. Jenkins, Phil. Mag. 26 (1972) 747.

[6] R.C. Crawford, D. Phil. Thesis, University of Oxford (1971).

[7] R.C. Crawford, I.L.F. Ray and D.J.H. Cockayne, J. Microsc. 98 (1973) 196.

[8] R.C. Crawford, I.L.F. Ray and D.J.H. Cockayne, Phil. Mag. 27 (1973) 1.

[9] R.W. Bicknell, Phys. Stat. Sol. 7 (1971) K1.

[10] M.L. Jenkins, D.J.H. Cockayne and M.J. Whelan, J. Microsc. 98 (1973) 155.

[11] M.L. Jenkins, Phil. Mag. 29 (1974) 813.

[12] F. Haussermann, Proc. Seventh Int. Congress on Electron Microscopy, Grenoble (1970) p. 225.

[13] D.J.H. Cockayne, M.L. Jenkins, I.L.F. Ray and M.J. Whelan, Proc. Fifth Eur. Congress on Electron Microscopy, Manchester (1972) p. 530.

[14] D.J.H. Cockayne, I.L.F. Ray and M.J. Whelan, Proc. Fourth Eur. Congress on Electron Microscopy, Rome (1968) p. 129.

[15] A. Howie and Z.S. Basinski, Phil. Mag. 17 (1968) 1039.

[16] P.B. Hirsch, A. Howie and M.J. Whelan, Phil. Trans. Roy. Soc. A252 (1960) 499.

[17] P.P. Ewald, Ann. Phys. 54 (1917) 557.

[18] D.J.H. Cockayne, D. Phil. Thesis, University of Oxford (1970).

[19] D.J.H. Cockayne, Z. Naturforsch. 27a (1972) 452.

[20] A. Howie and C.H. Sworn, Phil. Mag. 22 (1970) 861.

[21] R. De Ridder and S. Amelinckx, Phys. Stat. Sol. (b) 43 (1971) 541.

[22] R.W. Bicknell, J. Microsc. 98 (1973) 165.

[23] P.K. Madden, D. Phil. Thesis, University of Oxford (1974).

[24] S.M. Holmes, D.J.H. Cockayne and I.L.F. Ray, Proc. 8th Int. Congress on Electron Microscopy, Canberra (1974) p. 290.

[25] R. Sandstrom, A. Melander and R. Sandstrom, Phys. Stat. Sol. (a) 22 (1974) 587.

[26] D.J.H. Cockayne, M.L. Jenkins, I.L.F. Ray and M.J. Whelan, Proc. 25th Anniv. Meeting of EMAG, Cambridge (1971) p. 108.

[27] W.M. Stobbs and C.H. Sworn, Proc. 25th Anniv. Meeting of EMAG, Cambridge (1971) p. 118.

[28] M. Wilkens and K.H. Katerbau, Proc. Fifth Eur. Congress on Electron Microscopy, Manchester (1972) p. 414.

[29] R. Sandstrom, Phys. Stat. Sol. 18 (1973) 639.

[30] I.L.F. Ray and D.J.H. Cockayne, Proc. R. Soc. (London) A325 (1971) 543.

[31] I.L.F. Ray and D.J.H. Cockayne, J. Microsc. 98 (1973) 170.

[32] F. Häussermann and H. Schaumberg, Phil. Mag. 27 (1973) 745.

[33] M.J. Whelan, Proc. R. Soc. 249 (1959) 114.

[34] M. Wilkens and E. Hornbogen, Phys. Stat. Sol. 4 (1964) 557.

[35] M.J. Norgett, R.C. Perrin and E.J. Savino, J. Phys. F 2 (1972) L73.

[36] R.C. Perrin and E.J. Savino, J. Microsc. 98 (1973) 214.

[37] D.J.H. Cockayne and V. Vitek, Phys. Stat. Sol. (b) 65 (1974) 751.

[38] R. Bullough, D.M. Maher and R.C. Perrin, Phys. Stat. Sol. 43 (1971) 689.

[39] R.C. Perrin and B.L. Eyre, J. Microsc. 98 (1973) 200.
[40] P.K. Madden and S.M. Davidson, Rad. Effects 14 (1972) 271.
[41] P. Guyot, J. Microsc. 98 (1973) 180.
[42] F. Häussermann, K.H. Katerbau, M. Rühle and M. Wilkens, J. Microsc. 98 (1973) 135.
[43] M. Wilkens, Phys. Stat. Sol. 6 (1964) 939.
[44] P.B. Hirsch, A. Howie, R.B. Nicholson, D.W. Pashley and M.J. Whelan, Electron Microscopy of Thin Crystals (Butterworths, London, 1965).
[45] A.R. Thölén, Phys. Stat. Sol. 2 (1970) 537.
[46] M. Bouchard, R.J. Livak and G. Thomas, Surface Sci. 31 (1972) 275.
[47] I. Nordlander and A.R. Thölén, J. Microsc. 98 (1973) 221.
[48] M.J. Goringe, E.A. Hewat, C.J. Humphreys and G. Thomas, Proc. Fifth Eur. Congress on Electron Microscopy (1972) p. 538.
[49] R. Sandstrom, Phys. Stat. Sol. 19 (1973) 83.
[50] W.L. Bell and G. Thomas, Electron Microscopy and Structure of Materials (University of California Press, Berkeley, 1972) p.23.
[51] A. Melander and R. Sandstrom, Phil. Mag. 32 (1975) 1089.
[52] D.J.H. Cockayne, J. Microsc. 98 (1973) 116.

Diffraction and Imaging Techniques in Material Science,
eds. S. Amelinckx, R. Gevers and J. van Landuyt
© *North-Holland Publishing Company, 1978*

IDENTIFICATION OF SMALL DEFECT CLUSTERS IN PARTICLE-IRRADIATED CRYSTALS BY MEANS OF TRANSMISSION ELECTRON MICROSCOPY

M.WILKENS

Max-Planck-Institut für Metallforschung, Institut für Physik,
Stuttgart, Germany

1. Introduction

For about ten years it has been known that particle irradiation causes damage in crystals which appears on the transmission micrographs in general as "black dots" or "black spots" with diameters $d \lesssim 100$ Å, i.e. small compared with the extinction length ξ_g of the operating diffraction vector $\mathbf{g}$. Consequently the geometrical structure of the lattice defects, giving rise to the black dot contrast, is in general not resolvable. As examples we mention the early work of Pashley and Presland [1], who observed black dots in gold foils which were irradiated with O^- ions inside the microscope.

At about the same time Makin and coworkers [2,3] studied neutron-irradiated copper. They found a small number of large, well resolved dislocation loops with perfect Burgers vector $\mathbf{b} = \frac{1}{2} \langle 110 \rangle$ and, apart from these, a high density of black, unresolved dots. In the present paper we will deal only with the nature and the analysis of the small black dots. The large, well resolved loops, which were found also in other irradiation-damaged metals, for instance in neutron-irradiated platinum by Ruedl, Delavignette and Amelinckx [4,5], will not be treated in this contribution.

In the above mentioned papers the black dots were inspected mainly under so-called kinematical image conditions resulting in contrast figures of rather unspecific shape (fig. 1). Therefore the crystallographic nature of the irradiation-induced lattice defects could not be derived from the micrographs.

A certain progress was made when Essmann and Wilkens [6] detected that the black dots in neutron-irradiated copper reveal a characteristic black-white structure, if the foils are imaged under two-beam dynamical contrast conditions

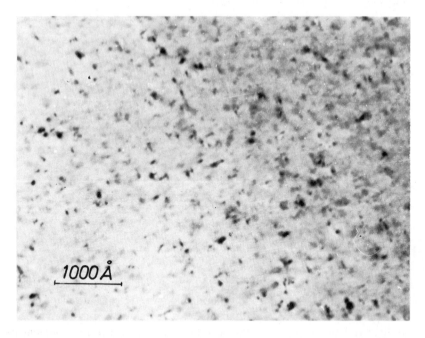

Fig. 1. Small Frank dislocation loops in copper, irradiated at $\approx 80°C$ with 6×10^{17} fast
neutrons/cm^2. Foil plane $\approx (001)$, bright field, black dots revealed under kinematical
contrast conditions.

(excitation error $s \cong 0$) (figs. 2 and 3). These black-white contrast figures re-
sembled to some extent the black-white contrast from spherical inclusions
which was studied rather extensively a little earlier by Ashby and Brown [7].
From the observed crystallographic orientation of the black-white contrast
streaks (figs. 2 and 3), Essmann and Wilkens [6] concluded that the lattice
defects giving rise to the black dot or to the black-white dot contrast (depending on the image conditions) are small Frank dislocation loops, i.e. dislocation
loops with habit planes parallel to a (closed-packed) {111}-plane and with
Burgers vectors $\mathbf{b} = \frac{1}{3} \langle 111 \rangle$ perpendicular to the loop habit plane (such a loop
will be called an "edge loop"). However, the fundamental question whether
these loops were due to agglomeration of (irradiation-produced) vacancies or
interstitials could not be answered. It was in fact concluded that the diffraction contrast theory for small elastic strain centres, as published at that time
mainly by Ashby and Brown [7,8], was insufficient to resolve this problem.
    Stimulated by this lack in theoretical background, Rühle, Wilkens and

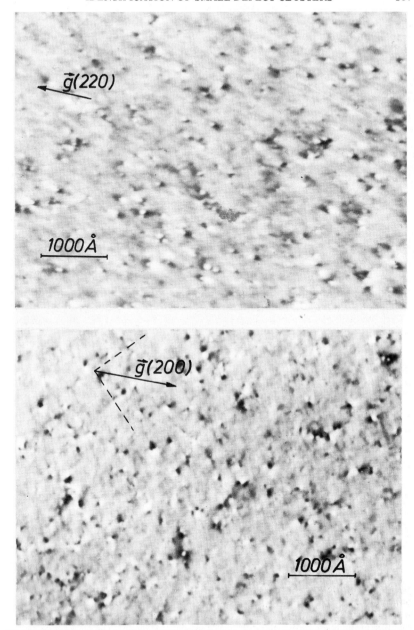

Fig. 2. The same as fig. 1, dynamical bright field contrast ($s=0$). Some of the black dots of fig. 1 appear now as black-white dots. The black-white vectors **l** are mainly parallel or antiparallel to **g** in fig. 2a and at $45°$ or $135°$ to **g** in fig. 2b as expected for **b** parallel to $\langle 111 \rangle$.

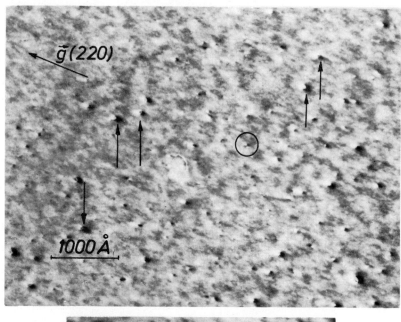

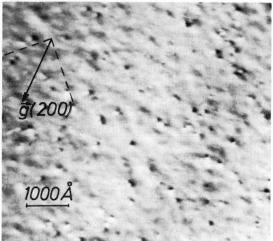

Fig. 3. Black-white contrast figures from Frank loops of vacancy type in copper foils irradiated with 100 keV O⁻ ions, foil plane ≈ (001), bright field. All the black-white dots
reveal the same sign of $(\mathbf{g}\cdot\mathbf{l})$. With respect to the direction of $\mathbf{l}$ see fig. 2. Notice the fine
structure of the black-white separation line of the indicated loops. The black-white con-
trast figure enclosed by a circle was explained by Rühle [11] as due to a Frank loop of
special diameter with its centre just between the layers L1 and L2. In fig. 3a a thin gold
layer was evaporated on the ion-irradiated foil surface for the stereo measurements.

Essmann [9] and Rühle [10,11] made an extensive theoretical study of the diffraction contrast from small Frank dislocation loops, which was later confirmed and in some points extended by McIntyre and Brown [12,13]. On the basis of these calculations Diepers and Diehl [14,15] and Rühle [10,11] developed experimental methods designed to differentiate between vacancy and interstitial type loops. In the mean time these methods have been applied by different workers to various kinds of point defect agglomerates in irradiation-damaged crystals,(sect. 6).

So far, mainly the comparatively simple damage structure in fcc metals was studied. It was in fact found that in fcc metals the overwhelming majority of the small point defect clusters created by particle irradiation are Frank loops. However, during a recent investigation of the neutron-irradiation damage in niobium [16] it was concluded that the contrast calculations for edge loops are presumably not sufficient for an analysis of the black dots in bcc metals. From a theoretical point of view it is expected that in bcc metals the irradiation-induced small dislocation loops may have a large shear component implying that the Burgers vector may be inclined to the loop normal. This shear component of the Burgers vector can modify to some extent the results of the contrast calculations valid for pure edge loops. The present paper summarizes the state of our present knowledge.

In this paper we restrict ourselves mainly to the analysis of the contrast from small dislocation loops, where the term "small" means "small compared with the extinction length ξ_g". With respect to the problems connected with the identification of other defect configurations, as for instance large dislocation loops (which are resolved as loops on the micrographs), voids, tracks from fission fragments, and stacking fault tetrahedra, we refer to the recent survey papers of Wilkens [17] and Rühle [18]. Sect. 2 contains the main results of the contrast calculations for small edge loops. Some preliminary results for loops with shear components are discussed in sect. 3. The results of sects. 2 and 3 are, as usually, obtained by numerical integrations of the differential equations which describe the electron diffraction in a distorted lattice. In order to obtain a quicker qualitative understanding of the type of black-white contrast which is expected for a given type of elastic strain centre it is expedient to solve the differential equations approximately in an analytical way. This is outlined in sect. 4. In sect. 5 the experimental procedures for the application of the theoretical contrast calculations are described. Sect. 6 presents a short review of those experimental results which confirm the applicability of the theoretical results and experimental methods as outlined in the foregoing sections.

A more complete review of the experimental results on the structure of the radiation damage in crystals is given in the survey papers of [17,18].

2. Theoretical results of the contrast calculations for small dislocation loops of edge type

For a proper description of the black-white contrast figures on the micrographs we define a vector **l** which points from the centre of the black part to the centre of the white part of the contrast figure ("black" and "white" on positive prints). It is expedient to discern between the direction of **l**, irrespective of the sign, and the sign of **l** as determined by the sign of the product $(\mathbf{g}\cdot\mathbf{l})$. The following contrast properties for edge loops have been derived [9–11].

(1) A loop oriented with $(\mathbf{g}\cdot\mathbf{b}) \neq 0$ (**b** is the loop's Burgers vector) and with its centre close to one of the foil surfaces reveals under dynamical image conditions $(s \cong 0)$ a black-white contrast. The orientation of the black-white vector **l** is independent of the direction of **g** and lies parallel (or antiparallel) to the Burgers vector **b** or to its projection onto the image plane (= plane perpendicular to the electron beam). Small, but insignificant deviations from this direction are expected for large angles between **b** and **g**.

(2) The sign of $(\mathbf{g}\cdot\mathbf{l})$ depends on the actual depth position of the loop centre and on whether the loop is of vacancy or interstitial type. The results for a vacancy loop are schematically shown in fig. 4. For interstitial loops the direction **g** in fig. 4 must be reversed. The regions near the foil surfaces are divided into the layers L1, L2, ... The sign of $(\mathbf{g}\cdot\mathbf{l})$ changes if the loop centre changes from one layer to the adjacent layer, thus leading to "depth oscillations" of the black-white contrast. The thickness of layer L1 amounts to about 0.3 ξ_g, depending slightly on the loop size, whereas the inner boundaries of the subsequent layers L2, L3 ... correspond to distances of $\frac{3}{4} \xi_g$, $\frac{5}{4} \xi_g$ ... to the adjacent foil surface. The sign of $(\mathbf{g}\cdot\mathbf{l})$ for loops in layer L1 is the same as was predicted by Ashby and Brown [7] for (large) spherical inclusions, which do not show the depth oscillations of the sign in the subsequent layers (see point (8)).

(3) Due to the anomalous absorption the black-white contrast is damped with increasing distance of the loop centre from the adjacent foil surface. For the frequently used value $\xi_g'/\xi_g = 0.1$ ($\xi_g' =$ anomalous absorption length) [19–21,7,10] the black-white contrast is expected to be observable only in the first two or three layers. For smaller values of ξ_g'/ξ_g the observable depth oscillations extend deeper into the foil.

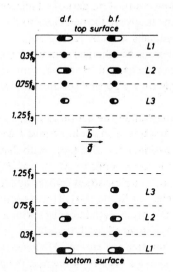

Fig. 4. Schematic plot of the depth oscillation of the black-white contrast figures from small dislocation loops of vacancy type; the contrast figures are drawn at those depth positions at which the loop centres were assumed. d.f. = dark field, b.f. = bright field. For loops of interstitial type the direction of g must be reversed.

Actually, the boundaries between L1 and L2, and between L2 and L3 etc. have a finite thickness of about 0.1 ξ_g which means that for loops whose centres are within these intermediate layers the black-white contrast is too weak to be observable. Consequently these loops reveal only a black-dot contrast.

(4) For loops in the middle region of the foil, i.e. outside the region of observable black-white contrast, the contrast consists of a black dot of unspecific shape.

(5) Loops oriented with $(\mathbf{g \cdot b}) = 0$ show only a very weak contrast which is due to the displacement field transverse to $\mathbf{b}$ (residual contrast, Querkontrast). Therefore, the well-known $(\mathbf{g \cdot b}) = 0$ extinction rule for the determination of $\mathbf{b}$ may be applied, provided care is exercised.

(6) For large excitation errors $s(|s| \cdot \xi_g \gg 1)$, which corresponds approximately to kinematical diffraction, only a black contrast remains for all loop positions. The black dot diameter, measured for instance at the 20% image width (for definition see ref. [7]) corresponds within 10% to the projected loop width. Therefore measurements on the size distribution functions of the radiation

damage should be performed under kinematical image conditions. For $|s| \cdot \xi_g \lesssim 1$ the black-white contrast on dark-field images depends in a critical manner upon whether the loops are located close to the top or the bottom surface respectively, for details see refs. [22,23,10].

(7) For small strain centres of spherical symmetry most of the above summarized properties remain unchanged. However, contrary to point (1) the black-white vector l turns always parallel (or antiparallel) to g [7] for spherical strain centres.

(8) The question as to whether the depth oscillations of the black-white contrast depend on the amount of the volume misfit ΔV of the strain centre demands a separate discussion. (For edge loops with diameter d and Burgers vector b the volume misfit corresponds to $\Delta V = \frac{1}{4} \pi d^2 b$.) This question has been studied especially for spherical strain centres by McIntyre and Brown [12] and by Chik, Wilkens and Rühle [24]. It was found that the sign of $(g \cdot l)$ oscillates with depth only for strain centres with a sufficiently small volume misfit ΔV. This is explained by the modification of the strain field due to the adjacent traction-free foil surface. With increasing ΔV, the width of the contrast profile increases. As a consequence, the contrast profile is influenced more by the modification of the strain field, resulting in an increase of the thickness of the layer L1 at the expense of the layer L2.

If ΔV exceeds a critical value $\Delta V_c = \pi \cdot \xi_g^2/g$, the layer L2 for which the sign of $(g \cdot l)$ is reversed as compared with L1 and L3 is completely suppressed. Since for reasonable values of the anomalous absorption parameter ξ_g'/ξ_g the black-white contrast in the layer L4 is hard to observe, the depth oscillations of the sign of $(g \cdot l)$ are practically suppressed for $\Delta V \gtrsim \Delta V_c$. Thus on dark field images $(g \cdot l)$ assumes a unique sign, which depends upon whether the strain centre is of vacancy type $((g \cdot l)) > 0)$ or of interstitial type $((g \cdot l) < 0)$. In the first paper, dealing with the properties of the black-white contrast, Ashby and Brown [7] treated only this special case, occasionally referred to as "Ashby-Brown rule".

In principle, the same influence of the traction-free surface on the strain field and, consequently, on the thicknesses of the layers L1 and L2 exists for dislocation loops. However, using the "infinitesimally small loop approximation" for the correction of the strain field as due to the adjacent traction-free surface, McIntyre and Brown [12] have shown that, for low order reflexions g and for b in the order of the lattice spacing, the critical misfit volume for suppressing the depth oscillations is reached only for loops with diameters d in the order of, or larger than, the extinction length ξ_g. However, loops with $d \gtrsim \xi_g$ are in general resolvable on the micrographs. Consequently, a decision as to whether they are of vacancy or interstitial type may be obtained by means of "conventional" methods based on the properties of the dislocation contrast. We conclude that for loops, too small to be resolved, i.e. $d \lesssim \xi_g/3$, the sign of $(g \cdot l)$ oscillates with depth. The thickness of the critical layer L2 in this size region is not expected to be very sensitive to the loop size. On the other hand some uncertainties remain concerning the black-white contrast from loops with diameters d between $\xi_g/3$ and ξ_g. For loops of this size the infinitesimal loop approximation, which has been used so far for the contrast calculations [12], fails to give reliable results for the surface corrections of the loop strain field. For some properties of the contrast from loops of this size region we refer to [25].

3. Contrast from small loops containing a shear component of the Burgers vector

Using the theoretical prediction of the direction of the black-white vector l as an indicator, several authors have found that small point defect agglomerates in radiation-damaged fcc metals are mainly of Frank type. Thus, for a differentiation between vacancy and interstitial loops it was justified to use the above summarized properties of the black-white contrast from edge loops. However, the formal application of these theoretically predicted properties to point defect clusters in bcc metals may give rise to complications: Tucker and Ohr [26] and Huber, Rühle and Wilkens [27,16] concluded from the observed directions of the black-white vector l in neutron irradiated niobium that the small point defect agglomerates may be interpreted as small dislocation loops with Burgers vectors b parallel to the directions $\langle 111 \rangle$, $\langle 110 \rangle$ or $\langle 100 \rangle$. Assuming that all these loops have been nucleated by agglomeration of single point defects on closed packed $\{110\}$ planes, one must expect that the Burgers vector of those loops with b parallel to $\langle 111 \rangle$ or $\langle 100 \rangle$ has an appreciable shear component b_s ($b = b_e + b_s$, b_e = edge component). If a loop of this kind is oriented with respect to g in such way that $|g \cdot b_s|$ is small compared with $|g \cdot b_e|$ one may assume that the properties of the black-white contrast remain practically the same as calculated for pure edge loops. In fact, for configurations so far treated, the direction of l coincides, as was found for pure edge loops, with the direction of b (or its projection onto the image plane), thus justifying the Burgers vector determination of [26,27] in niobium. If, however, $|g \cdot b_e|$ is small compared with $|g \cdot b_s|$, one must be aware of essentially different properties of the black white contrast. This is confirmed by preliminary results of corresponding contrast calculations. It is interesting to note that for special configurations of loops, containing an appreciable shear component, not only the thickness of the most important layer L1 is changed, but that in some cases also the sign of $(\mathbf{g}\cdot\mathbf{l})$ within the layer L1 is reversed. Extended calculations on this rather complicated problem which is important for the analysis of the structure of radiation damage in bcc metals are under way [28].

4. Some remarks on the analytical calculations

Let us assume that the primary electron beam is represented by a plane wave

$$\psi_o = \exp\,(2\pi i \mathbf{k}_o\cdot\mathbf{r})\;,$$

which penetrates the top surface of the transmission foil exactly under the Bragg angle (excitation error = 0). Inside the crystal foil the electrons propagate in the form of two Bloch waves $\psi^{(1)}$ and $\psi^{(2)}$ (notation similar as in [22])

$$\psi = \varphi^{(1)}\cdot\psi^{(1)} + \varphi^{(2)}\cdot\psi^{(2)}$$

with

$$\psi^{(1)} = \frac{1}{\sqrt{2}}\exp-\pi(\tau_o+\tau_g)z\cdot\exp 2\pi i(\mathbf{k}_o\cdot\mathbf{r}+\tfrac{1}{2}\sigma z)\cdot[1+\exp 2\pi i(\mathbf{g}\cdot\mathbf{r})]\;,$$
$$\tag{1a}$$

$$\psi^{(2)} = \frac{1}{\sqrt{2}}\exp-\pi(\tau_o-\tau_g)z\cdot\exp 2\pi i(\mathbf{k}_o\cdot\mathbf{r}-\tfrac{1}{2}\sigma z)\cdot[1-\exp 2\pi i(\mathbf{g}\cdot\mathbf{r})]\;;$$
$$\tag{1b}$$

$\tau_o^{-1} = \xi_o' =$ normal absorption length, $\tau_g^{-1} = \xi_g' =$ anomalous absorption length, $\sigma^{-1} = \xi_g =$ extinction length. z-axis parallel to the electron beam (column approximation), origin at the top surface. $\mathbf{g} =$ diffraction vector of the two-beam reflexion.

In a perfect crystal foil and under the assumed condition $s = 0$, the two Bloch wave amplitudes $\varphi^{(1)}$ and $\varphi^{(2)}$ are given by

$$\varphi^{(1)} = 1/\sqrt{2}\,,\qquad\qquad \varphi^{(2)} = -1/\sqrt{2}\,.$$

At the exit surface at $z = t_o$ the Bloch waves split into the transmitted (ψ_t) and reflected (ψ_g) plane waves respectively,

$$\psi_t = \frac{1}{\sqrt{2}} \exp\left[-\pi\tau_o t_o\right] \{\varphi^{(1)} \cdot \exp\left[-\pi\tau_g t_o\right] \cdot \exp\left[\pi i \sigma t_o\right]$$

$$+ \varphi^{(2)} \cdot \exp\left[+\pi\tau_g t_o\right] \cdot \exp\left[-\pi i \sigma t_o\right]\} \exp\left[2\pi i(\mathbf{k_o \cdot r})\right] , \quad (2a)$$

$$\psi_g = \frac{1}{\sqrt{2}} \exp\left[-\pi\tau_o t_o\right] \{\varphi^{(1)} \cdot \exp\left[-\pi\tau_g t_o\right] \cdot \exp\left[\pi i \sigma t_o\right]$$

$$- \varphi^{(2)} \cdot \exp\left[+\pi\tau_g t_o\right] \cdot \exp\left[-\pi i \sigma t_o\right\} \exp\left[2\pi i(\mathbf{k_o + g \cdot r})\right] . \quad (2b)$$

In a distorted lattice the bending of the reflecting planes is described by the displacement component $u(z)$ parallel to the diffraction vector $\mathbf{g}$. If the derivative $du/dz = u_z \neq 0$, a scattering between the two Bloch waves is induced which is controlled by the differential eqs. [22]

$$\frac{d\varphi^{(1)}}{dz} = i\pi u_z \exp\left(2\pi\tau_g z\right) \exp\left(-2\pi i \sigma z\right) \cdot \varphi^{(2)}(z) , \quad (3a)$$

$$\frac{d\varphi^{(2)}}{dz} = i\pi u_z \exp\left(-2\pi\tau_g z\right) \exp\left(+2\pi i \sigma z\right) \cdot \varphi^{(1)}(z) , \quad (3b)$$

with the boundary conditions $\varphi^{(1)}(0) = 1/\sqrt{2}$, $\varphi^{(2)}(0) = -1/\sqrt{2}$. The radiation-induced defects, which are of interest to us, are small compared with the extinction length ξ_g. Consequently, u_z will essentially be $\neq 0$ only in an interval $\ll \xi_g$. The centre of the defect lies in the depth position z_o. Then eq. (3) can be integrated in a Born first approximation. For this purpose we set on the right hand sides of eq. (3) $\varphi^{(1)}(z) = \varphi^{(1)}(0)$ and $\varphi^{(2)}(z) = \varphi^{(2)}(0)$. Furthermore the absorption factors $\exp\left(\pm 2\pi\tau_g \cdot z\right)$ can be considered as slowly varying functions over that region, in which u_z is essentially $\neq 0$. We obtain as the first approximation

$$\varphi^{(1)}(t_o) = \frac{1}{\sqrt{2}} - \frac{\pi}{\sqrt{2}} \exp\left(2\pi\tau_g z_o\right) [S + iC] , \quad (4a)$$

$$\varphi^{(2)}(t_o) = -\frac{1}{\sqrt{2}} - \frac{\pi}{\sqrt{2}} \exp\left(-2\pi\tau_g z_o\right) [S - iC] , \quad (4b)$$

$$S = \int_0^{t_o} u_z(z) \sin 2\pi\sigma z \, dz \, , \qquad C = \int_0^{t_o} u_z(z) \cos 2\pi\sigma z \, dz \, . \quad (5)$$

In the "thick foil approximation", it is assumed that the foil is thick enough to suppress the Bloch wave $\psi^{(1)}$ which is weakened much more strongly by anomalous absorption than the Bloch wave $\psi^{(2)}$, consequently we assume

$$\exp(-\pi\tau_g t_o) \ll 1, \qquad \exp(+\pi\tau_g t_o) \gg 1 \, .$$

Let us first consider a strain centre close to the top surface which corresponds to $\exp(\pm 2\pi\tau_g \cdot z_o) \approx 1$. Then the bright field contrast $|\psi_t|^2$ and the dark field contrast $|\psi_g|^2$ are given by

$$|\psi_t|^2 \cong |\psi_g|^2 \cong |\varphi^{(2)}(t_o)|^2 \cdot \exp\left[-2\pi(\tau_o - \tau_g)t_o\right] \, .$$

Therefore, in "linear approximation" (linear in u_z) the contrast is essentially given by

$$|\psi_t|^2 \cong |\psi_g|^2 \propto \tfrac{1}{2}[1 + 2\pi \cdot \exp(-2\pi\tau_g z_o) \cdot S] \, . \quad (6)$$

If the defect lies close to the exit surface (bottom surface) we have to assume that

$$\exp\left[\pm 2\pi\tau_g(z_o - t_o)\right] \approx 1 \, .$$

One obtains with eqs. (2)–(4) after some simple rearrangement in the linear approximation

$$|\psi_t|^2 = \tfrac{1}{2}\{1 - 2\pi \exp\left[-2\pi\tau_g(t_o - z_o)\right] \cdot S'\} \exp\left[-2\pi(\tau_o - \tau_g)t_o\right] \, , \quad (7a)$$

$$|\psi_g|^2 = \tfrac{1}{2}\{1 + 2\pi \exp\left[-2\pi\tau_g(t_o - z_o)\right] \cdot S'\} \exp\left[-2\pi(\tau_o - \tau_g)t_o\right] \, , \quad (7b)$$

$$S' = \int_0^{t_o} u_z(z) \sin 2\pi\sigma(z - t_o) \, dz \, . \quad (8)$$

The linear approximation is valid only for the tails of the contrast profiles. This, however, is sufficient to determine the essential properties of the black-white contrast. In [22] the analytic calculation was extended to a quadratic approximation (proportional to S^2 and C^2).For thick foils the quadratic terms, which will not be considered here, result in a reduction of both, $\varphi^{(1)}$ and $\varphi^{(2)}$.

We state that our approximation, i.e. eqs. (6) and (7), obeys the well-known symmetry properties of diffraction contrast: the contrast from defects close to the top surface are similar in bright and dark field; the contrast from defects close to the bottom surface are complementary in bright and dark field. Hence, in the following it is sufficient to consider defects close to the top surface, although the same considerations can be applied in a similar way to defects close to the bottom surface.

Now let us consider as the simplest case a Frank loop (which may be of interstitial type) with **b** parallel to **g**, as shown in fig. 5a. The corrections of the strain field due to the traction-free surfaces are neglected. Then, the dis-

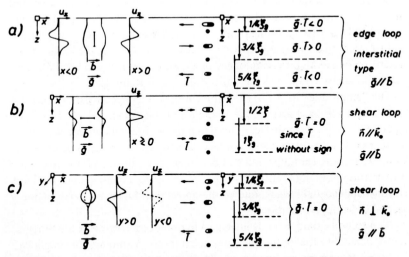

Fig. 5. First order calculation of the black-white contrast from small dislocation loops with **g**‖**b**, schematically. (a) edge loop of interstitial type. (b) and (c) shear loop, **n**= loop normal. In (c) the full lines represent the bent lattice planes and the function u_z for $y > 0$ (above the drawing plane). The dotted lines refer to $y < 0$ (below the drawing plane).

placement derivative u_z may be idealized by an antisymmetric double-peak function with the depth position z_0 of the loop centre between the two peaks. As shown in fig. 5a u_z changes its sign when changing from one side of the loop to the other. As a consequence, a positive sign of S on the one side (bright contrast tail) corresponds to a negative sign of S on the other side (dark contrast tail). Thus, the black-white contrast is explained in our linear approximation as a consequence of the symmetry of the loop strain field. From the antisymmetry of $u_z(z)$, it follows directly that S vanishes, if z_0 coincides with the extrema of $\sin 2\pi\sigma z$, i.e. $S = 0$ for $z_0 = \frac{1}{4}\xi_g + \frac{1}{2}n\xi_g$, n is an integer. These depth positions determine the boundaries of the layers L1, L2, ... Loops with their centres such that $S = 0$, i.e. just between the layers, reveal only a comparatively narrow black dot contrast, which follows from the quadratic approximation [22] which is not treated here.

For z_0 within the layers the sign of $S \neq 0$ is the same for layers with odd and with even numbers respectively. Consequently S changes its sign when z_0 changes from one layer to the adjacent layer (depth oscillations). Due to the antisymmetric shape of u_z, S assumes maximum values for those values of z_0 for which $\sin 2\pi\sigma z_0$ vanishes, i.e. for $z_0 = n \cdot \xi_g/2$. Loops within the first layer require an additional consideration. The adjacent foil surface must be assumed to be traction-free. This modifies that peak of u_z that lies just beneath the surface more than the other peak. As a consequence the value of S is enhanced and the first vanishing position of S (i.e. the boundary between L1 and L2) is shifted to slightly higher z-values. For a more detailed analytical discussion of the modification of the black-white contrast as a result of the elastic boundary conditions see Chik, Wilkens and Rühle [24].

The "amplitude" of the black-white contrast is damped by the absorption factor $\exp(-2\pi\tau_g z_0)$ for z_0 close to the top surface or $\exp(-2\pi\tau_g(t_0-z_0))$ for z_0 close to the bottom surface. This damping factor limits the number of layers in which the black-white contrast is sufficiently strong to be observable. Therefore, for loops in the middle region of a thick foil, the first approximation does not contribute to the contrast. As a consequence the loop contrast appears only black, due to the above mentioned property of the second order approximation.

As a second example let us imagine a hypothetical loop with the Burgers vector parallel to the loop plane (pure shear loop). Assuming, for simplicity, **b** parallel to **g**, there are two essentially different configurations as shown in fig. 5b and c. In the case of fig. 5b the strain parameter $u_z(z)$ is the same on either side of the loop. Consequently the tails of the contrast figure are expected to be either black or white on both sides, depending on the actual depth position of the loop centre. Since u_z is a symmetric function of $z-z_0$

the first order perturbation integral S vanishes for $z_0 = \frac{1}{2}n\,\xi_g$, i.e. in comparison to fig. 5a the thickness of the first layer of the depth oscillations is changed to $\frac{1}{2}\,\xi_g$. In the case of fig. 5c, the strain parameter u_z changes its sign when changing from one side to the other side of the loop. Therefore the contrast is of the black-white type. Furthermore, due to the antisymmetry of u_z as a function of $(z-z_0)$ the depth oscillations obey the same periodicity as has been found for pure edge loops.

The sign of the $(\mathbf{g}\cdot\mathbf{l})$ product of the contrast figure from edge loops depends upon the actual loop position, z_0, and upon whether the loop is of vacancy or interstitial type. For a shear loop in the position of fig. 5b the contrast is symmetric, so that a vector $\mathbf{l}$ cannot be defined, whereas in fig. 5c $\mathbf{l}$ points perpendicularly to $\mathbf{g}$. Consequently we may say that $(\mathbf{g}\cdot\mathbf{l}) = 0$ for both cases. This appears satisfactory, since shear loops are neither of vacancy nor of interstitial type.

5. Experimental methods

For an understanding of the mechanisms of the radiation damage in crystals the following points are of considerable interest:

(i) Identification of the symmetry of the lattice defects;

(ii) Determination of the Burgers vector of small dislocation loops;

(iii) Differentiation between strain centres of vacancy and interstitial type.

(iv) Determination of volume density and of the size distribution of the lattice defects.

(i) In order to decide as to whether a small point defect agglomerate has a strain field of spherical or non-spherical symmetry, the transmission foils must be imaged under dynamical two-beam conditions with different (non-parallel) diffraction vectors $\mathbf{g}$ [6–10]. If a defect, giving rise to a black-white contrast, turns its black-white vector $\mathbf{l}$ always parallel (or antiparallel) to $\mathbf{g}$, the strain field is, at least approximately, of spherical symmetry.

In this context we mention the experiments of Chik [29] on stacking fault tetrahedra in quenched and subsequently annealed gold. When the tetrahedra revealed a black-white contrast, the direction of $\mathbf{l}$ turned always parallel to $\mathbf{g}$, thus indicating that, with respect to the direction of $\mathbf{l}$, a tetrahedron may be considered as a strain centre of spherical symmetry.

(ii) If, for different dynamical images, obtained with different $\mathbf{g}$, the direction of $\mathbf{l}$ remains unaltered irrespective of the direction of $\mathbf{g}$, one may conclude that the defect consists of a dislocation loop with its Burgers vector $\mathbf{b}$, or with the projection of $\mathbf{b}$ onto the image plane, parallel to $\mathbf{l}$. Thus, by observing the directions of l for different g and for different foil orientations, the loop Burgers vectors may be determined rather definitely.

That line on the micrograph, along which the black and the white dot of the black-white contrast figure meet each other, is sometimes called "line of no contrast". Some authors [30–32] have tried to use the line of no contrast as an indicator for the identification of the loop Burgers vector or the loop habit plane. In these papers it was assumed that the line of no contrast, which is really defined only for spherical inclusions [7], extends always perpendicular to the loop Burgers vector or to its projection onto the image plane. However, this method is not justified by the theoretical contrast calculations. On the contrary, the line of no contrast displays in some cases a peculiar fine-structure (compare [11] and fig. 3a), which is not yet understood and which in the future may allow further conclusions to be drawn on details of the structure of the loops

(iii) In order to discriminate between loops of vacancy and interstitial type, it is necessary to observe the sign of $(g \cdot l)$ on dynamical images and to determine the depth position of the loop centres with respect to the adjacent foil surface. For the latter several methods have been proposed which are based on the following idea: If one takes micrographs of the same foil area with different extinction lengths (i.e. by changing from g_1 to g_2 with $\xi_{g_1} \neq \xi_{g_2}$, by varying the acceleration voltage or by changing the excitation error s) some of the loops may change their "black-white" layers, resulting in a reversal of the sign of their $(g \cdot l)$ products. Then, by more or less reliable statistical considerations, these sign reversals may allow a decision as to whether the loops are of vacancy or interstitial type. This method have been applied by several authors [33,34,11], however, the results were not very convincing.

So far, the best technique for the determination of the depth position appears to be the method of stereo microscopy in the form as developed by Diepers and Diehl [14,15] and by Rühle [10]. For this technique two micrographs of the transmission foil must be taken, one with a tilting angle $+\beta$ (in the order of $10°$) and the other with a tilting angle $-\beta$, both measured with respect to the foil orientation perpendicular to the electron beam as the reference orientation and with the operating diffraction vector g as the tilting axis. In order to achieve the necessary accuracy of the depth measurements the two tilting angles must be measured with high accuracy (using Kikuchi patterns). To obtain comparable images of the defects on the two stereo micrographs, it is necessary to perform the stereo micrographs under kinematical contrast conditions ($|s| \cdot \xi_g \gg 1$) for the following reasons: according to the contrast calculations the shape of the contrast figures from small dislocation loops depends for $|s| \cdot \xi_g \gg 1$ only insensitively on the actual image conditions, i.e. the black dot contrast coincides rather well with the position of the loop.

However, under dynamical contrast conditions ($|s| \cdot \xi_g \lesssim 1$), the structure of the contrast figures of those loops, which give rise to a black-white contrast, is rather sensitive to the image conditions. Thus, for $|s| \cdot \xi_g \lesssim 1$, it is difficult to obtain an equivalent pair of stereo micrographs.

Since the distance of the defects from the adjacent foil surface must be measured (for instance by an optical stereo device), it is necessary to mark the position of the foil surface. In the case of copper and niobium foils the following procedure has been applied with success: after obtaining the dynamical images for the determination of the signs of (g·l) of the individual defects, a small amount of gold is evaporated onto one side of the foil, condensing on the foil surface in the form of small islands of about 50Å diameter and less than 10Å thickness. Then the kinematical stereo micrographs are performed. The small gold islands are easily observed in the optical stereo viewer, thus defining the reference mark for the depth measurements. However, special care must be taken to avoid any amorphous layer on the foil surface, as produced before the gold evaporation, for instance by a non-appropriate electro polishing method or by carbon contamination inside the microscope. After the gold evaporation such a layer simulates a wrong position of the real specimen surface.

A critical discussion of the error sources involved in the stereo measurements indicates that an accuracy of about ± 20Å is achievable. Since the thickness of the critical first layer of the black-white contrast, L1, ranges in the order of 50–100Å, this accuracy should be just enough to discern between the loop depth positions in the most important layers L1 and L2.

(iv) We add some remarks on the accuracy of the loop size measurements. Although the contrast calculations may give predictions of the relation between the true loop size and the contrast width as defined by a given percentage deviation from the background intensity level, the experimental methods for measuring the diameter of the small unresolved black dots are rather uncertain. This is due to different reasons: (i) everyone has his own peculiarities in measuring the black dot diameter, (ii) within each of these individual techniques there exists a rather large uncertainty especially for dots with diameters smaller than $\approx$ 50Å, (iii) the apparent dot sizes on the kinematical micrographs depend in a critical way, which is difficult to control in practice, on the film exposure, the film processing and the positive printing procedures. Consequently, size distribution functions obtained on the same subject but by different research groups are difficult to compare quantitatively. Deviations in the order of ± 30% may easily occur. With respect to further details of the experimental procedure we refer to [18].

6. Experimental results

Before the calculations of the black-white contrast from small dislocation loops were performed, the most striking feature was observed and interpreted intuitively in a correct sense by Essmann and Wilkens [6] : Studying the damage in neutron-irradiated copper, they found that the direction of the black-white vector l of individual black-white dots remains fixed, when the same foil area is dynamically imaged with different diffraction vectors g. In the mean time this property has been used by various authors to determine the Burgers vector of defect agglomerates in crystals damaged by irradiation with fast neutrons, ions or high-energy electrons, compare [17,18]. It appears that in pure fcc metals small point defect agglomerates occur mainly in the form of Frank loops with b parallel to $\langle 111 \rangle$. In most of the fcc metals only a small fraction of perfect loops with b parallel to $\langle 110 \rangle$ have been found [6,10]. As an interesting exception, not yet understood, we mention neutron-irradiated platinum [35,17,18], where the number of loops with b parallel to $\langle 110 \rangle$ was comparable with the number of Frank loops. In neutron-irradiated copper a high fraction of $\langle 110 \rangle$ loops has been found only after the specimens (irradiated at $80°C$ or at $4°K$) had been annealed at $300°C$ [35,17,18].

In bcc metals, so far only the black-white contrast in neutron-irradiated niobium has been studied in detail (Tucker and Ohr [26], Huber, Rühle and Wilkens [27, 16]. As already mentioned in sect. 3, loops with Burgers vectors b parallel to the directions $\langle 111 \rangle$, $\langle 110 \rangle$ and $\langle 100 \rangle$ have been identified. All three kinds of loops were found with about the same frequency.

Strain centres whose black-white vector l turns parallel to g for all directions of g have been observed by Bourret and Dautreppe [36] in neutron-irradiated nickel and by Rühle et al. [35,17,18] in neutron-irradiated platinum.

In the case of nickel it was concluded from the geometrical shape of the contrast figures on kinematical images that the lattice defect has tetrahedral symmetry. Consequently the authors interpreted these defects as being tetrahedral voids or stacking fault tetrahedra. In platinum, even on well focussed kinematical images, no geometrical structure of these "spherical" strain centres (diameter in the order of $50Å$) could be detected. Perhaps these defects may be identified as the zones of extremely high concentration of point defects that have been observed in neutron-irradiated platinum by means of field ion microscopy [37].

The first attempts to apply the method of stereo microscopy to the discrimination between vacancy and interstitial loops have been published by Diepers and Diehl [14,15]. The authors found by stereo microscopy that the damage produced by the impact of 5 keV argon ions on the surface of copper foils consists of small Frank loops located at a rather sharply defined distance of about $100 - 200\,\text{Å}$ (depending on the irradiation conditions) below the irradiated surface. From the mean depth of the loops in connection with the predominantly observed sign of the $(\mathbf{g}\cdot\mathbf{l})$ products, the authors concluded that the loops are mainly of interstitial type.

A more rigorous analysis of the vacancy or interstitial nature of small loops was performed by Rühle [10,11] and Rühle and Wilkens [38]. More than 200 loops were registrated with respect to the sign of their $(\mathbf{g}\cdot\mathbf{l})$ product and their depth position inside the foil as determined by stereo microscopy. In fig. 6 the numbers of loops found in a certain depth interval were plotted above the abscissa for $(\mathbf{g}\cdot\mathbf{l}) > 0$ and below the abscissa for $(\mathbf{g}\cdot\mathbf{l}) < 0$. The plot displays just that change in the sign of $(\mathbf{g}\cdot\mathbf{l})$ and at that depth position expected from theory for vacancy loops. Thus, it is indicated that the depth measurement by means of stereo microscopy is sufficient to discriminate between the different layers of the black-white depth oscillations. With respect to further results mentioned below it must be said that in this work [10,11,38] only loops with diameters between 30 and 50 Å were stereo-analysed since experience shows that the stereo technique is most easily applied in this size range. This restriction in size was not stated in the original papers.

In the following time the stereo experiments of Rühle on neutron-irradiated copper were repeated by several authors, who found only vacancy loops (Crump III [39]) or only interstitial loops (McIntyre [40]) or either vacancy or interstitial loops depending on the atmospheric environment of the copper specimens during the neutron-irradiation (Bourret and Dautreppe [41]). In order to clarify these striking discrepancies Rühle et al. [35] repeated the measurements under careful control of the conditions for specimen preparation and irradiation. Furthermore, in contrast to the former work, loops with diameters between about 15 and 150 Å were analysed. Similarly as in fig. 6 black-white dots belonging to the two first layers L1 and L2 of the depth oscillations were found. The results are plotted in the diagram of fig. 7.

At a certain variance with the earlier results it was found that small loops with diameters $d \lesssim 75\,\text{Å}$ are predominantly of vacancy type, whereas the loops with $d \gtrsim 75\,\text{Å}$ are mainly of interstitial type. This separation in size may account for the above mentioned discrepancies. Presumably different authors stereo-measured different size groups. Furthermore, the critical size, at which vacancy and interstitial loops are separated, may depend on details of the irradiation conditions.

In addition to the already mentioned work on neutron-irradiated and 5 keV Ar^+ ion-irradiated copper we refer to some further results.

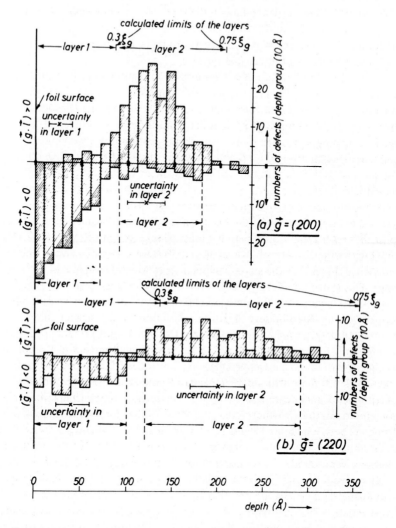

Fig. 6. Results of the stereo analysis of the black-white contrast figures from Frank loops with diameter d between 30 and 50 Å in neutron-irradiated copper [10,11,38]. The number of black-white dots with $(\mathbf{g}\cdot\mathbf{l}) > 0$ and $(\mathbf{g}\cdot\mathbf{l}) < 0$ are plotted against the distance of the defect centre from the bottom surface of the transmission foil (bright field, positive prints). The depth oscillations of the sign of $(\mathbf{g}\cdot\mathbf{l})$ are clearly demonstrated. Thus, according to fig. 4, the loops are mainly of vacancy type. The extinction length ξ_g used in the figure is corrected for many-beam effects.

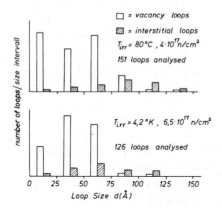

Fig. 7. Vacancy and interstitial loops in neutron-irradiated copper as a function of the loop diameter [27,35].

Neutron-irradiation: In nickel, Bourret and Dautreppe [36] found only interstitial loops. However, since only loops with $d > 40$Å were analysed, the nature of the high number of loops with $d < 40$Å remain, up to now, undetermined. In analogy to copper, the smaller loops may be predominantly of vacancy type [17]. Brimhal and Mastel [42] studied the damage in rhenium (hcp). From the direction of $\mathbf{l}$ they determined the Burgers vector to be parallel to $\langle 11\bar{2}0 \rangle$. The depth measurements of the loops with d between 40 and 100Å, which revealed the sign change of $(\mathbf{g} \cdot \mathbf{l})$ from layer L1 to layer L2, resulted in mainly interstitial loops. In platinum, Rühle, Häussermann, Rapp and Wilkens [35,17] identified the small loops as being mainly of vacancy type, which holds also for the already mentioned "spherical" strain centres. Vacancy loops were found also in gold by Eades [43].

The damage structure in niobium was studied by Huber, Rühle and Wilkens [16,27]. Under the assumption that the signs of $(\mathbf{g} \cdot \mathbf{l})$ and the thicknesses of the layers L1, L2, ..., as calculated for pure edge loops, are valid also for the loops with shear components occurring in particle irradiated bcc metals, the authors found about $\frac{2}{3}$ of the small loops to be of interstitial type and $\frac{1}{3}$ of vacancy type. However, since there were some indications for a large shear component of the loop Burgers vectors, it is just this assumption which must be confirmed by further contrast calculations.

Ion-irradiation: If the energy of heavy ions, irradiated on fcc specimens, are high enough (energies transferred to the lattice atoms higher than about 10 keV) the damage consists of small Frank loops close to the irradiated specimen surface. By stereo technique these loops have been identified as

vacancy loops (Rühle and Wilkens [44,11], Norris [45]). These loops
are presumably produced by displacement cascades or depleted zones. In
the case of extremely low ion energies (too low to produce depleted zones)
only "half loops" of interstitial type are produced, which are intersected by
the irradiated surface (Bowden and Brandon [46]; Thomas and Balluffi [47]).
However, compared with the vacancy loops, as produced by high energy ions,
these interstitial loops require a much higher irradiation dose for their formation.

Electron-irradiation: Bourret and Dautreppe [36] irradiated nickel below
the annealing stage III ($\approx 100°C$). Only interstitial loops were found. As an
interesting result of annealing experiments, it came out that the total number
of interstitials, agglomerated in the loops, increased by about a factor of 2,
when the specimens were annealed at $100°C$ (i.e. within stage III). In copper,
irradiated at $120°K$ and inspected in the electron microscope at room temperature (several weeks after irradiation) a mixture of about the same number
of vacancy and interstitial loops was found (Häussermann et al. [48]).

Finally, we mention a significant difference between the damage, as visible
on the micrographs, due to neutron or electron irradiation and the damage
by heavy ions respectively.

For fast neutron and high energy electron irradiation the damage must be
expected to be homogeneously distributed over the entire depth of the transmission foil. Thus, even on dark field images and even for defects of either
only vacancy or only interstitial type, due to the depth oscillations, both signs
of $(g\cdot l)$ occur on the micrographs.

On the other hand, the penetration depth of heavy ions, falling onto specimens which are prepared for transmission microscopy before irradiation, is extremely small. Consequently one expects that the damage is produced within
a thin surface layer. In fact, several authors [11,34,44,49,51] have found
that the damage consists of small Frank loops, all of which reveal the same
sign of $(g\cdot l)$. As an example we refer to fig. 3 which shows micrographs from
copper foils irradiated with 100 keV O^- ions. Under the assumption that all
the loops lie within the first layer L1 of the depth oscillations, it was concluded from the observed sign of $(g\cdot l)$ that the loops are of vacancy type.
(Apart from this rather indirect conclusion, the vacancy nature of the loops
have now been confirmed also by the stereo technique, see above.)

Acknowledgement

The author thanks his colleagues Dr. M.Rühle and Dipl. Phys. F. Häussermann for their helpful and stimulating discussions.

APPENDIX ADDED FOR THE SECOND EDITION

1. Introduction

In the past years after the completion of the preceding article (in the following quoted as [1]) considerable progress has been achieved in the identification of small point defect agglomerates in particle-irradiated crystals. This progress was summarized in a number of review articles, e.g., by Eyre [52,53], Rühle [54], and Wilkens and co-workers [55–57].

Instead of giving a full account of the recent developments this appendix is restricted to a brief discussion of some selected aspects of the matter in which the author and his co-workers are mainly involved. Of course, such a restriction implies some arbitrariness which can hardly be avoided. Furthermore, the appendix is understood merely as a guide to the corresponding literature. Therefore illustrations (e.g., micrographs etc.) are not included.

2. Crystallographic analysis of dislocation loops containing shear components

2.1. *Application of the black-white contrast technique*

Up to 1969 the study of radiation damage in metals was mainly concerned with the analysis of small point defect agglomerates (PDA) in f.c.c. metals. Using the direction of the black-white (BW) vector l as the characteristic parameter of the BW contrast figures on dynamical two-beam images, it was found that the majority of the PDA in f.c.c. metals can be interpreted as Frank loops on {111}-planes with $b = \frac{1}{3}\langle 111 \rangle$ perpendicular to the loop plane (loop of pure edge type). Consequently the theory of the BW contrast figures was mainly worked out for pure edge loops.

At that time the application of the BW contrast technique to small loops in radiation damaged b.c.c. metals did not result in simple and straightforward answers, cf., for instance, the results of Tucker and Ohr [26] and Rühle et al. [27] (cf. also [17]) which were briefly discussed in [1]. In the view of the following paragraphs these results appear now to be somewhat doubtful.

According to theoretical considerations of Eyre and Bullough [58] it is probable that in radiation damaged b.c.c. metals small loops are nucleated as pure edge loops on {110}-planes. In a subsequent shear process the Burgers-vector $b = \frac{1}{2}\langle 110 \rangle$ is converted into $b = \frac{1}{2}\langle 111 \rangle$ or, less probably, into $b = \langle 100 \rangle$. Thus, loops with shear components are expected to be dominant. The strength of the shear component may be characterized by the angle γ between b and n

(n = loop plane normal). For $b = \frac{1}{2}\langle 111 \rangle$ ($b = \langle 100 \rangle$) we have $\gamma \simeq 35°$ ($\gamma = 45°$). As compared with the situation in f.c.c. metals (only Frank loops) this model for loops in b.c.c. metals contains a much higher number of possible loop configurations. This has two implications:

(i) It is not expected that one particular property of a contrast figure, e.g., the direction of the BW vector l would be sufficient for the analysis of the loop configuration (determination of b and n).

(ii) Contrast calculations by numerical integration of the differential equation become extremely tedious.

At this stage it was found to be extremely expedient to solve the differential equation of Bloch wave type (specialized for the dynamical two-beam case, cf. section 4 in [I]) in the first order perturbation only. For small dislocation loops this is in general quite sufficient for a semi-quantitative calculation of the corresponding BW contrast figures. If the displacement field of a dislocation loop is approximated by the so-called infinitesimal loop approximation the final equations for the equal-intensity contour diagrams are expressed in simple analytical terms which depend on the direction cosines of n and b and on the depth position of the loop centre inside the foil. For details we refer to Wilkens and Rühle [59]. Using these equations one can conveniently survey all the possible kinds and shapes of BW contrast figures which may occur if the direction of n and b are varied with respect to the direction of the electron beam and the direction of the operating two-beam diffraction vector g. For instance it is easy to verify that the BW contrast figures deviate strongly from the "normal" shape which was mainly considered in [I] if b and n approach the plane perpendicular to g. On the other hand it has been found that in all cases where the BW contrast figures are "normal" enough in order to allow the determination of a BW vector l the formal rules for the differentiation between loops of vacancy and interstitial type remain applicable, independently of the shear angle γ. Accordingly the corresponding part of the work of Rühle et al. [17,27] on neutron-irradiated Nb still remains valid.

One disadvantage of the infinitesimal loop approximation should be noted. In this approximation the displacement field and, consequently, the first order solution of the corresponding BW contrast figure remains unchanged if the direction of b and n are interchanged. However, this ambiguity is not so serious since the possible directions of b are restricted by crystallographic arguments. As a further help for the appropriate selection of the direction b we mention a peculiar fine structure of the BW contrast figures which occur at the separation line of the black and the white part of the contrast figure and which was first described by Rühle [11]. It was shown by Eyre [52] that this type of fine structure is evidence of fairly large values of $[g \cdot b]$ ($\gtrsim \frac{4}{3}$).

Comparisons of first order solutions with BW contrast figures as observed in ion-bombarded tungsten and (hexagonal) cobalt have shown that this technique is quite successful and leads to a fairly unambiguous determination of the directions of **b** and **n**. In tungsten (Häussermann et al. [60], Jäger and Wilkens [61]) the majority of the loops could be indexed with $\mathbf{b} = \frac{1}{2}\langle 111 \rangle$ and $\mathbf{n} = \{110\}$. No evidence for loops with $\mathbf{b} = \langle 100 \rangle$ was found. In cobalt (Föll and Wilkens [62]) nearly all loops could be indexed with $\mathbf{b} = \frac{1}{3}\langle 1\bar{1}20 \rangle$ and $\mathbf{n} = \{10\bar{1}0\}$. No radiation-induced loops on the basal plane could be detected.

The contrast calculations treated so far are based on the assumption of elastic isotropy. It should be mentioned that the first order perturbation solution is also suitable for a comparatively easy estimate as to what extend the BW contrast figure of a given loop is modified by the elastic anisotropy of the specimen, cf. Yoffee [63,64], Mc Intyre et al. [65].

BW contrast figures of the type described above are best observed in foils which are thick enough so that the surface-near regions (layers L1, L2, etc., cf. [I]) which give rise to detectable BW contrast figures are separated. With decreasing foil thickness t these regions begin to overlap. Then the shapes of the BW contrast figures are modified: Depending on the actual foil thickness the black or the bright part of the contrast figure is increasingly suppressed (cf. Ruault et al. [66], and also Katerbau [68]). For $t \lesssim 2\xi_g$ essentially black or bright dots appear which are hard to discriminate from the contrast dots of dynamically imaged small cavities [67].

2.2. Inside-outside contrast

If dislocation loops are large enough in order to be resolved as loops on the micrographs the method of inside-outside contrast ($\mathbf{g} \cdot \mathbf{b} \cdot s$-rule [69]) has proved successful for the discrimination between loops of vacancy and interstitial type. This method was originally established for loops of pure edge type. Maher and Eyre [52,70] have shown that some modifications and precautions are required if loops with shear components are to be analysed. If these precautions are not taken into account a formal application of the $\mathbf{g} \cdot \mathbf{b} \cdot s$-rule in its original form would give the wrong answer.

3. Number density, size and depth distribution

3.1. Dynamical two-beam imaging conditions

The contrast figures of dynamically imaged PDA depend sensitively in shape and size on the actual depth position of the defect centre inside the foil. Therefore this imaging mode is in general not suitable for quantitative counting and measuring. This is especially true for the measurement of the depth distribution by means of the stereo technique. However, if small PDA with a weak strain field are located close to either of the foil surfaces their visibility is strongly increased under dynamical imaging conditions (Häussermann [71]). In this case size measurements are rather uncertain.

3.2. Kinematical imaging conditions

Using kinematical diffraction conditions (i.e., no low order reflection strongly excited) the depth dependence of the sizes and shapes of the contrast figures are much less pronounced. Therefore most of quantitative measurements in the literature are taken under these imaging conditions. Rühle [10,11] has studied the relationship between the true loop size and the width of the contrast figure applying a kinematical two-beam calculation. Since this relationship which is occasionally used in the literature was derived for particular, surely oversimplified diffraction conditions, its accuracy should not be overestimated.

"Conventional" contrast calculations usually neglect implications of the electron optical limitations of the microscope. This is certainly justified for contrast details $\gtrsim 50$ Å. However, for PDA with diameter $d \lesssim 30$ Å the visibility on the transmission images may be substantially influenced, e.g., by the chromatic aberrations of the imaging lenses. In this size range the counted number densities, n_1, and the measured loop sizes, d, may depend on the foil thickness t and the electron optical magnification M: an apparent decrease of n_1 and apparent increase of d is expected if t is too large and M is too low. Perhaps some discrepancies in the literature concerning n_1 in this critical size range may be due to the fact that in some cases M and/or t were inadequately chosen. If these items are properly taken into account reproducible data concerning number densities and size distribution functions for d as low as $15-20$ Å can be obtained, cf., for example, the comparative study of the damage in neutron-irradiated copper by Rühle (Stuttgart) and Crump (Oak Ridge) [72]. A systematic investigation of the influence of the chromatic lens aberration on the visibility of small PDA was performed and theoretically interpreted by Noggle et al. [73]. With decreasing foil thickness the chromatic aberrations become less important. Bourret et al. [74,75] have shown that small stacking fault tetraheder with edge lengths down to ≈ 25 Å can be identified on the transmission images by means of the geometrical shape of their contrast figures if the imaged region of the foil is not thicker than about two extinction lengths.

3.3. Imaging under weak-beam conditions

Cockayne et al. [76,77] have shown that the contrast of dislocations is considerably sharpened and enhanced if the image is taken with a weakly excited beam (excitation error $s_{WB} \gtrsim 0.02 \, \text{Å}^{-1}$). This technique is advantageous also for the imaging of dislocation loops. The lower limit of the applicability of the "inside-outside contrast" (or $\mathbf{g} \cdot \mathbf{b} \cdot s$-rule) is shifted to loops with $d \approx 70$–$80 \, \text{Å}$ (Jenkins et al. [78], Häussermann et al. [79]). Furthermore, due to the sharpening of the contrast lines of the dislocation surrounding the loop area, the size measurement becomes more accurate. However, for loops with diameters comparable with, or smaller than, the effective extinction length ξ_{WB} of the weakly excited beam ($\xi_{WB} \approx s_{WB}^{-1}$) the resulting contrast figures depend, throughout the foil thickness, sensitively on the actual depth position of the loop centre (depth periodicity $= \xi_{WB}$). By these depth oscillations not only the shapes and sizes but also the strengths of the contrast figures are strongly modulated [79]. Therefore any naive counting and measuring of the small contrast dots on weak-beam images of radiation-damaged specimens may lead to considerable errors which are difficult to estimate. Perhaps the depth oscillations can be suppressed, at least partly, if the foil is imaged with a converging beam (illuminating beam optimally focused onto the specimen). Then the incoming electron beam is represented by an interval of excitation errors (rather than by a discrete value) which corresponds inside the foil to an interval of extinction lengths. Experiments must show to what extend the depth oscillations can be suppressed by this method.

4. Defocusing contrast of small cavities

Initiated by the development of hightemperature nuclear reactors the TEM investigation of cavities (voids, bubbles) in crystalline materials has become of considerable interest, cf., for instance, the survey article of [54]. The diffraction contrast of cavities was investigated theoretically and experimentally, e.g., by Van Landuyt et al. [80], Ingram [81], Ruedl and Staroste [82,83], and Magee et al. [84]. Accordingly, small cavities are best visible at the flanks of low-order thickness fringes produced by a low-order reflection. In [81] and [84] special emphasis was put on the contrast of small cavities by which the surrounding matrix is strained (due to surface tension or a high pressure of insoluble gas inside the cavity).

In comparatively thick foils the thickness fringes are damped out due to anomalous absorbtion. The visibility of small cavities decrease rapidly with decreasing diameter d if cavities in such "thick" foils are imaged with the objective lens focused on the specimen (in-focus mode). Thus, in the in-focus mode, which is usually applied, accurate counting and measuring of small cavities with $d \lesssim 50 \, \text{Å}$ may become a serious problem.

As first shown by Harkness and Li [85] and by Rühle [54] the contrast of small cavities in such "thick" specimens is considerably enhanced if the specimen is imaged with the objective lens focused on a plane at a distance ζ of the order of 1 μm from the specimen (defocus mode). By this technique cavities with diameters of 10 Å or even less are clearly visible.

A theory of the defocus contrast of small cavities in crystalline specimens was developed by Rühle and Wilkens [54,56,86,87]. It was shown that cavities degenerate with increasing foil thickness into "pure phase objects" in the electron optical sense (Hanssen [88]). Such pure phase objects are invisible under in-focus conditions. One essential part of the phase shift is given by $\Delta V = V_{o,c} - V_{o,m}$, where $V_{o,c}$ and $V_{o,m}$ are the mean inner potential inside the cavity and in the surrounding crystalline matrix, respectively. In the defocus mode the contrast figure consists of a central dot which is bright or dark depending on the signs of ΔV and ζ and which is surrounded by a number of Fresnel fringes of alterating sign. For reasonable values of d and ζ the inner diameter of the first Fresnel fringe represents a fairly good measure of d. Of course, the diameter of the entire contrast figure may exceed d considerably.

If a cavity is large enough to be detectable under in-focus conditions the in-focus contrast is independent of the value of ΔV. However, if such a "large" cavity is imaged under defocus conditions the resulting contrast depends sensitively on sign and magnitude of ΔV. Therefore, through-the-focus series can be used in principle for an estimate of ΔV. First results of Merkle and Rühle [89] and Ruedl and Rühle [90] indicate that this method may reveal interesting information regarding $V_{o,c}$ which are hard to obtain by other methods.

Acknowledgement

The author thanks all his colleagues, especially Dr. M. Rühle and Dipl. Phys. K.-H. Katerbau, for their continuous collaboration.

References

[1] D.W.Pashley and A.E.B.Presland, Phil. Mag. 6 (1961) 1003.
[2] M.J.Makin, A.D.Whapham and F.J.Minter, Phil. Mag 6 (1961) 465; 7 (1962) 285.
[3] M.J.Makin and S.A.Manthorpe, Phil. Mag. 8 (1963) 1725.
[4] E.Ruedl, P.Delavignette and S.Amelinckx, Radiation Damage in Solids (Vienna, 1962) p. 363.
[5] E.Ruedl and S.Amelinckx, J. Phys. Soc. Japan 18, Supp. III (1963) 195.

[6] U.Essmann and M.Wilkens, Phys. Stat. Sol. 4 (1964) K53.
[7] M.F.Ashby and L.M.Brown, Phil. Mag. 8 (1963) 1083.
[8] M.F.Ashby and L.M.Brown, Phil. Mag. 8 (1963) 1649.
[9] M.Rühle, M.Wilkens and U.Essmann, Phys. Stat. Sol. 11 (1965) 819.
[10] M.Rühle, Phys. Stat. Sol. 19 (1967) 263.
[11] M.Rühle, Phys. Stat. Sol. 19 (1967) 279.
[12] K.G.McIntyre and L.M.Brown, J. Phys. Radium 27 (1966) C3-178.
[13] K.G.McIntyre and L.M.Brown, Symposium on the Nature of Small Defect Clusters, Harwell, AERE Report R 5269 (1966) p. 351.
[14] H.Diepers and J.Diehl, Phys. Stat. Sol. 16 (1966) K109.
[15] H. Diepers, Phys. Stat. Sol. 24 (1967) 235, 623.
[16] P.Huber, M.Rühle and M.Wilkens, to be published.
[17] M.Wilkens, Studies of Point Defect Clusters by Transmission Electron Microscopy, in: Vacancies and Interstitials in Metals, eds. Seeger et al. (North-Holland, Amsterdam, 1970) p. 485.
[18] M.Rühle, Proc. of the Symposium on Radiation Damage in Reactor Materials Vol. 1 (Vienna, 1969) p. 113.
[19] N.Hashimote, A.Howie and M.J.Whelan, Phil. Mag. 5 (1960) 967.
[20] F.Häussermann and M.Wilkens, Phys. Stat. Sol. 18 (1966) 609.
[21] J.W.Steeds, Phil. Mag. 16 (1967) 785.
[22] M.Wilkens, Phys. Stat. Sol. 6 (1964) 939.
[23] W.L.Bell and G.Thomas, Phys. Stat. Sol. 12 (1965) 843.
[24] K.P.Chik, M.Wilkens and M.Rühle, Phys. Stat. Sol. 23 (1967) 113.
[25] W.L.Bell and G.Thomas, Phil. Mag. 13 (1966) 395.
[26] R.P.Tucker and S.M.Ohr, Phil. Mag. 16 (1967) 643.
[27] M.Rühle, F.Häussermann, P.Huber and M.Wilkens, Proc. 4th European Reg. Conf. of Electron Microscopy, Vol. I (Rome, 1968) p. 397.
[28] M.Rühle and M.Wilkens, to be published.
[29] K.P.Chik, Phys. Stat. Sol. 16 (1966) 685.
[30] W.L.Bell, D.M.Maher and G.Thomas, Lattice Defects in Quenched Metals (Academic Press, New York, London, 1965) p. 739.
[31] L.M.Howe, J.F.McGurn and R.W.Gilbert, Acta Met. 14 (1966) 801.
[32] P.Rao and G.Thomas, Acta Met. 15 (1967) 1153.
[33] J.L.Brimhal, H.E.Kissinger and B.Mastel, J. Appl. Phys. 37 (1966) 3317.
[34] W.L.Bell, D.M.Maher and G.Thomas, Symposium on the Nature of Small Defect Clusters, Harwell AERE Report R 5269 (1966) p. 314.
[35] M.Rühle, F.Häussermann, M.Rapp and M.Wilkens, to be published.
[36] A.Bourret and D.Dautreppe, Phys. Stat. Sol. 29 (1968) 283.
[37] M.J.Attardo and J.M.Galligan, Phys. Rev. 161 (1967) 558.
[38] M.Rühle and M.Wilkens, Phil. Mag. 15 (1967) 1075.
[39] J.C.Crump III, Bull. Am. Phys. Soc. 13 (1968) 462.
[40] K.G.McIntyre, Phil. Mag. 15 (1967) 205.
[41] A.Bourret and D.Dautreppe, Phys. Stat. Sol. 24 (1967) K174.
[42] J.L.Brimhall and B.Mastel, Phys. Stat. Sol. 27 (1968) K89.
[43] J.A.Eades, Phil. Mag. 19 (1969) 47.
[44] M.Rühle and M.Wilkens, Proc. 6th Intern. Conf. for Electron Microscopy, Vol. I (Kyoto, 1966) p. 379.

[45] D.I.Norris, Phil. Mag. 19 (1969) 527.
[46] P.B.Bowden and D.G.Brandon, Phil. Mag. 8 (1963) 935.
[47] L.E.Thomas and R.W.Balluffi, Phil. Mag. 15 (1967) 1117.
[48] F.Häussermann, M.Rühle, G.P.Scheidler and G.Roth, Phys. Stat. Sol. 32 (1969) K103.
[49] K.L.Merkle, L.R.Singer and R.K.Hart, J. Appl. Phys. 34 (1963) 2800.
[50] K.L.Merkle, Phys. Stat. Sol. 18 (1966) 173.
[51] R.V.Hesketh and G.K.Richards, Phil. Mag. 13 (1966) 1069.
[52] B.L.Eyre, in: Proc. Intern. Discussion Meeting on Defects in Refractory Metals, Mol, 1971, eds. R.De Batist et al. (S.C.K./C.E.N., Mol., 1972) p. 311.
[53] B.L.Eyre, J. Phys. F: Metal Phys. 3 (1973) 422.
[54] M.Rühle, in: Proc. Intern. Conf. on Radiation-Induced Voids in Metals, Albany, 1971, eds. J.W.Corbett and L.C.Ianiello (U.S.A.E.C., 1972) p. 255.
[55] M.Wilkens, M.Rühle and F.Häussermann, J. Microscop. 16 (1973) 199.
[56] M.Wilkens, in: Proc. Intern. School on Electron Microscopy in Materials Science, Erice, 1973 (C.I.D. Luxemburg, in press).
[57] M.Wilkens, in: Proc. Intern. Conf. on Application of Iron Beams to Metals, Albuquerque, 1973 (in press).
[58] B.L.Eyre and Bullough, Phil. Mag. 11 (1965) 31.
[59] M.Wilkens and M.Rühle, Phys. Stat. Sol. (b) 49 (1972) 749.
[60] F.Häusserman, M.Rühle and M.Wilkens, Phys. Stat. Sol. (b) 50 (1972) 445.
[61] W.Jäger and M.Wilkens, to be published.
[62] H.Föll and M.Wilkens, to be published.
[63] E.H.Yoffe, Phil. Mag. 21 (1970) 833.
[64] E.H.Yoffe, Phil. Mag. 25 (1972) 935.
[65] K.G.McIntyre, L.M.Brown and I.A.Eades, Phil. Mag. 21 (1970) 853.
[66] M.O.Ruault, B.Jouffrey and P.Joyes, Phil. Mag. 25 (1972) 833.
[67] J.Van Landuyt, R.Gevers and S.Amelinckx, Phys. Stat. Sol. 10 (1965) 319.
[68] K.-H.Katerbau, to be published.
[69] P.B.Hirsch, A.Howie, R.B.Nicholson, D.Pashley and M.J.Whelan, Electron Microscopy of Thin Crystals (Butterworths, London, 1965).
[70] D.M.Maher and B.L.Eyre, Phil. Mag. 23 (1971) 409.
[71] F.Häussermann, Phil. Mag. 25 (1972) 537.
[72] M.Rühle and J.C.Crump, III, Phys. Stat. Sol. (a) 2 (1970) 257.
[73] T.S.Noggle, O.S.Oen and J.C.Crump, III, Proc. 28th Annual EMSA Meeting, Houston, Texas (1970) p. 406.
[74] A.Bourret and D.Dautreppe, Phys. Stat. Sol. 29 (1968) 283.
[75] A.Bourret and A.M.Levelut, Phys. Stat. Sol. 37 (1970) K101.
[76] D.J.H.Cockayne, I.L.F.Ray and M.J.Whelan, Phil. Mag. 20 (1969) 1265.
[77] D.J.H.Cockayne, Z. Naturf. 27a (1972) 452.
[78] M.L.Jenkins, D.J.H.Cockayne and M.J.Whelan, J. Microscop. 98 (1973) 155.
[79] F.Häussermann, K.-H.Katerbau, M.Rühle and M.Wilkens, J. Microscop. 98 (1973) 135.
[80] J.Van Landuyt, R.Gevers and S.Amelinckx, Phys. Stat. Sol. 10 (1965) 319.
[81] J.C.Ingram, J.Appl. Phys. 40 (1969) 5030.
[82] E.Ruedl and E.Staroste, in: Proc. 7th Intern. Congress for Electron Microscopy, Grenoble, Vol. II (1970) p. 343.

[83] E.Ruedl, in: Radiation Effects on Structural Alloys for Nuclear Reactor Applications, ASTM, Special Technical Publication, No. 484 (1970) p. 300.

[84] T.J.Magee, R.H.Morris and C.D.Melvin, Phys. Stat. Sol. (a) 13 (1972) 107.

[85] S.D.Harkness and C.Y.Li, Met. Trans. AIME 2 (1971) 1457.

[86] M.Rühle and M.Wilkens, in: Proc. 5th European Reg. Conf. on Electron Microscopy, Manchester (1972) p. 416.

[87] M.Rühle and M.Wilkens, to be published.

[88] K.-J.Hanssen, in: Advances in Optical and Electron Microscopy, Vol. 4 (Academic Press, New York, London, 1971) p. 1.

[89] K.L.Merkle and M.Rühle, to be published.

[90] E.Ruedl and M.Rühle, to be published.

Diffraction and Imaging Techniques in Material Science,
eds. S. Amelinckx, R. Gevers and J. van Landuyt
© *North-Holland Publishing Company, 1978*

SOME APPLICATIONS OF TRANSMISSION
ELECTRON MICROSCOPY TO PHASE TRANSITIONS

G.THOMAS

Inorganic Materials Research Division, Lawrence Radiation Laboratory,
Department of Materials Science and Engineering, College of Engineering,
University of California, Berkeley, California, USA

1. Introduction

The most important advantage of transmission electron microscopy in materials science is its ability to provide almost all the data needed to characterize completely the microstructure of materials [1,2] as indicated by the scheme shown in fig. 1. Today it is possible to resolve substructural details down to $\approx 20\,\text{Å}$ (discrete particles) and atomic plane spacings $\approx 1\,\text{Å}$ can be

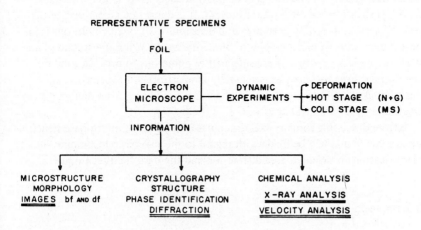

Fig. 1. Scheme illustrating the main functions of the electron microscope.

imaged. The new technique of velocity analysis (e.g. refs. [3–5]) has considereable promise for obtaining information regarding the chemistry of the specimen down to the resolution limits of the instrument.

The applications of the technique are almost unlimited [1,2] and it is obviously impossible to describe all of them here. However, some general methods of identification are discussed as applied to two or more phase systems resulting from phase transformations, excluding martensites.

Most commercially useful alloys contain two or more phases as a result of thermal or more complex thermal-mechanical processing. It is important to characterize the structure in terms of alloy composition and treatment as this approach is a necessary part of efforts to control alloy performance through control of structure. This chapter is not intended to be comprehensive, but is representative of some typical research work in materials science and engineering at Berkeley.

In the analysis of structure equal attention must be given to the diffraction pattern, corresponding bright and dark field images, and how these change upon tilting. As indicated in fig. 2 of the chapter on Kikuchi diffraction, only two orientations are necessary for the analysis of microstructure, namely (a) the symmetrical orientation, to provide accurate crystallographic information, e.g. orientation relations, identification of phases by utilizing the camera constant equation, and so on, and (b) the systematic two beam orientation so that contrast effects can be investigated in terms of various $g \cdot R$ conditions.

The interpretation of the image and the diffraction pattern is of course facilitated by careful selected area diffraction analysis, together with dark field investigations of the features present. It is important to emphasize that several photographs of a given area under various controlled conditions is far better than random photography of numerous areas. When the second phase particles are large enough or are sufficiently numerous to provide good diffraction patterns the analysis is generally straightforward except that care must be taken to isolate diffraction phenomena resulting from double diffraction as will be indicated in sect. 3.

Before discussing some typical examples of analysis of multiphase structures some points will be made with regard to the two basic techniques of identification viz selected area diffraction and the dark field technique.

2. Basic techniques

2.1. Selected area diffraction

This technique [1,2] provides a means for selecting various features of the

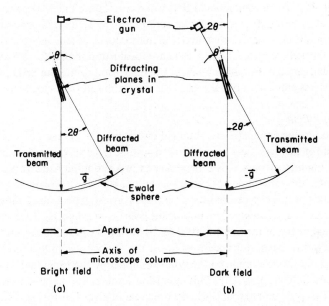

Fig. 2. Sketches showing that for maximum contrast gun tilt the dark field image must be formed of the negative diffraction vector corresponding to the bright field image; thus the sign of **g** is reversed from bright to dark field. The specimen is not tilted.

image for examination by diffraction and dark-field imaging. In order to distinguish between several different regions of the specimen it is necessary to be able to select the smallest possible area e.g. in diffraction analysis of small and different particles [1]. The minimum selected area (ΔA) contributing to the diffraction pattern is limited chiefly by the spherical aberration $\{C_s\}$ of the objective lens as follows:

$$(\Delta A) \cong C_s \theta_B^3 = C_s (\lambda/d)^3$$

where θ_B is the Bragg angle of a set of reflecting planes spacing d for incident wavelength λ.

Since C_s is roughly proportional to λ^{-1}, then $\Delta A \approx \lambda^2$ and decreases rapidly with increasing accelerating voltage (decreasing λ). Thus, there are advantages in high voltage microscopy for identifying small particles by selected area diffraction, e.g., at 100 kV $\Delta A \approx 2\,\mu$m, while at 1 meV $\Delta A \approx 0.02\,\mu$m.

The procedures which must be observed to eliminate errors and misinterpretation in carrying out selected area diffraction (SAD) are discussed in detail in ref. [2] . It must be remembered that when correlating the SAD pattern to the image, all rotations (optical and magnetic) must be accounted for and pre-calibration is essential. For example, in microscopes of lens sequence objective, intermediate, projector there is an optical rotation of 180° between image and pattern. For alignment fix the image and rotate the SAD pattern (both plates emulsion up) 180° plus the magnetic rotation, clockwise.

2.2. Dark field

High resolution images are obtained only when the diffracted beam to be utilized for the dark field image is tilted so that is passes down the optical axis of the microscope. This is necessary in order to minimize errors such as chromatic aberration and spherical aberration, but objective aperture images of off axis beams can be used for preliminary investigations since these can be obtained very quickly. The important point is that in order to obtain the dark-field image of maximum intensity by tilting the illumination and without tilting the specimen, it is necessary to tilt the optical system in a direction which translates the origin to the point occupied by the Bragg spot responsible for bright field contrast [6] . This operation reverses the sign of g as shown in fig. 2. This procedure applies whether manual or electrical tilting systems are to be used. The advantages of the electrical system include ease and speed of operation and fast switching from bright to dark field and vice-versa.

The advantages of dark field imaging are many as some of the illustrations indicate. Also the images of defects near either the top or bottom surfaces can be selectively brought into contrast by dark field imaging at $s < 0$ and $s > 0$, respectively [7] e.g. fig. 5a. As an example of the combined use of diffraction pattern and dark field imaging consider fig. 3 which is of a commercial aluminium alloy designed for cryogenic applications*. The two beam bright field image at $s \approx 0$ of the 200 reflection (fig. 3a) shows strain contrast from plate shaped particles. No strain contrast images are seen for $g \cdot R = 0$. For fig. 3 the plates on (100) are visible, and so R is normal to (100). The orientation is [011] (fig. 3b) and the inclined plates on (010) and (001) are not in suitable orientation for strain contrast since they (and hence R) are inclined at 45° to the foil plane normal. In order to obtain strain contrast $g \cdot R$ must be a maximum i.e., R should lie in the foil plane. Thus plates must be oriented to be nearly parallel to the incident beam. In fig. 1c a dark field image is obtained of the streak near the 200 spot. No strain contrast is observed, only "structure factor contrast". In order to utilize such dark field images small objective apertures are required so that only one diffraction

* I'am grateful to Dr. D.Rowcliffe of Lockheed, Palo Alto, for providing this specimen.

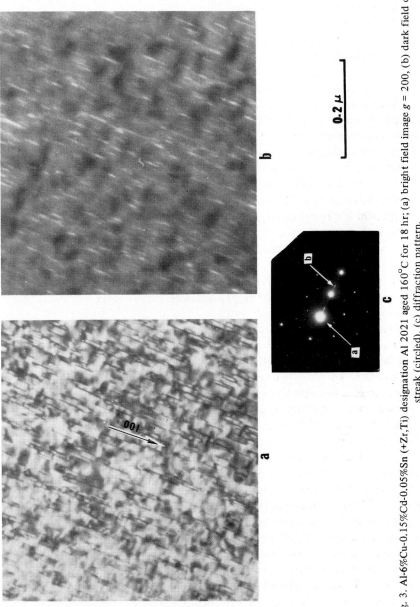

Fig. 3. Al-6%Cu-0.15%Cd-0.05%Sn (+Zr,Ti) designation Al 2021 aged 160°C for 18 hr; (a) bright field image $g = 200$, (b) dark field of streak (circled), (c) diffraction pattern.

phenomenon is to be imaged at a time. This is not always possible of course, when reflections are close together.

3. Double diffraction

The complexities of a diffraction pattern are most easily solved with the aid of dark field analysis of the various features present. In this way the maximum information can be obtained with minimum errors of identification. In two phase structures it is essential to recognize special effects due to double diffraction in order to correctly identify the phases which are present. This is also effected by dark field experiments.

In single phase BCC or FCC structures, double diffraction does not produce reflections of zero structure factor in the pattern since multiple reflections yield only allowed positions, e.g., in $[1\bar{1}0]$ BCC orientations

$$002 \pm 110 \leftrightharpoons 112 \text{ or } \bar{1}\bar{1}2$$

or

$$110 \pm 112 \leftrightharpoons 222 \text{ or } 00\bar{2} \text{ and so on.}$$

Twinning in these systems can however produce double diffraction [2], and it also occurs in less symmetrical structures such as diamond cubic or HCP, e.g., 200 (DC) and (0001) HCP.

In situations where two (or more) phases can exist, then double diffraction becomes more probable and care must be taken to identify spots which are due to this phenomenon. A spot which is present as a result of double diffraction, when used to form a dark field image will simultaneously reverse contrast in the corresponding diffraction regions of the phases responsible.

As an example consider fig. 4 taken from a Fe-Ni-Co maraging alloy which consists of a Widmanstatten pattern of austenite plates in martensite [8,9] (for review see ref. [10]). The SAD pattern consists of a mixture of the basic BCC $[0\bar{1}1]$ orientation (martensite) on which is superimposed several FCC orientations (austenite) in $\langle 111 \rangle$. For example, spot C is a 220 austenite reflection which in the dark field image (fig. 3c) reverses contrast only at those austenite plates that have this particular orientation. Spot d is a double diffraction spot produced by interactions of BCC and FCC reflections as shown by its dark field image in fig. 3d; similarly for spot b. Thus, the "quartets" of spots along $\langle 112 \rangle$ BCC in the pattern are mixtures of FCC reflections and

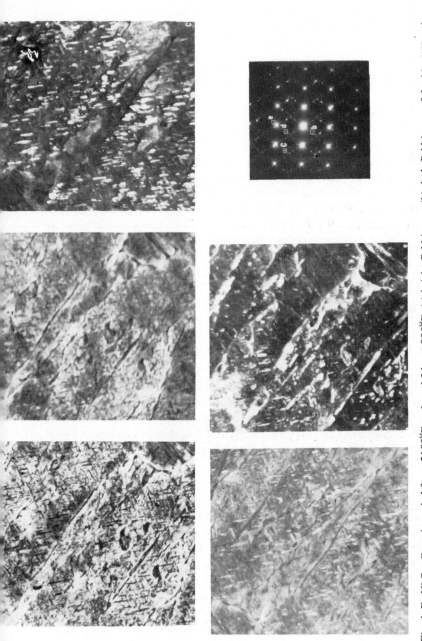

Fig. 4. Fe-Ni-Co alloy air cooled from 2100°F and aged 3 hr at 900°F. (a) bright field image, (b) dark field image of double diffraction spot b, (c) dark field image of austenite spot c (220 type), (d) dark field image of double diffraction spot d notice weak dark field contrast of precipitate and matrix, (e) dark field image of austenite spot e (220 type). The diffraction pattern shows the [011] symmetrical BCC with three superimposed FCC patterns in ⟨111⟩ orientations corresponding to the {011} Widmanstatten plates of austenite. Spots such as at b and d are due to double diffraction of austenite and martensite reflections.

double diffraction. They are not due to any intermetallic compounds. Similar arguments apply to any multiphase structure.

4. Detection and identification of small coherent particles

When second phase particles are large enough to give diffraction effects which are recognizable from those due to the matrix, their contrast can be reversed by dark field imaging and detection is not difficult. However situations can arise when it is not easy to be certain that the microstructure is indeed two-phase or not since the diffraction pattern may remain single crystal orientation with no extra spots visible and other diffraction effects due to second phases (strain, shape factor) may be too diffuse to be easily detected. Thus in characterizing the microstructure of alloys, it is important to attempt to utilize all possible pieces of information which may be present — observable or otherwise. This requires painstaking work in bright and dark field, obtaining high resolution, well exposed diffraction patterns, and ensuring that no spurious effects due to foil preparation (e.g. rough surfaces) do not confuse the issue. As will be illustrated in sect. 4.2, even though individual particles may not be resolvable, evidence for decomposition into two (or more) phases can be obtained by considering various possible contrast effects. Thus it is convenient to consider two general cases (a) when individual particles can be resolved and (b) when they cannot. Case (b) seems to be characterized by systems in which small, very coherent particles form in very large densities ($> 10^{17}$ cm^{-3}) so that any strain fields overlap and strain contrast images reveal net matrix strains rather than individual particle strain contrast. Examples include Cu-Be [11], short range ordering in alloys such as in Fe-Al [12], Fe-Si [13], Cu-Al [13], Ni-Mo [14] and possibly in interstitially ordered alloys such as Ta-C [15].

4.1. Resolvable particles
The visibility of precipitate particles depends on one or more different contrast mechanisms as discussed in detail in ref. [2], e.g., (a) diffraction contrast due to coherency strain fields, resulting from the matrix deforming locally to accommodate the precipitate, e.g., fig. 3a, (b) contrast due to the differences in structure factor between the phases present e.g. fig. 3b, (c) interface contrast in the form of fringes due to misorientation, phase contrast (as with stacking faults or antiphase boundaries) or geometrical effects such as at wedges, (d) Moiré contrast due to overlapping reflecting planes diffracting simultaneously in matrix and precipitate, (e) contrast due to the matrix being

in diffracting orientation when the particle is not (or vice versa), (f) thickness differences due to preferential thinning of the one phase with respect to its neighbor when preparing foils, (g) interface dislocation contrast when phases are partially coherent (e.g. figs. 14, 15).

When the precipitate particles are coherent, of similar lattice spacings, and are small with respect to the extinction distance (≈ 100 Å or less) only the first two contrast mechanisms are significant. Such cases of precipitation occur generally in alloys which undergo decomposition from supersaturated solid solutions such as age-hardening alloys (see e.g. ref. [16] for review).

In the early stages of precipitation when large numbers of small particles can be formed several factors influence the microstructure and observed contrast, e.g., (a) coherency strains, (b) volume fraction, (c) elastic anisotropy, represented by the ratio of the shear moduli G $\langle 110 \rangle$: G $\langle 100 \rangle$.

In aluminum alloys where the anisotropy is ≈ 1, the shapes of particles are determined by the atom size factor. Spherical (as in Al-Ag) needle-like (Al-Mg_2Si) and plate-like (Al-Cu) particles have all been identified [16]. Needles and plates are most easily distinguished in the early aging stages when particles are very small by analysis of the SAD pattern since this is modified by the shape factor. Needles give rise to rel-sheets of intensity perpendicular to their axes while plates give rise to rel-rods, normal to the plane of the plate [1,2]. Fig. 5 shows examples of needles in Al-Mg_2Si and the diffraction pattern shows the curved streaks which are produced when the reflecting sphere intersects the sheets of intensity which are normal to $\langle 100 \rangle$ for all needles which do not lie normal to the beam. By comparison to fig. 5b the straight streaks in fig. 6 are due to small plates (GP zones) on {001}. Thus, the [110] orientation immediately distinguishes between plates and rods in these alloys. Shape factor effects can be understood geometrically by the superposition of all respective reciprocal lattices [17].

If the volume fraction of the particles is not too large so that individual small particles can be resolved by diffraction contrast, and the strain fields do not overlap to a considerable extent, qualitative information can be obtained as to the direction and magnitude of strain and the shape and dimensions of the particles by utilizing the strain contrast rules to dark-field images first developed by Ashby and Brown [18]. These rules can be summarized by reference to fig. 7 which shows the type of strain contrast images expected for different (simple) defects under conditions where $\mathbf{g} \cdot \mathbf{R} \neq 0$ (where $\mathbf{R}$ is the displacement vector). These images show dark contrast to the same side as $\mathbf{g}$ when the strain field is interstitial in nature and white when the strain field is of the vacancy type, provided that exactly $s = 0$ condition applies to the area being considered [18]. In principle, therefore, the sense of the image

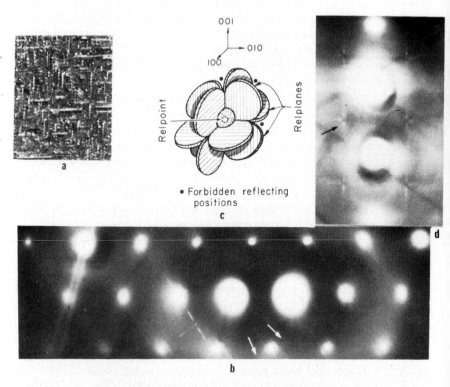

Fig. 5. a, foils of Al-Mg$_2$Si quenched and aged 5 hr 220°C; dark-field at $s < 0$, only precipitates near top surface are in good contrast. The needles along [100] and [010] inclined at 45° exhibit extinction contrast and strain contrast. The strain contrast indicates interstitial strain fields. b SAD pattern of a, notice parabolic streaks spread about [002] due to the [100] and [010] needles, and straight streaks along [220] due to the [001] needles. c. Schematic representation of the intensity sheet distribution about rel-points. d. Diffraction pattern ($\approx$[103]) of needles showing cancellation of intensity at nonallowed reflecting positions (cf-c).

contrast with respect to the direction of **g** can be used to determine the sense of the strain fields. However, due to the periodic intensity oscillations with depth in the foil as illustrated in fig. 8, it is essential that the position of the particle in the foil be accurately known when the size of the particle is smaller than the extinction distance before this rule can be applied. Details of this type of analysis are described in the chapter by Wilkins. If precipitation has in fact occurred in the bulk of the material and not on the surfaces then roughly half

Fig. 6. [110] orientation of Al-Cu aged to form GP zones on {100} the streaks along [001] show that plates and not needles are present (compare to fig. 5b).

the particles have white contrast and half have dark contrast on the same side as the direction of g (fig. 9). Also, if the particle size is large (of same order as the extinction distance) there is no problem in defining the sense of displacement from the image e.g. the larger θ' plates in fig. 9, all have their white images on the same side while the GP zone images have mixed contrast.

4.2. Alloys containing very large volume fractions of small particles

The illustrations of figs. 3, 8 and 9 show that strain contrast images are determined by $g \cdot R$ where g is a matrix reflection and R represents the displacement(s) around the precipitate. If the precipitate reflection is used to

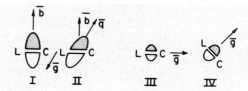

Fig. 7. Scheme illustrating strain contrast images expected from individual precipitates I plate shaped particle displacement vector **b** normal to habit plane or rods viewed with axes normal to the beam. II As I but displacement vector inclined to habit plane. III Similar to a screw dislocation end-on. IV Spherical particle or rod viewed end-on. In I and II the image (line of dividing contrast LC) is independent of **g**; in III LC is parallel to **g**, in IV LC is normal to **g**. These predictions may be modified when the volume fraction of particles is very large so that strain fields overlap and interact, and for more complex shaped particles.

form a dark field image, e.g., the streak in fig. 3, only structure factor contrast is observed. Such images thus may provide more accurate information regarding true particle size and shape than the strain contrast image.

Difficulties in resolving particles may be encountered when the volume fraction is very large and the particles are very small (<100Å) so that the strain fields overlap. The image contrast can then be determined by *net strains* rather than by individual particles and it is convenient to refer to this effect as net strain contrast. The simplest example is found in the Cu-Be precipitation hardening system [11] in which only ⟨110⟩ strain "striations" (also called tweed patterns) can be observed during the initial stages of aging (see fig. 10a). Tanner [11] in a detailed investigation concluded that the strain patterns were due to small plates on {100}, but with strain fields in ⟨110⟩. This result was inferred from a series of **g · R** experiments. However, in Cu-2% Be additional helpful information can be gained from the diffraction patterns, for example in fig. 10b streaks are observed in ⟨100⟩ from rel-point to rel-point proving that small plates with {001} habit must be present. The interpretation of strain fields in ⟨110⟩ is confirmed by the short ⟨110⟩ diffuse streaks observed in the pattern. The reason for {001}⟨110⟩ strains may be related to the anisotropy factor > 1*. When the volume fraction is high, fig. 7 is no longer

---

* The anisotropy factor is also important when coherency is lost; e.g. partially coherent dislocations are generated with minimum energy expenditure so that dislocations with **b** = ⟨110⟩ rather than ⟨100⟩ may exist (cf. figs. 14, 15).

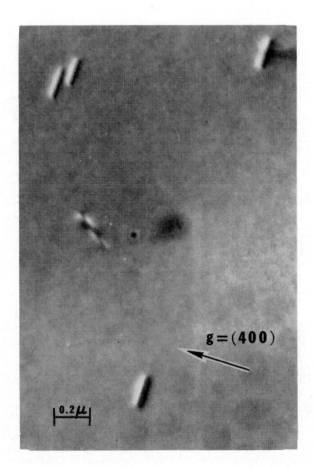

Fig. 8. Rods of precipitate formed in silicon doped with phosphorus strain contrast images; the rods lying normal to the beam indicate vacancy contrast (cf. fig. 7-I) but the inclined rod shows oscillatory contrast due to the depth dependence of the intensity.

an accurate guide to interpretation but the zones in Cu-Be if resolved should appear as in fig. 7 II with $b = [100]$ and $q = [110]$.

Similar but not identical results occur in short range ordered alloys. For example, fig. 11 shows a series of $g \cdot R$ experiments on Ni-20%Mo which indicate that R is principally along $\langle 110 \rangle$ but no individual particles can be resolved until aging is prolonged sufficiently so that superlattice spots can be

Fig. 9. Al-4% Cu dark field strain contrast image showing heterogeneously precipitated
θ' (large plates) and GP zones. Compare to figs. 3 and 7 I. Displacement **R** parallel to
g = 200. Foil orientation [001], plates on (010) are not visible since **g · R** is zero for these.

seen. In this case the dark field image of a superlattice spot reverses contrast
for particles of that particular orientation (fig. 11f). However, unless diffuse
or superlattice spots are present the net strain contrast image may be the only
indication that precipitation has occurred. If the individual particles cannot be
resolved and shape factor and/or strain diffuse streaks cannot be seen or dis-

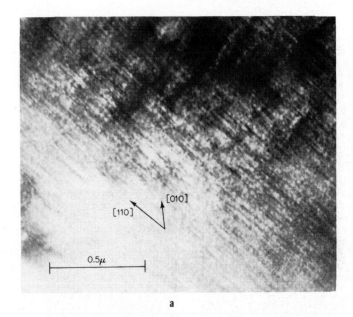

a

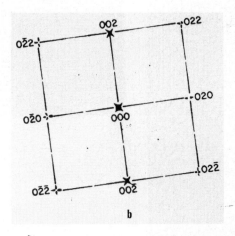

b

Fig. 10. Cu-2% Be aged to form GP zones (a) bright field image g = [220], (b) sketch of
SAD pattern to show ⟨110⟩ strain diffuse streaks and ⟨100⟩ form factor streaks.

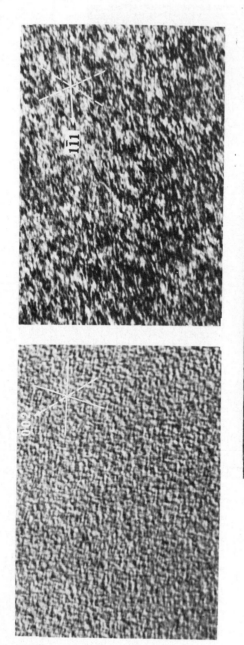

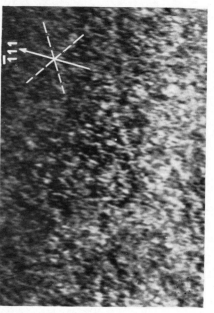

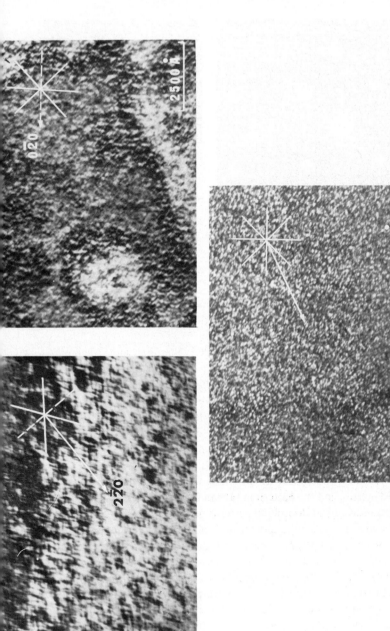

Fig. 11. Ni$_4$Mo quenched to ice brine from 1100°C aged 5 sec 750° (a−d) foil near [110]. Courtesy P.R.Okamoto. (a) bright field two beam g = 002 (b) bright field two beam g = 1̄11 (c) bright field two beam g = 1̄11 (d) bright field two beam g = 22̄0. Solid and dashed lines show traces of {110} planes. Strain contrast in ⟨110⟩ is parallel to solid lines. (e) bright field g = 02̄0 after tilting to near [001] zone. (f) dark field of superlattice reflection showing one of the six orientational variants possible for ordered Ni$_4$Mo particles.

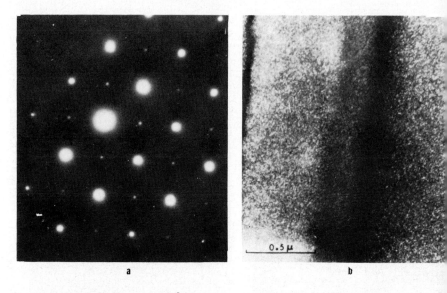

Fig. 12. Fe-19% Al aged 1 week 300°C, (a) diffraction pattern (b) dark field image of "superlattice spot", showing two-phase nature of the alloy.

tinguished, there is little more to be concluded other than some small particles, of undefined shape and associated strain vector are present. Considerable effort is currently being devoted to this problem in order to better define physically the meaning of short range order. For example fig. 12 shows a SAD pattern of Fe-19% Al after aging one week at 300°C [12]. This pattern may be interpreted to be single phase, single crystal, but ordered with superlattice spots at $\{h00\}$ and equivalent positions. However, a dark-field image of a "superlattice" spot, fig. 12b, clearly reveals small particles. The microstructure may thus be characterized as two phase with small ordered particles in a disordered matrix, and the pattern in (a) can be regarded as consisting of two superposed ordered and disordered patterns of the same [001] orientation and almost identical lattice parameter since no doubling of the spots is seen. Thus the two phases in (b) must be almost ideally coherent. This characterization seems to indicate that short range ordered alloys consist of small ordered particles in a disordered matrix. It should be emphasized that it is difficult to prove that two phases exist when the contrast is very weak and no obvious effects are to be seen in the SAD patterns. Other techniques such as field ion microscopy may then be combined to advantage [14].

5. Spinodal decomposition

In spinodal decomposition, periodic fluctuations in composition occur along the elastically soft directions (generally $\langle 001 \rangle$ in metals) [19]. The consequence of this on the diffraction pattern is to produce "side-bands", i.e., satellite reflections alongside the main reflections in a direction parallel to the direction of modulation. The important feature of the sidebands is that their spacing depends only on the wavelength of the compositional fluctuation. For cubic phases the wavelength can be calculated from [20]

$$\lambda = \frac{h(d_{h'k'l'}) \tan \theta}{(h^2+k^2+l^2)\Delta\theta}$$

where $h'k'l'$ is direction of fluctuation and $\Delta\theta$ the angular separation between spot and satellite. For high energy electrons and for fluctuations along [h00] this reduces to

$$\lambda = \frac{ha}{(h^2+k^2+l^2)} \left(\frac{g}{\Delta g}\right)$$

where a is the lattice parameter, and $g : \Delta g$ is given by the ratio of the distances from 000 and satellite to the hkl spot. Similar equations apply to the $0k0$, $00l$ directions of fluctuation. The wavelengths obtained from fig. 13 increase from 60Å (b) to 160Å (e) [21]. This method of measuring λ is more convenient than direct measurements of the image for two main reasons viz., (a) because the sideband spacing is independent of magnification and (b) because mean values are immediately obtained for all distributions of λ contributing to the pattern (i.e., within the selected area). When the phases are coherent with small strains involved the images do not show strong strain contrast. For Cu-Fe-Ni the strain is $< 0.6\%$ (fig. 17b). Interface fringes (δ-fringes [22]) typical of coherent boundaries can be observed when the interface plane is inclined to the incident beam. Many examples of δ-fringes have now been given, e.g. at domain interfaces [22–24]. The characteristic of these fringes is that their contrast is the opposite to that of stacking fault contrast in FCC systems. Delta fringes show asymmetry at the top and bottom of the foil in bright field, and are symmetrical in dark field. These fringe patterns occur due to the slight mismatch in lattice spacing at the interface giving rise to a Δg (and Δs) mismatch in the reciprocal lattice. In such cases splitting of the diffraction spots and Kikuchi lines may be resolved particularly at large 2θ values [25]. From measurements of the Kikuchi patterns the axial ratios

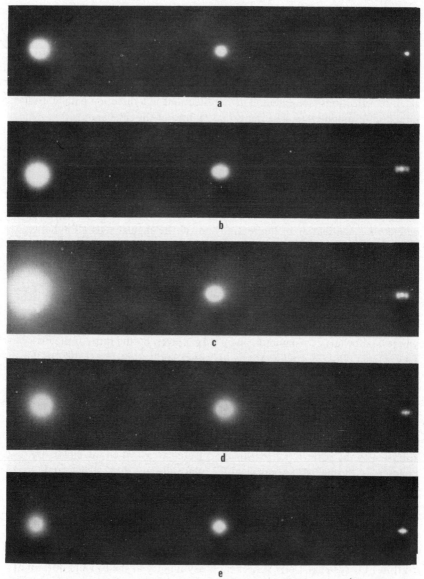

Fig. 13. 51.5 Cu-33.5Ni-15 Fe alloy quenched and aged at 625°C showing development of side-bands due to spinodal decomposition along {100}. (a) fast quenched (no decomposition), (b) 1 min, (c) 5 min, (d) 15 min, (e) 60 min. Notice decrease in satellite spacing at 400 reflection as aging increases (λ increases).

of non-cubic structures may be measured quite accurately [23]. It should be noted that satellites from modulated (side-band) structure can be distinguished from Δg splitting since the spacing of the former depends only on spinodal wavelength whereas the latter increases with $|g|$.

6. Partially coherent phases

When the misfit between two phases exceeds that which can be tolerated by elastic distortion (visible as strain contrast), coherency breaks down and interfacial dislocations can be generated. Mechanisms to account for loss of coherency have been investigated in several alloy systems by Weatherly and Nicholson [26]. In Al-4% Cu coherency between θ' plates and the matrix is lost by the generation of prismatic pure edge-dislocation loops inside the plates with the loop lying parallel to the habit plane $\{001\}$. The contrast from these loops is directly analogous to the contrast from large edge-loops in quenched or irradiated crystals. For a plate viewed with its normal parallel to the incident beam $g \cdot b = 0$ but the resolved components of the displacement normal to b, i.e., $b \times u$ where u is a vector normal to b are only normal to g where g is tangent to the loop ($g \cdot b \times u = 0$). This is the only condition when $g \cdot b = 0$, and $g \cdot b \times u = 0$ is simultaneously satisfied. The image has maximum contrast when g and $b \times u$ are parallel. Thus, the image consists of double arcs normal to g and the images are complementary on opposite sides since $g \cdot b \times u$ changes sign about a line through the center of the plate. An example is shown in fig. 14. The doublets and triplets in the images are due to the effect of foil thickness on image contrast. Triple images occur for loops near the bottom surface of the foil.

For precipitates, such as θ' in Al-Cu, which form on cube planes, the misfit dislocations are expected to have their Burgers vectors along $\langle 100 \rangle$ in the interface, i.e., be pure edge. However, this is not a universal rule and interesting differences occur in the Cu-Fe-Ni spinodal system when the wavelength > 1000 Å and coherency is lost [21].

Figs. 15a,b show the interface structure. Only one set of interface dislocations has been generated and these have b of the $\frac{1}{2} a$ [110] type. The mismatch $\delta = |b|/d$, where d is the spacing, is $\approx 0.6\%$. The corresponding diffraction pattern (fig. 16) shows a splitting in the [010] but not in the [100] direction, (e.g., the 440 spot). The mismatch in fig. 16 $\approx 0.7\%$. This result shows that as coherency is lost the structure must change from cubic to tetragonal. At later stages when a second set of dislocations has been generated so that all grains are relieved at the interface, the structure becomes cubic again [21].

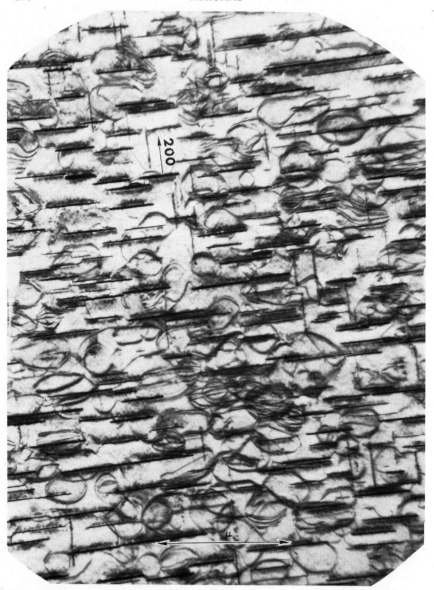

Fig. 14. Showing interfacial pure edge prismatic loops around partially coherent θ' plates in Al-4% Cu. Foil in [001]. Notice that $\mathbf{g} \cdot \mathbf{b}$ is zero for one set of edge-on plates and $\mathbf{g} \cdot \mathbf{b} \times \mathbf{u}$ and $\mathbf{g} \cdot \mathbf{b}$ is zero simultaneously for parts of loops with $b = [001]$ normal to the foil plane. Compare to strain contrast images of θ' in fig. 9.

Fig. 15. Interfacial dislocations in spinodal Cu-Fe-Ni alloy aged 200 hr 700°C visible for $g = 11\bar{1}$ in (a), but invisible for $\mathbf{g} = 1\bar{1}1$ in (b). The dislocations lie in [100]; their most probable Burgers vector is along [011].

Fig. 16. Diffraction pattern corresponding to area similar to that in fig. 15. Zone is [001].
The resolvable doublet at 440 is parallel to the interface normal. Notice that there is no
splitting along [100]. The structure is thus tetragonal.

The contrast experiments illustrated by fig. 15 prove that the Burgers vectors of these interface dislocations are parallel to ⟨110⟩ directions with the dislocations lines along ⟨100⟩. Thus roughly twice as many dislocation are required to relieve the mismatch than if dislocations of $b = a\langle100\rangle$ were formed. It is possible that nucleation of dislocations with $\frac{1}{2} a\langle110\rangle$ Burgers vectors is more favorable energetically than $a[100]$ type in this system and in view of the high anisotropy ratio.

7. Note on grain boundaries

Phase transformations from supersaturated solutions occur neither by nucleation and growth (N and G), homogeneously as in the spinodal, or martensitically. The latter case will not be discussed here. Homogeneous and heterogeneous decomposition can be distinguished morphologically since in the latter case nucleation is favored at defects such as dislocations, boundaries, faults, point defects, etc. Noticeable differences occur at and near grain boundaries as illustrated in fig. 17. Fig. 17a shows a grain boundary microstructure in Al-Zn-Mg alloy showing typical N + G conditions with precipitation along the boundary, precipitate free zones adjacent to boundaries (PFZ) [27] and a decrease in number (but increase in size) of particles in the matrix adjacent to the PFZ. The homogeneous microstructure resulting from spinodal decomposition of Cu-Fe-Ni on the other hand (fig. 17b) shows none of these features. Although it is easy to distinguish such heterogeneous and homogeneous transformations, it is not recommended as a general principle to use microstructure to define the type of transformation since this is determined by kinetic and thermodynamic principles, and usually the experimentalist never really "sees" the nucleation (or lack of) stage in the process, even when direct observations are possible.

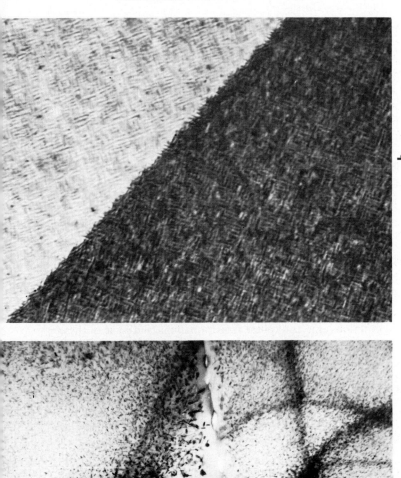

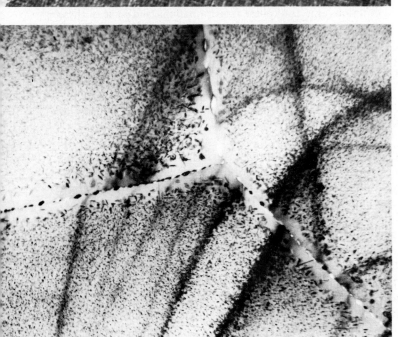

Fig. 17. a. Heterogeneous precipitation in Al-Zn-Mg. b. Homogeneous precipitation in Cu-Fe-Ni spinodal.

8. Dynamic studies of phase transformations

As indicated in fig. 1 it is possible to obtain direct observations of dynamic events, e.g., deformation, precipitation, recovery, etc., with the use of appropriate specimen stages and ciné techniques (see ref. [28] for review). The high voltage microscope may be useful in this regard since it will be possible to work with thicker specimens and possibly have fewer problems due to surface effects. Some examples have already been given by Fujita et al. [29].

This work was done under the auspices of the United State Atomic Energy Commission. I also acknowledge helpful discussions with Dr. Paul Butler and my graduate students.

APPENDIX ADDED FOR THE SECOND EDITION

Since the preceding chapter was written, several important advances have occurred in various aspects of phase transformations, and some of these are briefly reviewed in the following. The references given are representative of current work and are not meant to be comprehensive. The potential applications of the critical voltage effect are discussed at the end of the chapter on Kikuchi electron diffraction.

1. Interpretation of "tweed" structure

As discussed in section 4.2 of the main chapter, a diffraction contrast effect known as "tweed structure" is observed in many systems during initial stages of a transformation. For this effect, the description "net strain contrast" is also useful since it indicates that the strain contrast may not give a direct indication of the strain field of individual particles (e.g. fig. 11 of this chapter). The current interpretation of this type of contrast is that it arises from a preferential alignment of tetragonally misfitting particles [30]. This aligned morphology has been shown to reduce the total elastic energy of the two (or more) phase system [31]. Since tweed type contrast may also be observed in homogeneously transformed systems (e.g. spinodals) [32] and ordered alloys [33], it may not be uniquely a feature associated with small particles dispersed in a matrix. Lattice imaging may be most useful for sorting out such unresolved images (see section 3 of this appendix).

It should be noted that there are several additive contributions to contrast which are especially likely to occur simultaneously in spinodal systems viz., (a) strain contrast which will depend on the parameter $\bar{g} \cdot \bar{R}$, (b) structure factor (and absorption) contrast which arises from the differences in composition of the two phases, (c) Fourier fringe contrast due to beating between the satellite reflections and their adjacent main beams, (d) thickness differences due to foil preparation; in many systems, one phase preferentially polishes at a different rate from its neighbor e.g. Cu-Ni-Fe alloys [32].

2. Interpretation of diffuse scattering and short range order

Recent detailed analyses of electron diffraction patterns in Ni-(8–25 at%)Mo, Au_3Cr, and other ordered alloy systems [34] (reviewed by Das and Thomas in ref. [33]) have lead to some new suggestions concerning the structural interpretation of short range order. These results together with theoretical calculations [35] suggest that the short range ordered state may consist of microdomains of different superstructures. For a particular alloy, the most frequently occurring domain may or may not correspond to the equilibrium long-range ordered structure of that alloy. We have used the description "multiple microdomain" for theses cases [33].

Experimentally it is necessary to carry out careful analyses of the diffuse scattering. The detection of weak maxima at reciprocal lattice positions such as $\{1\frac{1}{2}0\}$ etc., depends critically on the examination of the appropriate reciprocal lattice sections for which long exposure times are necessary (several minutes). For example, fig. A1(a) is a [001] diffraction pattern of Ni_4Mo sample after quenching in iced brine from 1100°C. If one simply looks at the [001] diffraction pattern, it is not possible to tell whether there is any diffuse scattering present near Ni_4Mo and Ni_2Mo superlattice positions, because the diffuse peaks near $\{1\frac{1}{2}0\}$ positions dominate. However, a plot of iso-intensity contour maps, such as shown in fig. A1(b), reveals the diffuse scattering present near the Ni_4Mo and Ni_2Mo superlattice positions (marked by filled circles and filled triangles respectively). The detection of these weak superlattice reflections requires careful examination of certain favorable orientations where only the superlattice reflections lie on the Ewald sphere. The [110] orientation is very favorable for detecting Ni_2Mo spots and $[\bar{1}30]$ is suitable for detecting Ni_4Mo spots [34]. Fig. A2 shows an example of a [110] diffraction pattern taken from a Ni_3Mo sample after quenching from 1270°C in iced brine. The diffuse scattering near Ni_2Mo superlattice positions (marked by arrows) can be resolved. There are no Ni_4Mo nor $\{1\frac{1}{2}0\}$ reflections present in this orienta-

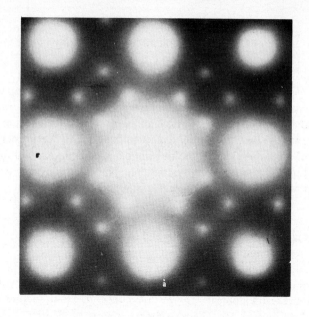

(a)

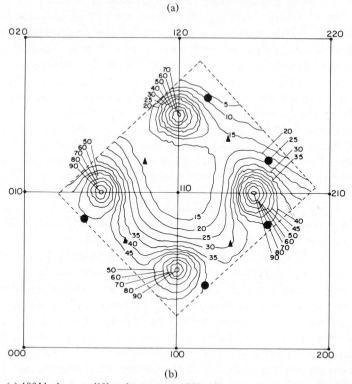

(b)

Fig. A1. (a) [001] electron diffraction pattern of Ni_4Mo quenched in iced brine from 1100°C. (b) Iso-intensity contour map of [001] electron diffraction pattern of quenched Ni_4Mo. The dotted line outlines the portion traced. The notations are: •: Ni_4Mo super-lattice positions; ▲: Ni_2Mo superlattice positions. (Ref. [34].)

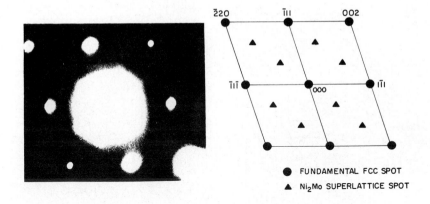

Fig. A2. [110] electron diffraction pattern of Ni_3Mo after quenching in iced brine from 1270°C. (Ref. [34].)

tion. A qualitative interpretation of the diffuse scattering observed near Ni_2Mo and Ni_4Mo positions is that there are microdomains present in the short-range ordered state with Ni_2Mo and Ni_4Mo structure. The presence of diffuse $\{1\frac{1}{2}0\}$ peaks in short-range ordered Ni-Mo alloys have been interpreted [36] to be due to the presence of imperfectly ordered domains with Do_{22} superstructure, resulting from the occurrence of nonconservative antiphase boundaries within the micro-domains. These qualitative observations imply that the short-range ordered Ni-Mo alloys (in the composition range 8–25 at% Mo) contain micro-domains with not one but three different superstructures, namely Do_{22}, Ni_4Mo and Ni_2Mo.

3. Lattice imaging

With the most recent generation of transmission electron microscopes, it has become almost a routine matter to achieve Fourier resolutions, or "lattice imaging", of 2–3 Å. The technique appears to be particularly useful for the study of fine structure, e.g. structures causing tweed contrast; spinodals and small coherent particles in alloys [37] (although care must be exercised in the interpretation of the images [38]), studies of so-called amorphous materials [39,40] structure analysis [41], and at Berkeley we are attempting to check the interpretation of short range order by lattice imaging ordered alloys (e.g. fig. A3). We believe it is essential to compute the image characteristics as well

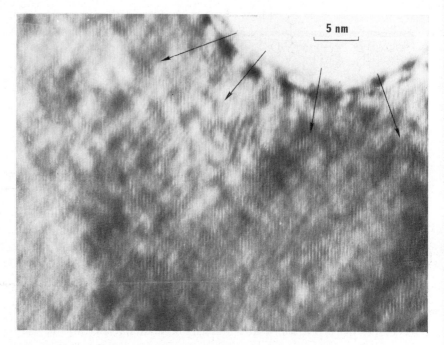

Fig. A3. A lattice image of the (200) planes (spacing 0.19 nm) in partially ordered Cu_3Au. Small ordered nuclei (arrowed) approximately 2.5 nm in diameter are present in a disordered matrix, and these are manifested in the lattice image by alternately wider and narrower white fringes. (Courtesy R.Sinclair.)

as to obtain high resolution images in order to clarify the interpretation, e.g. the appearance of fringes corresponding to fundamental or superlattice reflecting planes in the same specimen seems to be critically dependent on thickness.

4. Notes on contrast and resolution

The importance of several non-conventional techniques in transmission electron microscopy for the improved imaging of defects has already been recognized. Significant benefits of improved imaging of dislocation lines and quantitative applications to problems of dislocation structure and stacking fault energy measurements have been demonstrated at 100 kV by the dark-field weak-beam technique [42].

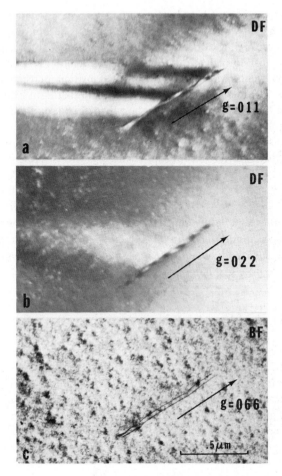

Fig. A4. Contrast examples showing defects in fully ordered $LiFe_5O_8$: (a) 011 superlattice reflection showing strong APB contrast (broad fringes due to large extinction distance; (b) fundamental 022 reflection resolving cation stacking faults (parallel to **g**); (c) high resolution 066 image resolving partial dislocations bounding the fault. (Courtesy O. van der Biest.)

Comparably narrow dislocation images have been produced by high voltage electron microscopy using bright-field images when the crystal is oriented near high order systematic reflections [43,44].

At 100 kV, dislocations images may normally be understood using two-beam theory which considers the two most strongly excited dispersion surface branches. As is well known, the image width is then about $\xi_g/3$ where ξ_g is the extinction distance ($\xi g \propto (\Delta k)^{-1}$, where Δk is the separation of the two branches). At higher voltages many-beam interactions become more important, and for an understanding of defect contrast a larger number of dispersion surface branches must normally be considered. For any order reflection along the systematic row, the Δk value of the dominant transition increases with increasing order. The implications for microscopy are that both high-order bright-field and weak-beam images may be narrow because of the large Δk values, and hence small ξ_g values, involved.

Applications of these principles to studies of defects in ferrites have enabled us to resolve $\frac{1}{4}\langle 110 \rangle$ partial dislocations associated with stacking faults. An example is shown in fig. A4. It should be noted here that in fig. A4(b) weak APB contrast is visible in spite of the fact that for the operating fundamental reflection 022, $\alpha = 2\pi\bar{g} \cdot \bar{R} = 0$. This is due to the systematic interference from the 011 and other superlattice reflections. Notice the very narrow images of the partial dislocations in fig. A4(c). This bright field method has the advantage of shorter exposure times compared to the weak beam method and thus is not as susceptible to potential hazards of vibration etc.

5. Dynamic (in situ) observations

High voltage electron microscopes have permitted a much wider range of dynamic events to be studied. The new developments include observations of phase changes in controlled environments and have come about from the advantages of increased electron penetration at high voltages coupled with ingenious designs of environmental chambers and specimen stages (e.g. ref. [45]). Several examples have been published in a recent symposium [46].

References

[1] G.Thomas, Transmission Electron Microscopy of Metals (John Wiley and Sons, New York, 1962).

[2] P.B.Hirsch et al., Electron Microscopy of Thin Crystals (Butterworths, London, 1965).

[3] A.J.F.Metherell and M.J.Whelan, J. Appl. Phys. 37 (1966) 1737.

[4] Electron Microscopy, Kyoto, ed. R.Uyeda (Maruzen Company, Tokyo, 1968) pp. 85–99.

[5] S.L.Cundy and P.J.Grundy, Phil. Mag. 14 (1966) 1233.

[6] W.L.Bell, D.M.Maher and G.Thomas, Lattice Defects in Quenched Metals (Academic Press, New York, 1965) p. 739.

[7] W.L.Bell and G.Thomas, Phys. Stat. Sol. 12 (1965) 843.

[8] G.Thomas, I-Lin Cheng and J.R.Mihalisin, Trans. ASM 62 (1969) 852.
[9] I-Lin Cheng and G.Thomas, ibid. 61 (1968) 14.
[10] S.Floreen, Met. Rev. (1968) p. 115.
[11] L.E.Tanner, Phil. Mag. 14 (1966) 111.
[12] H.Warlimont and G.Thomas, J. Mat. Sci. 4 (1970) 47.
[13] H.Warlimont (private communication).
[14] P.R.Okamoto and G.Thomas, Acta Met. 19 (1971) 825.
[15] P.Rao and G.Thomas, to be published.
[16] A.Kelly and R.B.Nicholson, Prog. Mat. Sci. 10 (1963) 151.
[17] G.Thomas, W.L.Bell and H.M.Otte, Phys. Stat Sol. 12 (1965) 353.
[18] M.F.Ashby and L.M.Brown, Phil. Mag. 8 (1963) 1083, 1649.
[19] J.W.Cah, Trans. TMS-AIME 242 (1968) 166.
[20] V.Daniel and H.Lipson, Proc. Roy. Soc. 182 (1943) 378.
[21] E.P.Butler and G.Thomas, Acta Met. 18 (1970) 347.
[22] R.Gevers, J.van Landuyt and S.Amelinckx, Phys. Stat. Sol. 11 (1965) 689;
     G.Gemant et al.Phys. Stat. Sol. 13 (1966) 125.
[23] R.E.Villagrana and G.Thomas, Phys. Stat. Sol. 9 (1965) 499.
[24] E.P.Butler and P.M.Kelly, Trans. TMS-AIME 242 (1968) 2107.
[25] G.Thomas, Trans. TMS-AIME 233 (1965) 1608.
[26] G.C.Weatherly and R.B.Nicholson, Phil. Mag. 17 (1968) 801.
[27] G.Thomas and J.Nutting, J. Inst. Metals 88 (1959-60) 81.
[28] G.Thomas, High Temperature High Resolution Metallography (Gordon and Breach,
     1967) p. 217.
[29] J.Fujita, Y.Kawasaki, E.Furubayashi, S.Kajiwara and T.Taoka, Jap. J. Appl. Phys. 6
     (1967) 214.
[30] P.J.Fillingham, H.J.Leamy and L.E.Tanner, in: Electron Microscopy and Structure
     of Materials, ed. G.Thomas (Univ. of Calif. Press, 1972) p. 163.
[31] P.Eurin, J.M.Pennisson and A.Bourret, Acta Met. 21 (1973) 559.
[32] R.J.Livak and G.Thomas, Acta Met. 19 (1971) 497.
[33] Many examples will be published in the Proceedings of the 1973 Conf. on Order-
     Disorder Transformations (Tübingen) to be published by Deutsche Gesellschaft für
     Metallkunde.
[34] S.K.Das, P.R.Okamoto, P.M.J.Fisher and G.Thomas, Acta Met. 21 (1973) 913.
[35] P.C.Clapp, Phys. Rev. B4 (1971) 255.
[36] P.R.Okamoto and G.Thomas, Acta Met. 19 (1971) 825.
[37] V.A.Phillips and L.E.Tanner, Acta Met. 21 (1973) 441.
[38] D.J.H.Cockayne, J.R.Parsons and C.W.Hoelke, Phil. Mag. 24 (1971) 139.
[39] M.L.Rudee and A.Howie, Phil. Mag. 25 (1972) 1001.
[40] A.Howie, O.L.Kritanck and M.L.Rudee, Phil. Mag. 27 (1973) 235.
[41] J.A.Allpress, E.A.Hewatt, A.F.Moodie and J.V.Sanders, Acta Cryst. A28 (1973) 528.
[42] D.J.Cockayne, I.L.F.Ray and M.J.Whelan, Phil. Mag. 20 (1969) 1265.
[43] W.L.Bell and G.Thomas, in: Electron Microscopy and Structure of Materials, ed.
     G.Thomas (Univ. of Calif. Press, 1972) p. 23.
[44] M.J.Goringe, E.A.Hewat, C.J.Humphries and G.Thomas, Proc. 5th European Congress
     Electron Microscopy (1972) p. 538.
[45] P.R.Swann, in: Electron Microscopy and Structure of Materials, ed. G.Thomas
     (Univ. of Calif. Press, 1972) p. 878.
[46] Proc. Symposium on High Voltage Electron Microscopy (Manchester) 1972, Royal
     Mic. Soc. (1972) p. 171, see especially the review by H. Flower, p. 171.

$$\mathbf{P} = \mathbf{I} + m\mathbf{dp}'$$

$$= \begin{pmatrix} 1 & 0 & 0 \\ 0 & 1 & 0 \\ 0 & 0 & 1 \end{pmatrix} + m[d_1 d_2 d_3](p_1 p_2 p_3)$$

$$= \begin{pmatrix} 1 + md_1 p_1 & md_1 p_2 & md_1 p_3 \\ md_2 p_1 & 1 + md_2 p_2 & md_2 p_3 \\ md_3 p_1 & md_3 p_2 & 1 + md_3 p_3 \end{pmatrix} \tag{1}$$

where $\mathbf{p}'$ (prime meaning transpose) being a plane normal with covariant components is written a row matrix, in contrast to $\mathbf{d}$, a lattice vector with contravariant components, which is a (3×1) column matrix.

It was both a triumph and disappointment for investigators [20] to realize that the measured shape strain, $\mathbf{P}$, when applied to the parent lattice did not generate the known product lattice — the case in general.

Another characteristic of martensitic transformations is the experimental fact that the martensite-parent interface or habit plane (usually referred to the parent phase) is not one of simple Miller indices as is often the case for solid state reactions, i.e. precipitation from solid solution. Various materials exhibit different habit planes, as shown in fig. 4 for several iron alloys. The scatter in habit plane indices for a given material is considered to be greater than that arising from experimental error [2]. In addition to the martensite habit plane being generally irrational, experiments have shown that the lattice orientation relationship is not a simple one. Important low-index planes and directions in the parent and product phases are usually non-parallel.

It has been observed that ordered phases will transform into other ordered phases (with a change in structure) martensitically and there is no evidence that diffusion occurs in martensitic transformations. Thus, martensitic transformations are often called diffusionless transformations. In some cases, i.e., steels, high speed experimental techniques [22] have established that an individual plate of martensite can form in less than a microsecond. Some other martensitic transformation appear to be considerably slower although the evolution of a plate in these cases may consist of a number of intermittently delayed rapid sequences.

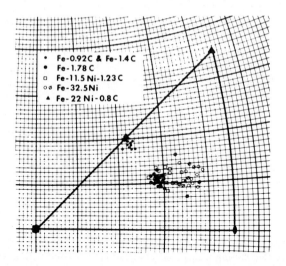

Fig. 4. Experimental results of martensite habit plane determinations for a number of
ferrous alloys [2].

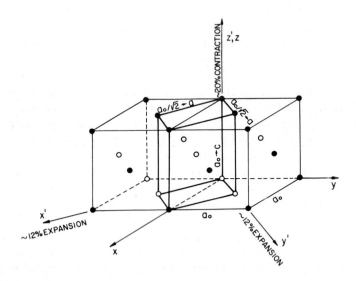

Fig. 5. Correspondence and distortion for the fcc to bcc (bct) transformation proposed by
Bain [22]. The delineated bct unit cell is simply "upset" to the proper dimensions. The
magnitudes of the principal distortions shown are typical of those for the martensite
transformation in iron alloys [2].

The rapidity of martensite formation in steels led Bain to propose his well-known model shown in fig. 5 for the fcc to bcc (or bct) martensitic transformations, according to which the delineated bct cell is simply upset to the proper dimensions [22]. This homogeneous distortion is a mode of atomic shift requiring minimum atomic motion and involves a *correspondence* which specifies a unique relation between lattice points in the parent and product lattices. There are other possible fcc–bcc correspondences and hence homogeneous strains, but it has been shown that the one proposed by Bain involves minimum atomic displacements [23]. For some transformations, for example the $\beta \to \alpha$ martensitic transformation in uranium, the choice of the likely correspondence is less obvious. That martensitic transformations exhibit an invariant plane strain shape change implies that a lattice correspondence exists because of the coordinated or "military" like atomic movements which must occur [24]. In a way of speaking, a correspondence means that each atom in the parent has a "predestined" position in the product [25].

According to the Bain correspondence shown in fig. 5, the pure distortion which generates martensite from the fcc parent is

$$\mathbf{B} = \begin{pmatrix} \sqrt{2}a/a_0 & 0 & 0 \\ 0 & \sqrt{2}a/a_0 & 0 \\ 0 & 0 & c/a_0 \end{pmatrix} \tag{2}$$

expressed with respect to the orthogonal axes defining the fcc unit cell. The principal axes are parallel to the delineated bct unit cell. For the fcc–bct (or bcc) transformation in iron alloys, when typical lattice parameters results are substituted for a_0, a, and c representative numerical values are

$$\mathbf{B} = \begin{pmatrix} 1.12 & 0 & 0 \\ 0 & 1.12 & 0 \\ 0 & 0 & 0.8 \end{pmatrix}. \tag{3}$$

Apart from its merits, the distortion proposed by Bain is inconsistent with a fundamental piece of evidence — that the habit plane is invariant, i.e., undistorted and unrotated. This is readily seen from the numerical values of the principal distortions η_i in eq. (3). As such the Bain distortion would provide only cones of unextended lines centered about the z axis. It is readily shown

that for a pure distortion to leave a plane invariant, the necessary and sufficient condition is that $\eta_i > 1$, $\eta_j < 1$ and $\eta_k = 1$. That is, one of the principal
distortions must be unity, and the other two must be respectively greater and
less than unity [26,27]. Correspondences in known martensitic transformations
which enable this condition to be fulfilled by the implied distortion are not
usual, and thus pure distortions such as the one proposed by Bain for iron
alloys are not in themselves a proper description of martensitic transformations. An exception to this has recently been pointed out by Bywater and
Christian [28], and this work is discussed later.

The present martensite crystallography theories [26,29–31] retain the
notion of a correspondence and Bain-type homogeneous strain but also incorporate an additional distortion to meet the requirement that the habit plane
be undistorted. Since the necessary lattice change is brought about by the
Bain distortion, any additional distortion is restricted to a lattice invariant
process or shear, such as slip or twinning. It can be shown mathematically that
a simple shear coupled with a homogeneous distortion such as the Bain strain
provides for an undistorted plane, if the plane, direction, and magnitude of
the simple shear are unique [27].

It is useful here to introduce an analogy to clarify the previous points. Considering, for example, the fcc to bct transformation as in iron alloys, a hypothetical unit sphere of the parent phase is transformed into an ellipsoid of
revolution as a result of the Bain distortion (eq. (2)). An undistorted contact
plane between the initial sphere and final ellipsoid does not exist because of
the relative magnitude of the principal distortions, as already pointed out. If
now the simple shear is properly chosen, as a result of its occurrence the
ellipsoid can be sheared into tangency with the initial sphere, the diametrically
opposed points of tangency defining a net principal distortion of value unity.
Thus, the necessary conditions for an undistorted contact plane (habit plane)
can be met as a consequence of the *two* distortions. A two-dimensional analogy
is given in fig. 6, showing the undistorted planes AC and BD. Note that these
planes although undistorted are rotated relative to their original positions, i.e.,
BD came from B′D′, and are thus not invariant planes, since invariant planes
are undistorted *and* unrotated. Therefore, in addition to the Bain distortion
and simple shear, a rigid body rotation must be incorporated into a overall
theoretical description.

The basic equation of the crystallography theories [26,29–31] is

$$P_1 = R\overline{P}B \qquad\qquad (4)$$

where B is the Bain distortion, $\overline{P}$ is a simple shear which is taken in the mathe-

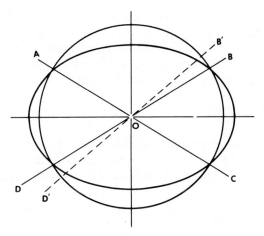

Fig. 6. Two dimensional example showing that even if a homogeneous distortion results in undistorted planes AOC and BOD, these planes are not invariant (undistorted and unrotated) unless a rigid body rotation is employed to restore, for example, BOD to its initial position B′O′D′ [2] .

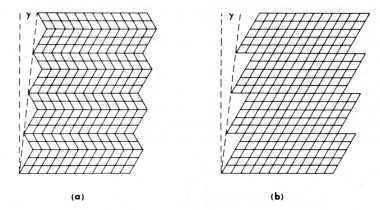

(a)   (b)

Fig. 7. Schematic representation of the mathematical equivalence of twinning (a) and slip (b). The same effective shear angle, γ, is involved in each case [2] .

matical sense to occur after the Bain distortion, $\mathbf{R}$ is a rigid body rotation, and $\mathbf{P}_1$ is the invariant plane strain shape change. $\mathbf{P}_1$, $\mathbf{R}$, $\overline{\mathbf{P}}$ and $\mathbf{B}$ are (3× 3) matrices, and the rotation $\mathbf{R}$ rotates the plane left undistorted by $\overline{\mathbf{P}}\mathbf{B}$ to its initial position. Thus $\mathbf{P}_1 = \mathbf{R}\overline{\mathbf{P}}\mathbf{B}$ is an invariant plane strain.

Although different in the physical sense, the same mathematical result can be produced by slip and twinning [26] , as shown in fig. 7. The same matrix describes both of these situations which are effectively simple shears, the shear angle being γ. Furthermore the same mathematical results are obtained by taking the shear to occur in the parent phase. There are certain computational simplifications when the simple shear is taken to precede the Bain distortion in which case the basic equation becomes

$$P_1 = RBP .\qquad(5)$$

Since P is a simple shear and is of the form $(I+m\mathbf{dp}')$, its inverse $P^{-1} = I - m\mathbf{dp}'$ represents a simple shear of the same magnitude on the same plane, but in the opposite direction [29]. Both P and P^{-1} are invariant plane strains.

It is convenient to rewrite (5), in the form

$$P_1 P_2 = RB\qquad(6)$$

where $P_2 = P^{-1}$. Since both P_1 and P_2 are invariant plane strains, their product, RB, is an invariant line strain, S, defined by the planes which are invariant to P_1 and P_2 [29]. Once S is known, all the crystallographic features of a given transformation can be predicted [29–31]. The Bain correspondence and distortion are known from the lattice parameters of the two phases and R can be determined once the plane (p_2') and direction (d_2) of P_2 are assumed. It is beyond the scope of the present account to go into the details of the invariant line strain analysis [29,30]. The important results are stated without proof after noting that the shape strain is $P_1 = I + m_1 d_1 p_1'$ and the simple shear (preceding the Bain distortion) is $P_2 = I + m_2 d_2 p_2'$. In the previous the magnitudes, directions, and planes of the component invariant plane strains are given by m, d, and p. The relevant equations are [2]

$$d_1 = [Sy_2 - y_2]/p_1' y_2\qquad(7)$$

$$p_1 = (q_2' - q_2' S^{-1})/q_2' S^{-1} d_1\qquad(8)$$

where y_2 is any vector lying in p_2' except the invariant line, x, and q_2' is any normal other than n' (the row unit eigenvector of S^{-1}, i.e., $n'S^{-1} = n'$) to a plane containing d_2. The normalization factor for d_1 in (7) is $1/m_1$, and thus P_1, m_1, d_1 and p_1' are determined. The matrix R is determined from the condition that x and n' which are displaced by the Bain distortion must be invariant. R defines the orientation relationship (within any small region of the martensite plate not involving P_2) [29–31]. Thus the assumed correspondence and lattice parameters fix B; the assumption of p_2' and d_2 allows R to be

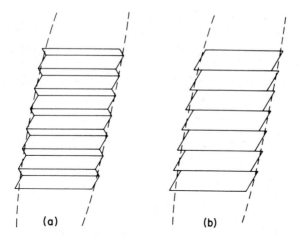

Fig. 8. Idealized representation of internally twinned (a) and slipped (b) martensite plates. These deformations ensure that the interface plane is macroscopically undistorted [2].

determined; $\mathbf{RB} = \mathbf{S}$ defines the elements of $\mathbf{P}_1$ from (5) and (1), and therefore the complete transformation crystallography is predictable in closed form.

The previous description parallels the theoretical formulation given by Bowles and Mackenzie [29–31]; however, the treatments of Wechsler et al. [26] and Bullough and Bilby [32] are entirely equivalent.

According to the previous discussion, martensite plates are expected to be inhomogeneous on a sub-microscopic scale, although the macroscopic shape change is homogeneous only on a larger scale. This is schematically shown in fig. 8.

The martensite transformation crystallography can also be viewed from the surface dislocation approach [32] when the simple shear of the theories corresponds to a slip process. In this case the interface contains a set of parallel dislocations. If these dislocations have a Burgers vector defined in either lattice or are pure screw, the parent-product interface will be glissile [13]. The movement of these dislocations accomplishes the simple shear or lattice invariant deformation. If the transformation inhomogeneity is twinning, interfacial dislocations are not expected. Fig. 9 is an idealized example of these two types of interface.

The theory just described may be justifiably confronted with two demands: (1) a consistent explanation of the transformation crystallography for a given material, and (2) the ability to account for various habit planes and other crystallographic features as in iron alloys.

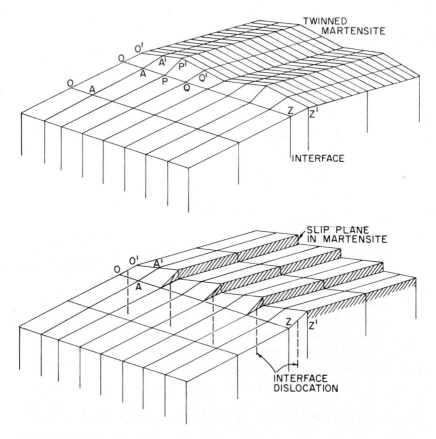

Fig. 9. (Top) Idealized description of the parent-martensite interface for internally twinned martensite. OA and O'A' are corresponding lattice vectors in the parent and one product (twin) orientation. PQ and P'Q' are corresponding vectors in the parent and other product orientation. (Bottom) Idealized description of the formation of internally slipped (single crystal) martensite. OA and O'A' are corresponding lattice vectors, and OZ and O'Z' are identical habit plane vectors. If the interface dislocations have a Burgers vector defined in either lattice or are pure screw the interface will be glissile and the movement of these dislocations accomplishes the simple shear (lattice invariant deformation) of the crystallographic theory [13].

For the fcc to bct transformation in Fe-22%Ni-0.8%C [26] and Fe-7%Al-2%C [19] and the fcc to bcc transformation in Fe-32%Ni [31] and Fe-24%Pt [16] the theoretical predictions are in very good agreement with the experimental habit plane and orientation relationship. By assuming that the martens-

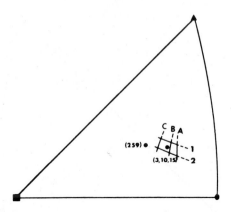

Fig. 10. The habit plane pole (3,10,15) is the mean result obtained by Greninger and Troiano [20] for an Fe-22% Ni-0.8%C alloy. The lines near (3,10,15) correspond to the theoretical predictions of Wechsler et al. obtained by assuming that the bct martensite is internally twinned on (112) [$\bar{1}\bar{1}1$]. Lines A, B and C represent different assumptions for the transformation volume change ratio (1.03, 1.04 and 1.05, respectively) and lines 1 and 2 are lines of constant axial ratio, being respectively 1.00 and 1.08. All predictions are near the observed habit plane pole [2].

ite is internally twinned on a $(112)_m$ plane (twinning direction [$\bar{1}\bar{1}1$]) or equivalently that the simple shear occurs on (101) [$\bar{1}01$]$_p$ in the parent phase*, the predicted habit plane comes very close to the mean experimental value $(3,15,10)_p$ as shown in fig. 10. The orientation relationship predictions are equally good, and more recent work [17] verifies that the theoretical and experimental magnitudes and directions of the shape strain are in good agreement. And finally, the predicted substructure consisting of $(112)_m$ twins is observed by transmission electron microscopy [33−36]. The unique variants of $\{112\}_m$ and $\{3,10,15\}_p$ go together as the theory requires. That is, a particular variant of $\{112\}_m$ predicts a particular variant of $\{3,10,15\}_p$, etc.

Within the theoretical framework of the original theory there have been two approaches to account for varying crystallographic features. These have most immediate bearing on iron alloys where the habit plane variation is considerable, although the principles involved are general. The explanation offered by Wechsler et al. [37,38] is that different habit planes and orientation relationships, etc., may be explained by varying the plane and direction of $\mathbf{P}_2$ (eq. (6)). On the other hand Bowles and Mackenzie [29−31] contended that (for iron alloys) $\mathbf{p}_2'$ and $\mathbf{d}_2$ were always the $\{112\} \langle \bar{1}\bar{1}1 \rangle_m$ twinning elements but that the inter-

---

* Subscripts p and m refer to the parent and martensitic phases respectively.

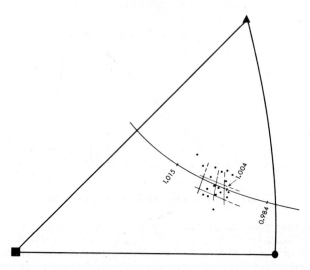

Fig. 11. Experimentally determined habit planes for Fe-32.5%Ni, for which the mean result is approximately $\{3,10,15\}_p$. The predictions of the Bowles-Mackenzie theory [31] (see text) as a function of the dilatation parameter, δ, follow the curved line [2]. The gridwork is the same as described for fig. 10.

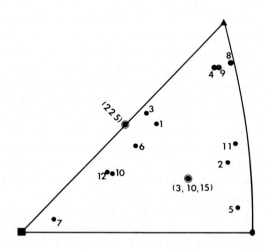

Fig. 12. Habit plane predictons for iron alloys [26] obtained by assuming that the martensite is internally slipped on (011) or equivalently that the parent phase undergoes slip on (111) [2].

face (habit) plane may depart from the exact invariant plane strain condition for certain transformations. The degree of departure was given by a dilation parameter δ, which varied from 1.000 (in which case the interface plane is invariant) to ≈ 1.015. According to their formulation

$$P_1 P_2 = \delta\, R B \tag{9}$$

and the scalar parameter δ represents a uniform expansion or contraction. The Bowles-Mackenzie predictions are given in fig. 11. A continuous variation of the habit plane occurs as δ increases and for $\delta = 1.000$ the predicted habit plane is $(3,10,15)_p$ as with the analysis of Wechsler et al.

The habit plane predictions of Wechsler et al. [38] taking the simple shear to occur on $\{110\}_m$ (equivalent to $\{111\}_p$) rather than $\{112\}_m$ are shown in fig. 12. More extensive calculations involving many different planes and directions for P_2 have been carried out more recently [39].

Considering other experimental information [15] is appears that neither the dilatation approach nor the one of varying elements of P_2 produces satisfactory agreement between theory and experiment. In addition, experiments [17,18] have shown that δ cannot be as large as 1.015. It thus appears that the transformation crystallography is more complicated for habit planes in iron alloys away from $\{3,10,15\}_p$; this is particularly so for the $\{225\}_p$ habit plane found in a number of alloys.

2.2. Crystallography theory involving multiple shears

Since the original invariant plane theories appeared, a number of calculations have been carried out, particularly with reference to the $\{225\}_p$ transformation. Both the dilatation parameter, δ, and the elements of p_2' and d_2 have been varied at the same time [14,15,39–41]. But again, predictions in the light of observed features were not satisfying. Further attempts were made by introducing what can be called a "sigma shear" into the theory. Accordingly, the inhomogeneous shear was expressed with respect to a direction in common to two planes (like the phenomenon of pencil glide in dislocation theory) with a parameter, σ, which gives relative weights to the two participating planes. As before, in consideration of observed crystallographic features for certain problem transformations such as the $\{225\}_p$ case in steels, the predictions were lacking [14,15,41].

In parallel with the theoretical difficulties just described, it is of interest that transmission electron microscopy studies of $\{225\}$ martensites indicate rather complex substructures, in contrast to the rather simple arrays of $(112)_m$ transformation twins which have been consistently verified in ferrous martensites for which the habit plane is $\{3,10,15\}_p$ [41]. Despite arguments that the more complex substructures found in non-$\{3,10,15\}$ martensites may be due to post-transformation accommodation distortions, as contrasted to transformation involved shears, it is natural to extend the original invariant plane theories. Thus, Ross and Crocker (RC) [42], Acton and Bevis (AB) [43], and Bowles and Dunne (BD) [17] suggested almost simultaneously that the original single shear of the theories be replaced by a combination of shears. These newer formulations will now be discussed.

The treatments of RC and AB involving two unrestricted shears are perfectly general in scope and involve, basically, the replacement of the original single shear by two unrestricted shears. The equation central to the RC and AB approaches is

$$P_1 = RBS_2S_1 \tag{10}$$

where R, B and P_1 have the same meanings as before, and S_2 and S_1 are simple shears which replace the single shear, P_2, of eq. (1). Since P_1, as before, must be an invariant plane strain, one of its principal distortions must be unity, and this us assured by the determinantal condition

$$|P_1'P_1 - I| = 0 . \tag{11}$$

Considering eq. (10), this can be written as $|Z - I| = 0$ where

$$Z = S_1'S_2'B'BS_2S_1 \tag{12}$$

and R is eliminated in transposition. Since the planes and directions of the shears S_1 and S_2 are assumed, the only unknowns in Z are the magnitudes s_1 and s_2 of the component shears. Eq. (12) thus defines the magnitudes s_1 and s_2 for which an invariant plane strain can exist and can be used to express the elements of the shape strain in terms of the diagonal entries Z_{ii} of the matrix Z according to

$$Z_{ii} = \delta^2 + 2\delta(u_ih_i) + 3 . \tag{13}$$

In this equation δ is the magnitude of the shape strain and u_i and h_i are, respectively, components of vectors defining the shape strain direction and the habit plane normal. The magnitudes s_1 and s_2 are obtained by manipulating eq. (12). From Acton and Bevis the resulting equation is

$$As_2^2s_1^2 + Bs_2^2s_1 + Cs_2s_1^2 + Ds_2^2 + Es_1^2$$

$$+ Fs_2s_1 + Gs_2 + Hs_1 + I = 0 \tag{14}$$

which establishes a necessary condition on the values of s_1 and s_2 for $\mathbf{P}_1$ to be an invariant plane strain. The coefficients A, B, C, etc., in eq. (14) are all combinations of the principal distortions of the Bain strain and the vector components of the two shear planes and directions. In general, there are two values of s_2 for each of s_1 and vice versa and eq. (14) is satisfied over a continuous range of these magnitudes once the shear magnitude limits for s_2 and s_1 have been established. Having obtained s_1 and s_2 the elements of Z can be evaluated and by equating corresponding terms of $\mathbf{P}_1'\mathbf{P}_1$ from Z, six equations are obtained in five unknowns which specify the invariant plane strain, $\mathbf{P}_1$.

It is to be noted that each pair of shear magnitudes s_1 and s_2 gives rise to one value of the magnitude of the invariant plane strain and to two solutions for the plane and the direction of the invariant plane strain. Since two values of s_2 are associated with each value of s_1 (and vice versa) there are thus four solutions for the invariant plane strain (as in the original theories). Note that as input data the magnitude of one of the shears, say s_1, is fixed and two values of the other are calculated.

In the double shear analysis the orientation relationship is determined from the matrix $\mathbf{R}$ according to

$$\mathbf{R} = \mathbf{P}_1\mathbf{S}_1^{-1}\mathbf{S}_2^{-1}\mathbf{B}^{-1} . \tag{15}$$

Thus $\mathbf{R}$ is determined as a residue.

In practice, the crystallographic predictions of the double shear theory are calculated as a function of incremental variations in s_1, having assumed the planes and directions for the component shears.

In applications of the double shear theory to transformations in steels, twinning on $(112)_m$, which has been observed by transmission electron microscopy, has been retained as one of the component shears, and the "supplementary" shear has been chosen from physically realizable slip and twinning modes in the austenite and martensite.

The first applications of the double shear theory [42,43] employed a nonexhaustive number of shear systems. At first sight, it appeared that predictions were in reasonable agreement with experimentally observed features. However, a detailed analysis of these predictions showed inconsistencies when the observed crystallographic variants of the habit plane, orientation relationship, and direction of the shape strain were mutually considered or when specific

numerical values (i.e., the magnitude of the shape strain) were viewed [41].
Further calculations employing additional shear systems were equally unfruit-
ful, and it was concluded that the double shear theory does not adequately
account for the $\{225\}_p$ transformation in steels [41,44]. Further extensions
of the combinations of input data were made by considering a given shear to
result from a shear on two planes containing a common direction [41,44].
That is, the two shears S_1 and S_2 were replaced by shears on four planes in
two directions. A given net shear on two planes containing a common direction
was determined by the parameters ρ and σ. But even these additional flexibili-
ties did not result in significant improvements between predicted and experimental quantities.

It remains, however, that even with guided insight, an infinite number of
shear combinations could be considered, and thus the task is virtually endless,
even with the aid of computers. A different approach was therefore taken by
Dunne and Wayman [44], who recognized that the strain $S_2 S_1$ must be an
invariant line strain, the invariant line being defined by the line of intersection
of the two shear planes. If the double shear theory is indeed applicable, then
the matrix product $(RB)^{-1} P_1 = S_2 S_1$ should also be an invariant line strain.
Since B is known from the lattice parameters and correspondence, R from the
experimental orientation relationship, and P_1 from the observed shape strain,
these "experimental" matrices, in principle, when multiplied should yield an
invariant line strain as determined from eigenvalue analysis. Accordingly,
allowance for experimental errors was made by computer "perturbations" and
over 200 "experimental" matrices were analyzed. In a few cases, the strains
$(RB)^{-1} P_1$ were indeed invariant line strains, a seemingly encouraging result.

An invariant line strain, as the result of two invariant plane strains, possesses
certain unique properties [29]. Given the invariant line strain and one of the
two component strains, the factorization in unique and the remaining strain is
determined. From the various invariant line strains resulting from experimental
data and computer variations, Dunne and Wayman [44] concluded that the
component strains must be generally irrational. If one of the component shears
was chosen to be consistent with the shear direction $[\bar{1}01]_p$ (i.e., martensite
internally twinned on $(112)_m$, in accord with experiments) the remaining shear
was clearly irrational. They therefore concluded that although the double shear
theory gives better predictions than the original single shear theories, it doe not
provide a completely satisfactory description of the crystallography of $\{225\}$
martensite, relative to the success of the single shear theory as applied to the
$\{3,10,15\}$ transformation.

2.3. *The plastic accommodation model and multiple shears*

Further attempts to explain the crystallography of $\{225\}$ martensite were made by Bowles and Dunne [17], who introduced the plastic accommodation model, In this case the shape strain is given by

$$\mathbf{P}_1 = \mathbf{RBC^{-1}P}. \tag{16}$$

In the above, $\mathbf{C}$ is a complementary shear and $\mathbf{P}$ is a "plastic" strain. Effectively the model involves three shears which occur, in general, on irrational planes but which can be resolved into rational component shears. The shear $\mathbf{C}$ occurs on any plane containing the $[\bar{1}01]_p$ direction and can be regarded as a combination of twinning on $(101)_p$ and slip on $(1\pm11)_p$. $\mathbf{P}$ consists of two shears in rational directions but on irrational planes, each of which can be represented by combining two $(111)_p$ planes.

The plastic accommodation model is not a general theory and applies only to the specific case where the habit plane is *(hhl)*. It has been applied with some success to Fe-C and Fe-Mn-C steels [17], but the predictions for an Fe-Cr-Mn-C steel are not encouraging [18,41]; for example, the predicted habit plane is some $4°$ from the mean experimental result.

2.4. *Some features of theories involving numerous shears*

Although for the $\{225\}$ case in steels the shortcomings of the double shear and plastic accommodation approaches are to be noted, the predictions in both cases are closer to the observed crystallography than previously has been possible. Thus, both theory and experiment (transmission electron microscopy) point to a more complex substructure. The same is inferred from recent work on martensite in Cu-15%Sn [45] from which it was concluded that neither the single shear nor double shear theories could explain the observed shape strain.

It seems that additional shears, i.e.,

$$\mathbf{P}_1 = \mathbf{RBS}_n \ldots \mathbf{S}_2\mathbf{S}_1 \tag{17}$$

will give even better predictions; however, the multiple shear theories are complex and provide no obvious selection rules for the initial choice of shear elements. For this, extremely detailed electron microscopy is required in the future. But even so, the observations are not straightforward because some of the inhomogeneities appearing in martensite plates, such as $\{011\}$ twins in Fe-C martensites [46] may be post-transformation deformations which are not related to the transformation mechanism per se. Another criticism [41] of the double (or multiple) shear theory is that the orientation relationship is not determined by first principles, but rather, referring to eq. (11), as a matrix product:

$$R = P_1 S_1^{-1} S_2^{-1} B^{-1} .$$ (18)

The multiple shear theories, however, can be subjected to eigenvalue analysis. This was not possible for the original single shear theories according to which $(RB)^{-1}P_1$ should be a shear. The eigenvalues are not distinct for a shear, and thus the matrix cannot be diagonalized.

Finally, a few comments on the order of shears may be appropriate. A simple interchange of S_2 and S_1 in eq. (10) is not ordinarily permissible. The shears must be suitably modified when the order is changed. For example, any given strain, S, can be written as the product of two strains, S_1 and S_2 (which are not necessarily invariant plane strains) [3]. Thus, for example

$$S = S_1 S_2 = (SS_2 S^{-1}) S_1$$
$$= (S_1 S_2 S_1^{-1}) (S_1) .$$ (19)

3. Applications of electron microscopy to various transformations

3.1. *The fcc to bcc transformation in ferrous alloys*

The excellent agreement between theoretical predictions and experimental observations for the $\{3,10,15\}_p$ transformation in Fe-22%Ni-0.8%C and Fe-~32%Ni alloys has been pointed out. Essentially similar crystallographic features (i.e., habit plane, orientation relationship, etc.) are also exhibited by certain Fe-Al-C alloys with M_s temperatures below room temperature. In this regard, we can consider an Fe-7%Al-2%C alloy, which has been extensively studied by optical metallography, X-ray diffraction, and transmission electron microscopy and diffraction [19]. Fig. 13 is a transmission electron micrograph showing four martensite plates, $m_1 - m_4$, and the surrounding austenite matrix, a. The inserts, (a) and (b), represent selected area diffraction patterns taken respectively from the encircled parent phase austenite (A) and the martensite (B). The transmission diffraction patterns allow the austenite-martensite orientation relationship to be obtained within the limitations of electrons diffraction. The fine striations seen in plate m_2 correspond to internal $(112)_m$ transformation twins 150–200 Å in width, as indicated by the diffraction pattern (b). The thinness of the twins gives rise to the observed relaxation of

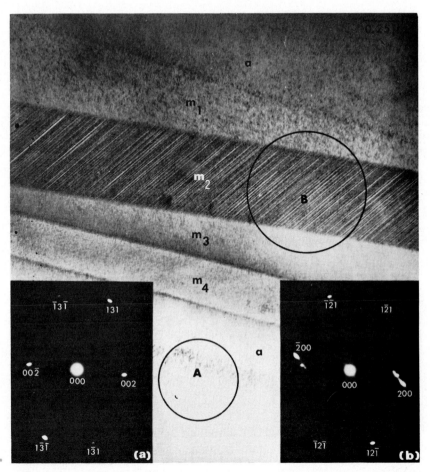

Fig. 13. Transmission electron micrograph showing four martensite plates (m_1-m_4) and retained austenite matrix (a) in Fe-7%Al-2%C alloy [19]. The inserts to the left and right are respectively transmission diffractions patterns from the encircled austenite (A) and martensite (B) regions. See text for discussion.

the Laue conditions (streaking). Plate m_2 is to be compared to the idealized schematic appearance of a martensite plate, due to the inhomogeneous shear of the theory, as shown earlier in fig. 8. Analysis of fig. 13 shows that the specific twin plane and habit plane variants are respectively $(112)_m$ and $(3,15,10)_p$. These two variants are mutually consistent within the framework of the crystallography theory, where for the $\{3,10,15\}_p$ transformation, the inhomogeneous

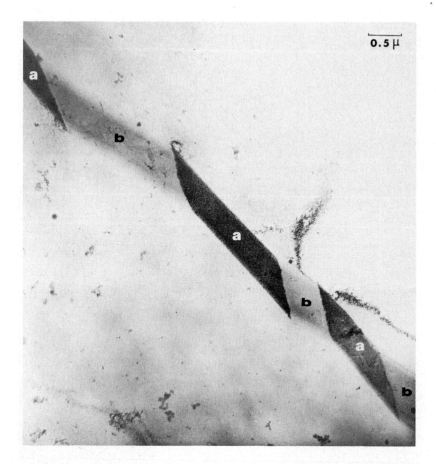

Fig. 14. Transmission electron micrograph showing zig-zag array produced by martensite plates of two habit plane variants in Fe-7%Al-2%C alloy [19]. Only alternate plates (a) are in strong Bragg contrast.

shear is taken as twinning on $\{112\}_m$, and thus the success of the phenomenological theory is also borne out by transmission electron microscopy and diffraction.

Fig. 13 also shows other martensite plates (m_1, m_3 and m_4) with no apparent substructure. These plates have crystallographically equivalent, but different habit planes (and hence different crystallographic variants of the orientation relationship), and as a consequence of the lattice orientation difference the substructure is not in strong Bragg contrast. Fig. 14 also for Fe-7%Al-2%C makes this point even more clear. Although internal twins are not in contrast in either case, martensite plates (a) of one habit plane variant are in relatively strong contrast while plates (b) of the same habit plane variant (but different from (a)) are barely discernible above background (austenite) contrast. These examples make it clear that a specimen tilting stage is required to reorient particular regions of a given specimen for a proper assessment of the substructure and other details.

3.2. *The fcc to bcc transformation in Fe-~25at.%Pt alloys*

A fcc to bcc martensitic transformation occurs in disordered Fe-Pt alloys of

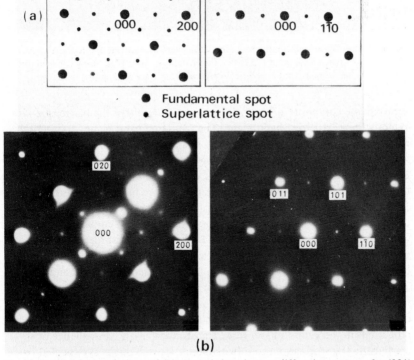

Fig. 15. Predicted (a) and observed (b) transmission electron diffraction patterns for (001) [left] and ($\bar{1}\bar{1}1$) [right] reciprocal lattice sections in martensite formed in an ordered Fe$_3$Pt alloy [48]. It is inferred from the superlattice reflections that the Bain correspondence applies.

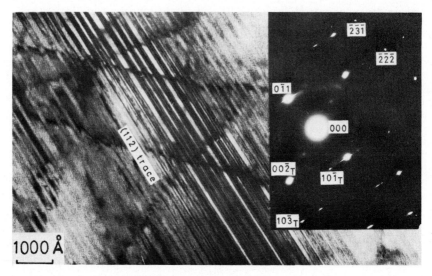

Fig. 16. Transmission electron micrograph and selected area diffraction pattern taken from ordered Fe_3Pt martensite plate [48]. The fine striations are $(112)_m$ transformation twins, and the habit plane (not in the field of view) from trace analysis is $(3, 15, 10)_p$.

approximate composition Fe_3Pt. It has been verified that the martensite also exhibits the $\{3,10,15\}_p$ habit plane. The measured habit plane, orientation relationship, and shape deformation for this case are in outstandingly good agreement with the corresponding theoretically predicted quantities [16], and the results obtained probably constitute one of the most convincing cases that the phenomenological theory is well founded. More recently, it has been found [47] that the austenite formed from ordered (Cu_3Au type) alloys of composition near Fe_3Pt transforms into martensite (at lower M_s temperatures, however) with crystallographic features identical to those of the disordered alloys. Tadaki and Shimizu [48] studied the parent-martensite transformation in ordered Fe_3Pt alloys by transmission electron microscopy and diffraction and in so doing took advantage of the ordering (it is well established that ordered phases remain ordered upon transformation) to suggest that the Bain correspondence clearly applies to this nominally fcc-bcc transformation. That is, superlattice reflections in the parent phase were "transformed", as a consequence of the martensitic transformation, to other superlattice reflections as expected from the Bain correspondence. Figs. 15a and 15b show the predicted and observed transmission diffraction patterns for both (001) and (111) reciprocal lattice sections. Fig. 16 [48] is a transmission electron micrograph and corresponding selected area diffraction pattern (insert) from the martensite formed ordered Fe_3Pt. The internal striations are $(112)_m$ transformation twins (see diffraction pattern) and from trace analysis, the interface plane (not within the field of view) is $(3,15,10)_p$. These variants are mutually consistent, theoretically, and such observations parallel those for a "disordered" transformation, e.g., Fe-7%Al-2%C [19].

3.3. The fcc to bcc transformation in Fe-Ni alloys

The austenite-martensite transformation crystallography in Fe-Ni alloys containing ~29–33%Ni is similar to that observed in other ferrous materials which exhibit the $\{3,10,15\}_p$ transformation. Although the habit plane in these alloys is slightly composition dependent, the martensite substructure is very composition (and hence M_s temperature) dependent. It would appear [35,36] that the extent of $(112)_m$ transformation twinning in Fe-Ni martensites depends on the M_s temperature. At high solute contents (i.e., 33%Ni) the martensite plates are completely internally twinned, as is the case for the Fe-Al-C and Fe-Pt alloys mentioned earlier. However, at lower Ni contents, the internal twin density decreases markedly. For example, fig. 17 is a trans-

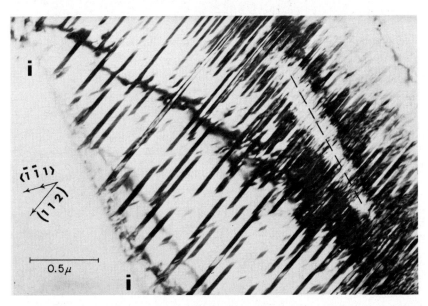

Fig. 17. Transmission electron micrograph of martensite plate in an Fe-32.5%Ni alloy showing a high density of $\{112\}_m$ transformation twins near the central, midrib region (dashed line) of the plate [36].

mission electron micrograph of a martensite plate in Fe-32.5%Ni showing a
high twin density near the central region of the plate (sometimes called the
midrib), which fades out as the martensite-austenite interface is approached,
It is implied in such cases that the mode of inhomogeneous shear changes from
twinning to slip as the plate thickens, although the same plane and direction
are maintained, and therefore the transformation crystallography is unaltered
[36].

    Fe-Ni martensites also reveal other interesting features, such as dislocation
arrays and secondary twins, which have been considered in Part I.

3.4. Transmission microscopy observations of $\{225\}_p$ martensites

    As mentioned earlier, the $\{225\}_p$ martensitic transformation in ferrous
alloys is highly complex, and the agreement between theory and experiment
leaves something to be desired. In the least, the martensite substructures, as

Fig. 18. Transmission electron micrograph taken from large martensite plate in Fe-1.3%C
alloy showing $\{112\}_m$ transformation twins of variable contrast owing to internal strains
and bend contours [49].

observed by transmission electron microscopy and diffraction, appears to be much more complex, compared to the "reference" case of the $\{3,10,15\}_p$ transformation for which good agreement generally obtains, considering the crystallography theory and experimental observations. A number of comments and examples to this effect were given in Part I. In the interest of brevity, these are not repeated here. However, certain observations which tend to reinforce previous conclusions are presented.

The classical $\{225\}_p$ transformation occurs in carbon steels containing from 0.9–1.4at.%C. However, the same habit plane and other crystallography is found in alloy steels with much lower M_s temperatures. Fig. 18 (also presented in Part I) is a transmission electron micrograph of a large martensite plate in an Fe-1.3%C alloy [49]. The vertical striations correspond to $\{112\}_m$ transformation twins, as determined from twinning reflections in transmission electron diffraction patterns. This micrograph is presented to exemplify the type of non-ideal contrast frequently found in the study of martensite by transmission electron microscopy. Fig. 18 shows a number of contrast reversals (i.e., light and dark colored internal twins). In this case, as with many others, it is to be noted that the stresses accompanying the parent-to-martensite transformation result in substantial buckling of thin films and preclude the attainment of ideal two-beam cases for analysis of the observed contrast. This is not always idealized.

In further comparison to the more or less idealized situation which holds for the $\{3,10,15\}_p$, transformation in iron alloys, mention is made of recent work [18] on an Fe-3%Mn-3%Cr-1%C alloy for which the martensite habit plane is near $\{225\}_p$, as determined by both bulk X-ray (two surface analysis) and thin foil (trace analysis) techniques. Despite the apparent constancy in habit plane, the martensite substructure, determined by transmission electron microscopy, was found to very considerably from plate to plate. In general, more than one type of internal inhomogeneity was observed in a given martensite plate, and a "typical" plate was not readily characterized. Fig. 19 is a transmission electron micrograph of a martensite plate in Fe-3%Mn-3%Cr—1%C. Two sets of internal striations can be noted. Trace T_3 corresponds to $(112)_m$ relative to the $(252)_p$ habit plane; trace T_2 appears to be related to and parallel with $(\bar{1}11)_p$ stacking faults in the austenite. However, there are other cases where the internal striations in the martensite, which appear to be related to austenite stacking faults, are actually transformed or displaced as the martensite forms (fig. 20). The displacement of austenite stacking faults by a growing martensite plate represents another method for estimating the martensite shape strain. With respect to the martensite orientation, traces T_1 and T_2 in the martensite plate of fig. 20 correspond, respectively, to $(101)_m$ and $(\bar{1}01)_m$ and it should

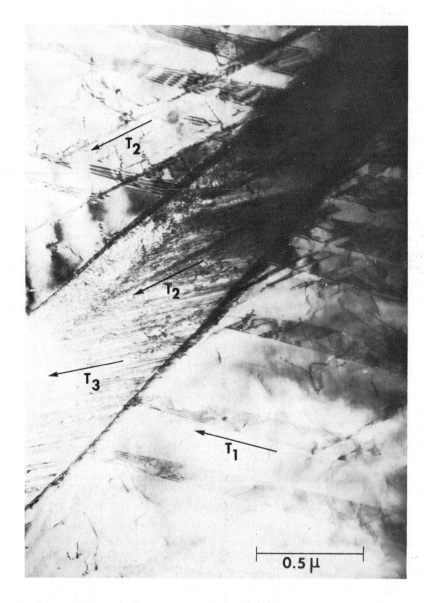

Fig. 19. Transmission electron micrograph of $(252)_p$ martensite plate and surrounding austenite region in Fe-3%Mn-3%Cr-1%C alloy [18]. Traces T_1, T_2 and T_3 respectively correspond to $(111)_p$, $(1\bar{1}1)_p$ and $(112)_m$.

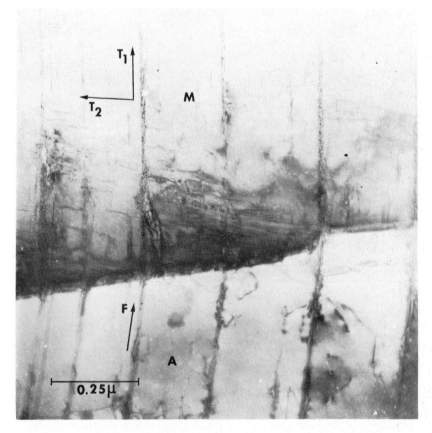

Fig. 20. Transmission electron micrograph of $(252)_p$ martensite plate in Fe-3%Mn-3%Cr-1%C alloy showing $(101)_m$ planar defect continuous with $(111)_p$ stacking faults (T_1) and $(\bar{1}01)_m$ planar defects derived from $(\bar{1}11)_p$ (T_2). The displacement of T_1 by about 10° is consistent with the magnitude of the shape strain.

be noted that $(112)_m$ twins are not seen in this orientation. The striations parallel to T_1 in fig. 20 represent an interesting contrast problem, assuming, as appears to be the case, that $\{111\}_{fcc}$ faults undergo an fcc to bct transformation. Multiple inhomogeneities observed in $\{225\}$ martensite plates are also considered later when transformations in this ferrous martensites are discussed.

Finally, as mentioned in Part I, no discussion of ferrous martensites should conclude without noting the morphological transition from lenticular plates to laths when the alloy content (either interstitial or substitutional) is decreased.

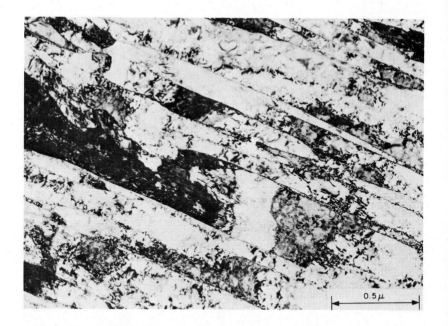

Fig. 21. Transmission electron micrograph showing typical morphology of "lath martensite" in Fe-4%Ni-0.05%C alloy [50].

Fig. 21 is a transmission electron micrograph showing untwinned laths of martensite in an Fe-4%Ni-0.05%C alloy [50]. The plate to lath transition, and, in addition, the characterization of the substructure in lath martensite in the light of the phenomenological theory, requires further investigation before these phenomena are properly understood.

3.5. The formation of TaO_y in oxidized Ta

When Ta is oxidized in an oxygen atmosphere at 400–500°C, an orthorhombic suboxide phase in the form of plates occurs [6]. These plates form from a supersaturated solid solution consisting of O_2 interstitially dissolved in Ta and their habit plane is irrational, $\approx(320)$ relative to the parent phase. This transformation has all the characteristics of a martensitic transformation. Once the cubic Ta lattice dissolves a certain amount of oxygen, it becomes unstable and transforms in a diffusionless manner (interstitial O_2 atoms remaining in phase) to a new orthorhombic phase TaO_y. It is not to be implied that TaO_y formation is an oxidation reaction in the usual sense.

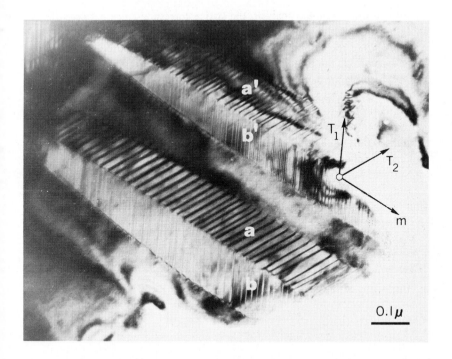

Fig. 22. Transmission electron micrograph showing two pairs of orthorhombic TaO_y plates joined along a pseudo-habit plane (m). Plates a and a' are of the same habit plane variant, whereas plates b and b' are also of the same variant (but different from a and a'). Traces T_1 and T_2 correspond to $\{110\}$ microtwins in the TaO_y [6].

The crystallography of the bcc (oxygen-saturated Ta) to bco (TaO_y) transformation has been studied in considerable detail [6]. The predicted crystallographic features (habit plane, orientation relationship, shape deformation, etc.) assuming that martensite crystallography analysis applies and that the inhomogeneous shear is twinning on $\{110\}_m$ in the product phase are in outstanding agreement with those determined experimentally. Fig. 22 is a transmission electron micrograph showing four TaO_y plates in an oxygen-saturated Ta matrix. Only two crystallographically different habit plane variants are involved. Plates 1 are of the same variant, and plates 2 are of a different variant; these plates have impinged along a pseudo-habit plane during growth. Transmission electron diffraction analysis confirmed that the fine striations within the plates are in fact $\{110\}_m$ twins of the proper theoretical variant consistent with the measured habit plane [6].

In the crystallographic analysis, the lattice correspondence between the two phases is given by the indentity matrix, i.e., the bcc cube axes become the **a**, **b** and **c** axes of the orthorhombic unit cell. From the measured lattice parameters of the two phases the principal distortions are 0.985, 0.964 and 1.087. The first of these is almost unity and the other two are of opposite sign; their magnitudes are such that the Bain distortion for this transformation is itself nearly an invariant plane strain. Therefore, the magnitude of the simple shear to effect an undistorted plane need not be large, and for the case of $\{110\}_m$ internal twinning is 0.0191. The relative volumes of the two twin orientations, taking into account the inclination of the transformation twins with respect to the foil surface, were found to be on the average 10 : 1. This corresponds to a simple shear of magnitude $m_2 = 0.0196$, in excellent agreement with theory (0.0191). Thus, in all respects the formation of TaO_y is consistent with the martensite crystallographic theory [6].

Fig. 23 is a selected area diffraction pattern from the double plates shown in fig. 22. The enlargement to the right is an interesting example of Frauenhofer diffraction [51,52] (near the narrow 1 at the 011 reflection) caused by the thin twins acting as diffraction slits.

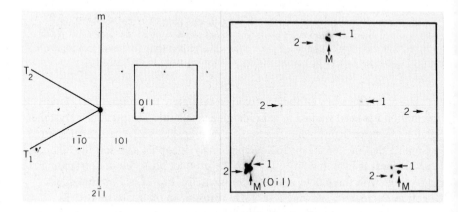

Fig. 23. Selected area diffraction pattern from region shown in fig. 22. The traces of the two sets of twins (T_1, T_2) and the midrib (m) are indicated. The enlargement of the insert, to the right, shows matrix reflections (M), reflections due to plate orientations b and b'(1), and reflections due to plate orientations a and a'(2). Frauenhofer splitting of the diffraction maxima can be seen near the (011) reflection at the arrow near (1) [6].

4. Recent developments

4.1. *Position of carbon atoms in martensite*

Thin foil studies of Fe-6%Mn-1%C steels have been employed [53] to study the positions of carbon atoms in martensite as well as their subsequent redistribution. Specimens while in the austentic state at room temperature ($M_s \approx -100°C$) were thinned to 100 kV electron transparency, placed in an electron microscope cooling stage, and cooled to effect transformation. A typical sequence of events, as indicated by selected area diffraction patterns from martensite is shown in figs. 24a–c. Fig. 24a is a diffraction pattern from freshly formed

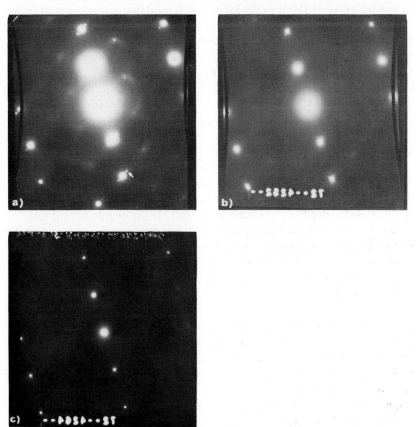

Fig. 24. (a) Transmission diffraction pattern taken near −196°C of freshly formed martensite in Fe-6%Mn-1%C showing extra spots (arrow) due to carbon clustering; (b) Same region after heating to room temperature; (c) Same region after cooling again to −196°C [53].

martensite taken near $-196°C$. The very sharp satellite reflections (indicated by arrow) cannot be indexed with respect to the substitutional atom lattice. When the same specimen is heated to room temperature (requiring about one hour) the extra spots disappear (fig. 24b), and after immediate recooling to $-196°C$ the diffraction patterns (fig. 24c) do not show the extra spots.

Analysis of diffraction patterns such as fig. 24a reveals that the extra spots show a $\frac{1}{6}\{110\}$ periodicity, which in the crystal lattice corresponds to some kind of ordering or clustering of the carbon atoms on each sixth $\{110\}$ plane. The significance of this will be reported pending further investigation [53]. There is some parallel considering the present results and those obtained recently by some Russian workers: In the present case, extra spots are present in freshly formed sub-zero martensite but disappear upon heating to room temperature. Kurdjumov and Khachaturyan [54] report that the tetragonality of freshly formed martensite is abnormally low but increases to nearly the "normal" value upon heating to room temperature. They suggest that some of the carbon atoms in as-formed martensite are in tetrahedral positions and thus do not contribute to tetragonality because of the isotropic strain symmetry of tetrahedal site; however, upon heating to room temperature, where atomic mobility is increased, the tetrahedrally disposed atoms can jump into octahedral sites, thus increasing the tetragonality.

A number of uncertainties remain, however, and in the least further work is required to clarify the electron diffraction observations. One difficulty is that the observed clustering of carbon atoms in $\{110\}$ planes indicates that this effect is probably due to octahedral sites, since $\{110\}$ planes do not contain tetrahedral sites. A second problem is that tetrahedral site occupancy in freshly formed martensite is inconsistent with the expected position of carbon atoms as a direct consequence of the Bain strain.

Observations similar to the above have also been made on an Fe-3%Mn-3%Cr-1%C alloy [55].

4.2. Substructure in thin foil ferrous martensites

The investigation of martensite formed in Fe-6%Mn-1%C thin foil below room temperature [53] has also revealed features which are either peculiar to thin foil martensites or which were previously overlooked in "bulk" martensites observed after thinning. For example, fig. 25 is a transmission electron micrograph (taken at room temperature) from thin foil martensite showing $\{110\}_m$ stacking faults, as determined by trace and projected width analysis. Similarly, fig. 26 shows $\{123\}_m$ stacking faults. The above observations imply that $\{110\}_m$ and $\{123\}_m$ stacking faults may be characteristic of bct and bcc materials.

Fig. 25. Thin foil martensite formed in Fe-6%Mn-1%C alloy showing {110} stacking faults in the bct martensite [55].

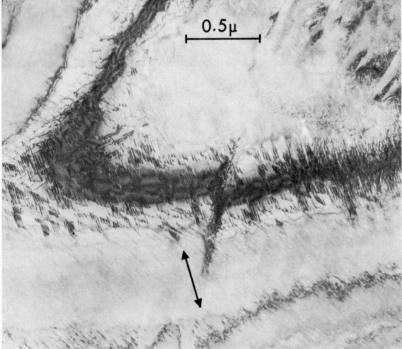

Fig. 26. Thin foil martensite formed in Fe-6%Mn-1%C alloy showing {123} stacking faults [55].

Fig. 27. Segmented {112} twins in thin foil martensite in Fe-6%Mn-1%C alloy. Dark field
micrograph using (112) twin reflection [55].

This foil martensites also show a striking tendency for the fragmentation of
internal $\{112\}_m$ twins, which are presumably transformation twins (inhomogeneous shear). This is seen clearly in fig. 27, a dark field micrograph obtained
using a $\{112\}_m$ twin reflection. Apart from the fragmented nature of the
twins, it should also be noted that some of the regions which are clearly in
twin orientation are not always crystallographically shaped, e.g., the curved
boundaries indicated by the arrows. The interpretation [53] of the crystallography of the twin segments may differ from previous analyses [36,56].

Fig. 28 is another dark field transmission micrograph (using a $\{112\}_m$ twin
reflection) from thin foil martensite formed in Fe-6%Mn-1%C showing very
finely divided twin fragments (~100 Å in size and ~100 Å in spacing) within a
martensite plate. The twin fragments are quite inhomogeneously distributed,
but as before [36] the direction parallel to the fragmentation is $\langle 111 \rangle_m$. At

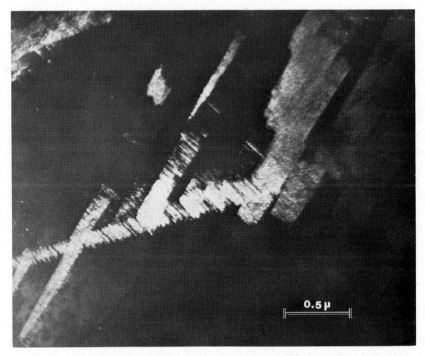

Fig. 28. Thin, segmented {112} twins in thin foil martensite in Fe-6%Mn-1%C. Dark field
image taken using (112) twin reflection [55].

present, the physical reasons (s) for the pronounced fragmentation are not
clear. Nevertheless, the above results indicate that the substructure in thin foil
martensites can be highly complex. Interestingly, the previous examples of
fragmented twins and $\{110\}_m$ and $\{123\}_m$ stacking faults were obtained
from martensites, which in bulk form exhibit the $\{225\}_p$ habit plane. Thus,
both present and previous observations point to the fact that $\{225\}_p$ martensites in ferrous alloys may involve more than one inhomogeneous shear system.

4.3. Results from "experimental variations" in the Bain strain

Two recent investigations [19,28] have shown that the principal distortions
of the Bain strain in ferrous martensitic transformations can be altered significantly by alloying. In both cases, the consequences are in complete accord with
expectations, considering the phenomenological crystallographic theory, and
thus serve to further substantiate the theory.

Bywater and Christian [28] observed the cubic-orthorhombic martensitic transformation in Ti-Ta alloys containing from 23–53wt%Ta. In alloys containing up to 32%Ta, the martensite plates were observed to be internally twinned, i.e., the inhomogeneous shear mode is twinning. However, at higher Ta concentrations the martensite is untwinned. This is explained on the basis that the Bain strain for alloys of these compositions is practically an invariant plane strain per se, and thus there is no necessity for an inhomogeneous shear, i.e., internal twinning. For a Ti-53wt%Ta alloy the principal distortious η_1, η_2 and η_3 are respectively 0.978, 1.026 and 1.000, which indicate that the Bain strain is very close to an invariant plane strain. Note that one of the three principal distortions (eigenvalues) is unity, and the other two are opposite in sign and differ from unity in nearly equal senses.

Whereas the Fe atom is 2.482 Å in diameter the Al atom is substantially larger, 2.862 Å. Consequently, Al expands considerably the Fe lattice. Considering the fcc → bct austenite-martensite transformation in Fe-Al-C alloys [19,57], the effect of the large Al atom (which substitutes for Fe) is to reduce the degree of "upsetting" in the Bain distortion. For an Fe-7wt%Al-2wt%C alloy, the Bain strain is given by

$$
\mathbf{B} = \begin{pmatrix} 1.083 & 0 & 0 \\ 0 & 1.083 & 0 \\ 0 & 0 & 0.873 \end{pmatrix}. \tag{20}
$$

The above can be compared with the fcc → bcc transformation in an Fe-31% alloy for which the lattice correspondence is the same and the Bain strain is given by

$$
\mathbf{B} = \begin{pmatrix} 1.132 & 0 & 0 \\ 0 & 1.132 & 0 \\ 0 & 0 & 0.801 \end{pmatrix}. \tag{21}
$$

Comparing the previous two matrices, it is clear that for the Fe-7%Al-2%C alloy, $\mathbf{B}$ is much closer to the identity matrix than for the Fe-Ni alloy. The Bain strain in Fe-Al-C is thus less "severe" and therefore requires an attendant inhomogeneous shear of relatively low magnitude to produce an undistorted habit plane. Correspondingly, a lower shape strain mahnitude is also expected.

The table below compares the principal distortions (η_i), shape strain magnitude (m_1) and magnitude of the inhomogeneous shear (m_2) for the Fe-7%Al-2%C and Fe-31%Ni alloys, and it is seen that the above mentioned expectations are confirmed

	Fe-7%Al-2%C	Fe-31%Ni
$\eta_1 = \eta_2$	1.083	1.132
η_3	0.873	0.801
m_1	0.138	0.223
m_2	0.162	0.263

The martensite plates in Fe-Al-C alloys are internally twinned on $\{112\}_m$ and other experimental observations are found to be in quite good agreement with the corresponding quantities predicted by the crystallographic theory [19]. Fe-Al-C alloys also present the interesting case where a fine ($\sim$50 Å) perovskite (Fe_3AlC) precipitate forms "epitaxially" in the austenite during quenching (evidently by spinodal decomposition). These precipitates are, in turn, transformed in situ, along with the austenite when martensite forms at sub-zero temperatures [58].

4.4. Phase transformations in β' CuZn alloys

Controversy has existed concerning the nature of the plate-shaped transformation product in Cu$\sim$40%Zn alloys isothermally transformed near 350°C. Among other difficulties, questions have been raised regarding the extent of diffusion (if any) involved during the transformation as well as the appropriateness of the terminology "bainite" which has been applied to this transformation because of certain similarities with the bainite transformation in steels. A recent investigation was thus undertaken to clarify certain issues [8]. In subsequent discussion, the transformation in question is referred to as the $\beta' \rightarrow \alpha_1$ transformation, which is nominally a bcc to fcc transformation.

Bulk crystallographic measurements of the α_1 habit plane, orientation relationship, and shape strain were recently made [8]. The irrational crystallographic features and reproducible surface tilt both indicate that the $\beta' \rightarrow \alpha_1$ transformation, which occurs at temperatures above the well known martensitic transformation, is also martensitic in nature. Transmission electron microscopy observations reveal a fine scale substructure in the α_1 plates. Fig. 29 is a transmission electron micrograph showing the typical appearance of "freshly formed" α_1 plates, while fig. 30 shows the appearance of α_1 plates at a later stage of isothermal transformation. The internal striations seen in the α_1 plates

Fig. 29. Transmission electron micrograph showing freshly formed α_1 plates in Cu-40%Zn alloy after a few seconds of isothermal transformation at 350°C. The internal striations are random stacking faults [8].

in fig. 29 are stacking faults, the density of which decreases substantially upon additional isothermal transformation time. It is also noted from fig. 30 that additional isothermal reaction time results in thicker α_1 plates which exhibit rather irregular interphase boundaries; in particular, the $\alpha_1 - \beta'$ boundary is highly non-planar in regions where the internal stacking faults have evidently "annealed out". It would appear that the $\alpha_1 - \beta'$ interface advances non-crystallographically (e.g., as in recrystallization) after, or concurrent with, the annealing out of the internal faults. Fig. 31 is a selected area diffraction pattern taken from a freshly formed α_1 plate. The 1/3 periodicity in reciprocal space (i.e., two weaker spots equispaced within the main diffraction maxima) indicates that the α_1 plates have a 3R long period stacking structure.

It should be stressed that the *observed* internal faults in the 3R α_1 plates are not considered fundamental to the 3R structure. Theoretically, the 3R structure can be generated by an $a/6 \langle 112 \rangle$ displacement (i.e., stacking shift) on

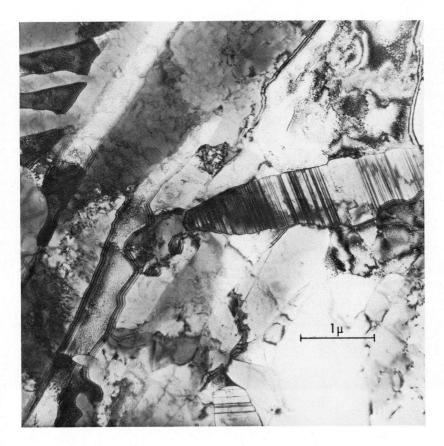

Fig. 30. Some as fig. 29, only isothermally reacted for longer time. Note the annealing out
of faults and the development of an irregular interface [8].

every third close packed {111} plane of the α_1 phase. Accordingly, the stacking
sequence changes from ...ABCABCABC... to ...ABCBCACAB... . Thus, the
"1/3 spots" in the diffraction patterns (i.e., fig. 31) can be ascribed to a periodicity of these ABC stacking modules, each of which is separated by a phase
shift in the fundamental ABCBCACAB unit cell.

The $\beta' \rightarrow \alpha_1$ transformation is considered to be basically a bcc (CsCl) → fcc
martensitic transformation, in which case the mode of inhomogeneous shear
is slip (or equivalently a stacking shift) on {111} planes of the product phase
which is initially fcc (disregarding ordering) after the Bain strain. When analyzed
according to the crystallographic theory of martensitic transformations, the

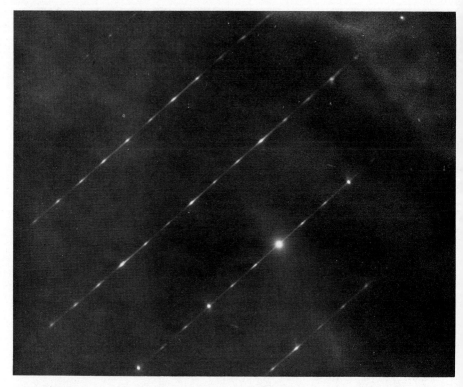

Fig. 31. Transmission diffraction pattern from freshly formed α_1 plate showing 3R, ...ABCBCACAB... stacking sequence [8].

observed habit plane, orientation relationship, etc. are nicely predicted for an inhomogeneous shear on $\{111\}_m$ of magnitude $m_2 = 0.234$, which is equivalent to a shear angle of 13.18°. This is in excellent agreement with the effective shear of 13.26° required for the change in stacking sequence from ...ABCABCABC... to ...ABCBCACAB... . It is thus emphasized, considering the excellent agreement between experiment (habit plane, orientation relationship, surface tilt, and inhomogeneous shear) that in addition to the martensitic nature of the $\beta' \rightarrow \alpha_1$ transformation per se, the observed 3R long period stacking sequence is a direct consequence of the martensitic transformation. That is, the inhomogeneous shear of the martensitic transformation generates the 3R structure. Thus, considering the $\beta' \rightarrow \alpha_1$ transformation in CuZn alloys as well as other similar cases, it would appear that "long period stacking structures" exist only because of a solid state phase transformation. Such structures are evidently extrinsic in nature and are not stable phases formed upon solidification, for example.

Several other aspects of the α_1 phase merit consideration. First random {111} stacking faults are observed in bright field transmission electron microscopy images (fig. 29). However, the density of these faults, which are regarded as "extra", is comparatively low; measurements reveal that the observed fault density represents about one fault on each 12 {111} planes, in contrast to one stacking shift (fault) on every third plane to generate the 3R structure. It appears likely that the "extra" faults are formed by accommodation strains, or else are required in addition to the 3R stacking shifts to produce a macroscopically undistorted habit plane. In any event, the *observed* faults represent a relatively minor component, considering their low density.

The observed internal striations ("extra" or random faults) in the α_1 plates give rise to the continuous streaks observed in the transmission diffraction patterns. In contrast, the regularly spaced stacking shifts (faults) are not observed in bright field images. This situation is analogous to, say, the fcc to hcp transformation in cobalt where formally, the $a/6 \langle 112 \rangle$ faults on every second plane of the fcc phase are invisible because they are intrinsic to the hcp cobalt. However, the stacking shifts on each third plane should be evident in images obtained by combining two of the "1/3 spots" (including principal maxima), in effect, a type of lattice resolution. For the α_1 case, the image should reveal the ABC stacking modules (three {111} planes), each of which is separated by the stacking shifts. The stacking shifts can be regarded as antiphase boundaries between fundamental ABC stacking modules.

Another point, with reference to the 3R α_1 structure is that the required stacking shift is unidirectional. That is, although there are three $a/6 \langle 112 \rangle$ fault directions for a given {111} plane, a little consideration shows that for an ordered alloy (i.e., the CsCl β' parent) only one of the three possible $\langle 112 \rangle$ directions will not disturb the ordering. This is consistent with the fact that the α_1 phase forms via the Bain strain from an ordered (β') parent, which in turn imposes restrictions on the nature of the inhomogeneous shear.

In further support of the martensitic nature of the $\beta' \rightarrow \alpha_1$ transformation is the result that no diffusion takes place during the initial formation of the α_1 plates [59]. However, diffusion does occur at later stages, but this causes disordering, removal of internal faults and the non-crystallographic, recrystallization-type movement of the $\alpha_1 - \beta'$ interface.

Finally, it should be mentioned that the widely studied martensitic transformation in β' brass in Cu~40%Zn which occurs at much lower temperatures than the $\beta' \rightarrow \alpha_1$ transformation is typified by internally twinned martensite plates, in contrast to the 3R stacking shifts (and random faults) found in the

α_1 plates [8]. This is consistent with the fact that internally twinned martensites exhibit the shape memory behavior, whereas the α_1 plates with a non-twinned substructure do not. Although the $\beta' \to \alpha_1$ transformation is also considered to be martensitic, the essential difference is that the α_1 plates, which form at a substantially higher temperature seem to incorporate internal slip (stacking shifts) as the dominant inhomogeneous shear mode in contrast to internal twinning, which apparently operates during the martensitic mode of transformations at substantially lower temperatures.

4.5. Ordering in CuAu thin films

In situ studies of the fcc (disordered) $\to$ CuAu II (orthorhombic) ordering reaction have recently been made using both epitaxial and polycrystalline films ~400 Å in thickness prepared by sputtering [60]. Specimens were heated and cooled within the electron microscope and observed over the temperature range from room temperature to 600°C [61].

Prior to previous work on evaporated Cu-Au thin films [62], Smith and Bowles [7] established that the fcc $\to$ CuAu II reaction is, at least formally, a martensitic transformation, attended by irrational crystallographic features, a substructure (see also ref. [62]) and well-defined surface relief. The application of the martensite crystallography theory gave predictions in excellent agreement with the observed crystallographic features. The fcc $\to$ CuAu II transformation exhibits C-curve kinetics, and the bried incubation time observed presents this transformation as a convenient one for studying the details of nucleation. This seemed an even more attractive possibility when preliminary in situ experiments revealed that there are no major kinetic differences comparing thin foils and bulk specimens [61].

Figs. 32 and 33 show some bright field images and diffraction patterns from epitaxial {001} sputtered films, deposited on NaCl and transformed in situ for various times at 385°C after removal from the substrates. The evolution of a CuAu II "particle" can be seen in figs. 32a–c (marked by arrow). Fig. 32d shows the end result after complete transformation. The diffraction patterns 33a, b, and c correspond to the images seen in figs. 32a, c and d. The internal striations observed within the CuAu II particles are {110} microtwins, which separate CuAu II domains whose **c**-axes are approximately perpendicular to each other. **c**-axes both parallel to and perpendicular to the film plane are found, although CuAu II variants with **c**-axes perpendicular to the film plane were more readily nucleated. The mean CuAu II habit plane (e.g., platelet X′ in fig. 32d is near $\{110\}_{fcc}$, which is the same as that observed when the transformation occurs in bulk crystals [7]. Moreover, both thin films and bulk specimens result in the preferential clustering of four near-{011} habit plane

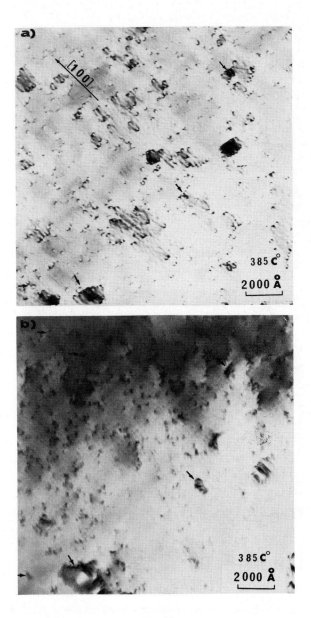

Fig. 32.

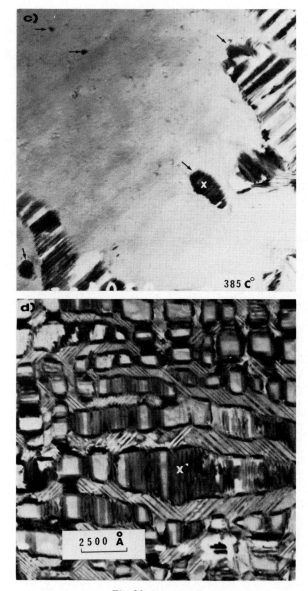

Fig. 32. (continued).

Fig. 32. Sequence showing formation of CuAu II in sputtered film at 385°C in the electron
microscope. See text [61].

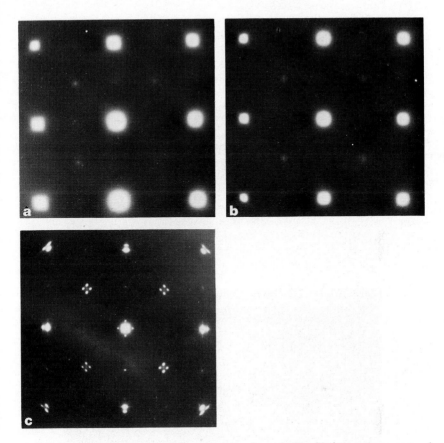

Fig. 33. Diffraction patterns taken from specimen shown in figs. 32, a, b, and c correspond to images a, c, and d of fig. 32 [61].

variants. Thus, the transformation crystallography is not substantially relaxed (i.e., completely two-dimensional) in thin foils, and the tendency still exists to form an invariant plane.

The transmission electron diffraction patterns show that CuAu I (fct) may be the actual nucleus for the CuAu II structure. This is inferred from the faint superlattice reflection at the center of the four satellite reflections at the {110} positions (fig. 33b). These central spots disappear after the isothermal transformation time has increased. The same behavior was also found for polycrystalline thin films and is consistent with the fact that the CuAu II unit cell is basically made up of ten CuAu I unit cells.

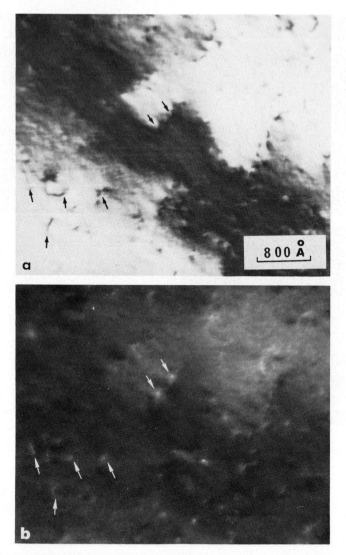

Fig. 34. Bright field (a) – dark field (b) pair showing nucleation of CuAu II at dislocations [61].

A decided preference for the nucleation of CuAu II at dislocations was found. Figs. 34a and b are a bright field-dark field pair ((110) reflection) showing small regions of CuAu II (or CuAu I nuclei) formed at dislocations. The dislocations

Fig. 35. Transmission electron micrograph showing continuity of 20 Å CuAu II domains across {110} twin boundaries T–T [61].

found in the fcc CuAu are purely screw in nature [62] (**b** = ⟨011⟩) and a detailed analysis of the coherent formation of the CuAu II within the dislocation strain fields has been made [61]. The results are in good agreement with the observation that nucleation always occurs to one side of the dislocation core; that is, dislocation-enhanced ordering is "one-sided". Even though nucleation is favored at dislocations in this films, the amount of time necessary to complete the transformation appears to be the same in both films and bulk crystals.

In addition to providing useful information on nucleation, sputtered CuAu films also serve as convenient specimens for the study of antiphase boundary arrangements. For example, fig. 35 is a bright field electron micrograph showing 20 Å antiphase boundaries (short striations) and {110} twin boundaries (long striations). The continuity of the antiphase boundaries across the twin boundaries gives rise to a herringbone structure as is seen. Fig. 36 is an example of CuAu II formed directly from CuAu I. The boundaries denoted 1 are antiphase boundaries within the CuAu I matrix, while the closed loops, designated 2, 20 Å apart, correspond to regions of CuAu II formed within the CuAu I.

Details on the formation of CuAu films by sputtering show that the overall composition is preserved by sputtering [60]. Moreover, the growth sequence

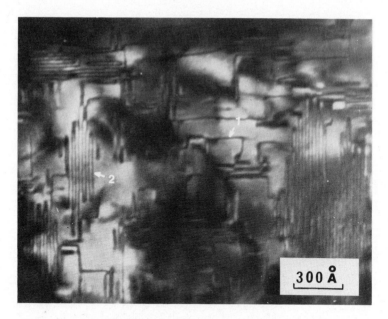

Fig. 36. Transmission electron micrograph showing the formation of CuAu II (closed loops designated 2) from CuAu I. Antiphase boundaries in the CuAu I are indicated by (1) [61].

for sputtered films closely parallels the classical behavior of evaporated films [63], involving nucleation, coalescence, a channel stage, and finally complete continuity.

4.6. High voltage electron diffraction and microscopy

The use of high voltage electron microscopy (HVEM) for the observation of thick specimens and for in situ studies of irradiation damage is well known and widespread. However, the advantages of high accelerating voltages for selected area diffraction are less commonly realized. As is known, a lack of correspondence exists between the apparent area contributing to diffraction and the area actually selected by the intermediate (selector) aperture [64]. Since the error is proportional to the objective lens spherical aberration coefficient, C_s, and the cube of the aperture angle, α, it follows that a significant reduction in error can be obtained at the lower Bragg angles characteristic of higher voltages and that it is therefore possible to take diffraction patterns from much smaller areas.

Shimizu and coworkers [65] have conducted "selected microarea diffraction" studies at 500 and 650 kV by using an electron microscope with a five-

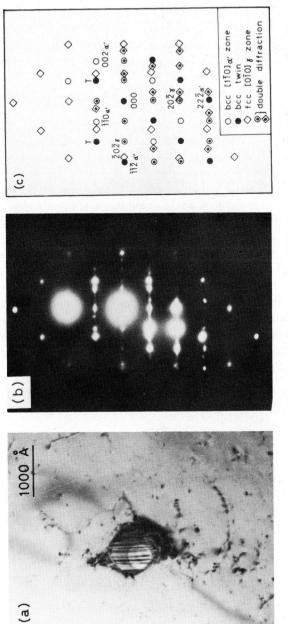

Fig. 37. (a) Transmission micrograph (650 KV) showing small particle of Fe precipitated in a Cu matrix. The diffraction pattern (b) which is indexed in (c) was taken from region indicated. The twinning reflections indicate that the iron particle has undergone a fcc to bcc martensitic transformation [66].

stage imaging lens system (objective, intermediate, first and second projectors, and supplemental lenses). A "supplemental" lens is located between the objective and intermediate lenses and permits areas 200–500 Å in diameter to be selected. The purpose of the supplemental lens (magnification 0–4X) is to allow the use of an intermediate aperture typically $10\,\mu$ in diameter for the selection of a specimen area 200–500 Å in size. For a reflection where $1/d = 1$ Å^{-1} the error in correspondence is 50 Å at 650 kV (80 Å at 500 kV). Two examples of microarea diffraction at high voltage follow.

Fig. 37a is a bright field image showing a small iron particle precipitated in a copper matrix [66]. Internal striations in the iron particles are to be noted. It has previously been reported [67] that the striations are thin discs of bcc martensite formed within fcc iron particles. However, the microarea area analysis shows that another interpretation is required. Fig. 37b is a selected area diffraction pattern taken from the round region in fig. 37a which was obtained by double exposure to reveal the aperture. The indexing of the diffraction pattern is given in fig. 37c, from which it has been concluded that the entire iron particle is bcc, the striations representing $\{112\}$ twin-related regions. Evidently the entire particle has undergone a fcc → bcc martensitic transformation, with internal twinning as the mode of inhomogeneous shear. This appears to be the case, even though the necessity to maintain an invariant (habit) plane does not appear to be required in the small particles. The fact that the particles are purely bcc is also deduced from the analysis of isolated particles such as the one shown in fig. 38.

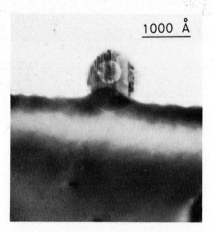

1000 Å

Fig. 38. Isolated Fe particle similar to that shown in fig. 37 used to show that the particle is not fcc (650 kV) [66].

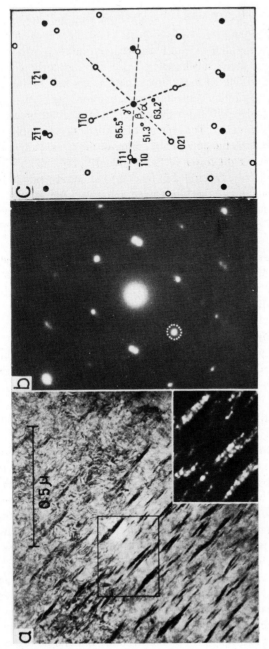

Fig. 39. (a) Electron micrograph (650 KV) of tempered martensite in 0.79%C steel showing ϵ carbide precipitates after aging for 3 days at 150°C. The insert, lower right, is a dark field image taken by using the 021_ϵ reflection. (b) Microarea electron diffraction pattern taken from light circular area in (a). (c) Indexing of (b); the filled circles represent martensite and the open ones are for ϵ carbide [68].

HVEM and microarea diffraction have also been used [68] for detailed studies of ϵ-carbide in tempered steels. Contrary to earlier conclusions, microarea diffraction indicates that ϵ is not hexagonal, but rather is orthorhombic. The HVEM technique allows small single carbides to be isolated, which avoids the interpretational difficulties previously experienced when several crystallographic variants of the carbide contribute to diffraction. Figs. 39a–c for a 0.79%C steel tempered at 150°C for three days show ϵ-carbide precipitates in a tempered martensite matrix. The selected area diffraction pattern, 39b, was taken from the carbide in the upper right corner of the framed area of fig. 39a. The insert in the lower right corner of fig. 39a is a dark field image taken by using the $(021)_\epsilon$ reflection (encircled in fig. 39b) and corresponds to the framed area. The indexing of fig. 39b is given in fig. 39c. The detailed examination of dark field images such as fig. 39a shows that each carbide platelet, apparently 1000 Å long, is actually made up of numerous smaller particles about 50 Å in size.

The previous examples clearly indicate that many of the ambiguities characteristic of conventional (i.e., 100 kV) electron diffraction are minimized by HVEM and selected microarea diffraction. This technique will undoubtedly lead to the clarification of other phenomena.

4.7. Long period stacking structures

An increasing number of references to "long period stacking structures" is appearing in the literature. Since these are observed primarily by transmission electron microscopy and diffraction, a few comments on this important area are appropriate.

In many cases, structures can be regarded to result from the stacking of close-packed planes in a particular sequence, e.g., ...ABCBCACAB..., ...ABCACBCABACABCB..., or ...ABCABCBCABCACABCAB.... Various notations have been used to describe these long period stacking sequences and no effort here will be made to justify or favor any of the proposed schemes. Rather, an attempt will be made to unify certain characteristics, considering these structures, and several examples will be presented for consideration.

As mentioned in section 4.4 concerned with the formation of the α_1 phase from β' brass [8], selected area diffraction patterns from the α_1 indicate nominally an ...ABCBCACAB... stacking sequence of close packed $\{111\}$ planes. The $\beta' \rightarrow \alpha_1$ transformation may be regarded [8] (ignoring order) as fundamentally a bcc → fcc martensitic transformation, in which case the inhomogeneous shear of the transformation is responsible for a stacking shift on each third $\{111\}$ fcc plane. The end result is the structure given by the ...ABCBCACAB... sequence. The observed structure is therefore regarded as

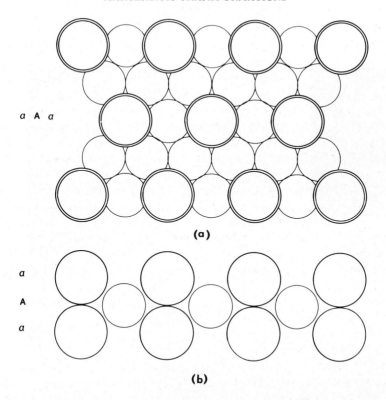

a **A** a

(a)

a

A

a

(b)

Fig. 40. Basic $\alpha A \alpha$ sandwich of the Laves phases. The large or double circles represent Ti atoms and the smaller circles represent Cr (or Co) atoms. (a) The plane of the drawing is parallel to the (000l) plane for the hexagonal or double hexagonal phase or to the (111) plane for the cubic phase. (b) Cross section showing the levels of the atoms [69].

one which results as a consequence of a phase (martensitic) transformation.

Similar situations exist for comparatively more complex materials. Allen, Delavignette and Amelinckx [69] have investigated "polytypism" in $TiCr_2$ and $TiCo_2$ Laves phases where a variety of layering sequences can form as a result of different variations in the stacking of fundamental layer units. It is implied from their work that the final structures (i.e., stacking sequences) result from a martensitic transformation where a regularly distributed shear (stacking shift) produce the new structure, or "polytype". In contrast to the $\beta' \rightarrow \alpha_1$ transformation in CuZn alloys, in the $TiCr_2$ and $TiCo_2$ Laves phases (and this would apply to other more complex intermetallics) the fundamental layering unit is not a single plane of atoms. In the Laves phases the analog of the single close-packed plane is a unit several layers thick as shown in fig. 40 [69]. Fig. 41

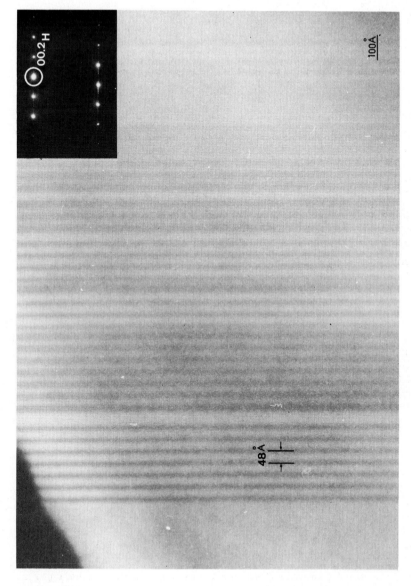

Fig. 41. Lattice imaging of faulted twelve-layer structure grown in a cubic phase of $TiCo_2$. The insert shows the corresponding diffraction pattern, and the encircled reflections were used to produce the image [69].

[69] is a lattice resolution micrograph showing a twelve layer stacking modulation observed in $TiCo_2$. The lattice image results from the interference of diffraction maxima within the objective aperture (encircled region).

Transformations from one stacking sequence (phase) to another in the Laves phases are ascribed to a shear mechanism [69].

As another example of the various kinds of long period stacking structures, mention is made of the work of Oka, Tanaka and Shimizu [70,71] who studied the various structures formed in an Fe-16.5%Mn-0.26%C alloy as a result of cyclic cooling and heating between -196 and $400°C$. This alloy is typical of a number of steels which undergo a γ (fcc) $\rightarrow \epsilon$ (hcp) transformation martensitically (as in the analogous case of cobalt). The observed microstructures and diffraction patterns are remarkably sensitive to the number of thermal cycles.

Figs. 42a–c (bright field transmission electron micrographs) and Figs. 42a'–c' (the corresponding selected area diffraction patterns) show observations made after various numbers of $400°C \rightleftarrows -196°C$ thermal cycles; a and a' correspond to 25 cycles, b and b' to 150 cycles, and c and c' to 400 cycles. Increased thermal cycling results in a complete deterioration of the γ and ϵ phases shown in fig. 42a (a'), in which case the extensive streaking in the diffraction patterns is ascribed to random faulting within the γ and ϵ; the striations seen in fig. 42a represent thin layers of the ϵ phase. Although the micrographs, figs. 42b and 42c are similar to fig. 42a, the corresponding diffraction patterns are decidedly different. Neither fig. 42b' not 42c' shows maxima characteristic of the γ and ϵ phases. Instead, reflections from both of these phases are replaced by other principal maxima, and, in addition, reflections characteristic of long period stacking structures appear in between the new principal maxima. Whereas fig. 42a–a' is attributed to the presence of the γ and ϵ phases, the diffraction patterns, figs. 42b' and 42c' are explained [71] as due to 15R (...ABCACBCABACABAB...) and 18R (...ABCABCBCABCACABCAB...) stacking sequences.

The previous observations indicate that the observed changes in stacking sequence as a result of increased thermal cycling are transformation related. The striations observed in figs. 42b and 42c are indicative of random stacking faults introduced by cycling (transformation); however, upon comparing the corresponding diffraction patterns, figs. 42b' and 42c' it was concluded [70] that the random stacking faults tend to "rearrange" in regular fashion upon increased thermal cycling.

In general, considering the aforementioned examples, it would appear that the observed structural changes are a direct consequence of systematic layer shearing, or equivalently a martensitic transformation. In the ideal cases the stacking modulation is revealed by lattice imaging using the dark field technique

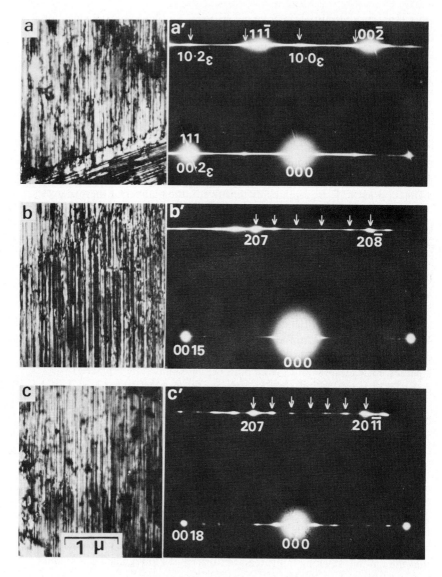

Fig. 42. Transmission electron micrographs and corresponding diffraction patterns taken from Fe-16.5%Mn-0.25%C specimens subjected to various heating and cooling cycles between +400 and −196°C: (a) and (a′) 25 cycles; (b) and (b′) 150 cycles: (c) and (c′) 400 cycles. Note the weaker reflections between (207) and (20$\bar{1}\bar{1}$) which correspond to an 18R long period structure [70].

(e.g., fig. 41). However, in most cases internal striations are also observed in the bright field image, and the corresponding diffraction patterns show extensive streaking. These "non-ideal" effects arise from the presence of random stacking faults which are probably incidental and are not themselves responsible for the stacking shifts and hence structure change. These random faults would also be responsible for relaxation of the Laue conditions, and hence the observed streaking. For the case of the ideal long period stacking structure, it is envisioned that perfect (i.e., no random faults) lamellae are separated with respect to each other by a precise stacking, and hence phase shift. One thus expects to see no random faults in the bright field image, and the streaking should be absent.

4.8. Direct observations of pretransformation lattice instabilities

Hunt and Pashley [62] in 1962, while investigating the fcc → CuAu II ordering reaction in evaporated films of stoichiometric CuAu ({001} epitaxial orientation) reported a "streaming" phenomenon prior to the actual formation of the orthorhombic CuAu II phase. From their description, streaming, as seen in a bright field transmission image, can be described as a cross-textured appearance with ⟨100⟩ directions in the film plane being brought into prominence. According to them the image shimmers continuously, giving the impression of some kind of flow along the ⟨100⟩ directions.

Until recently, the above observation has remained largely unnoticed and unconfirmed. However, similar, if not identical, effects are seen to precede martensitic transformations in a rather wide variety of materials [72]. The phenomenon appears to be general, and the terminology lattice oscillations (LO) (rather than streaming) has been applied [72]. To date, lattice oscillations have been observed above the transformation temparature (M_s) in Cu-Au, Cu-Zn, Ag-Cd, Fe-Ni, Fe-Mn-C, Fe-Cr-C, and Fe-Mn-Cr-C alloys [73].

In all the above cases [72], observations have been made by thin film (sputtered, or pre-thinned) transmission electron microscopy at 100 kV. The LO are highly orientation dependent and are most pronounced in regions of favorable Bragg contrast such as bend contours (principally) and thickness contours and dislocations. The oscillations invariably appear as a network of adjacent domains on the order of 100 Å in size * which go in and out of contrast with respect to each other. Collectively the image appears to shimmer. Since the oscillations are highly crystallographic, the observer senses the impression of a cooperative "boiling" or waterflow-like streaming, with a definite crystallographic accentuation. Further, the extent of the lattice oscilla-

---

* The domain size varies, depending upon the material.

tions is noticeably temperature dependent, becoming significantly more obvious as the transformation temperature is approached. For example, in CuAu [61] the LO are not observed at temperatures well above the transformation temperature. As a specimen is cooled (within the electron microscope) the oscillations become more noticeable and are independent of time; the oscillations only disappear when the actual transformation occurs. But if the transformation is reversed (i.e., CuAu II → disordered fcc) and the specimen is cooled again, the oscillations reappear in exactly the same manner.

Further evidence for the relation between lattice oscillations and martensitic transformations is obtained from the study of Cu-Zn alloys; only compositions capable of a martensitic transformation at a lower temperature show LO prior to the transformation. If such materials are more heavily alloyed (i.e., increasing the Zn content to 44%) the martensitic transformation is suppressed, and concurrently the lattice oscillations are not seen.

According to present thinking [72,73] the lattice oscillations are a manifestation of a pre-transformation instability. Although amplified by "thin foil" conditions, the LO are not necessarily a thin foil phenomenon. It would appear that thin foils act as a "sounding board" for a type of cooperative lattice instability. In a way of speaking a partial "Baining" and "unbaining" appears to

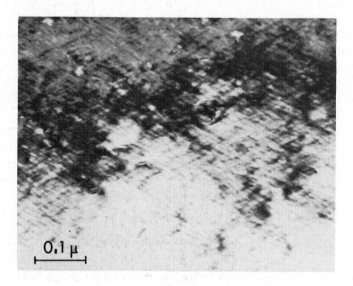

Fig. 43. Transmission electron micrograph showing "frozen-in" lattice oscillations in Cu-38%Zn-1%Sn alloy [73].

occur prior to the actual transformation. In bulk specimens, this is averaged out because the Bain contraction axes alternate in crystallographically equivalent directions. However, this does not occur in very thin specimens and thus, reciprocal lattice points oscillate across the Ewald sphere causing the observed "shimmering" in the image. Since the Bain strain is highly crystallographic in nature, it follows that the same symmetries might be seen in images of the lattice oscillations. This is observed. The crystallography of the oscillations can be directly related to the principal distortions of the Bain strain for a given material. Fig. 43 is a transmission electron micrograph taken at room temperature showing "frozen-in" lattice oscillations in a Cu-38%Zn-1%Sn alloy. Although the M_s tempereture for this alloy is about $-40°C$, the oscillations are clearly seen at room temperature, with a "wavelength" on the order of 50 Å.

Although only image observations have been considered thus far, it should be noted that corresponding effects are also noted in transmission diffraction patterns. In particular, the LO give rise to diffuse electron scattering, the enhancement of which increases as the transformation temperature is approached. This results in a broadening of diffraction spots as shown in fig. 44. Furthermore, the diffraction spots themselves exhibit a polygonal symmetry typical of the lattice oscillations, and in addition Laue conditions are relaxed along planes which correspond, in two dimensions, to cones of unextended lines of the Bain deformation. Symbolically, the lattice oscillations are depicted in

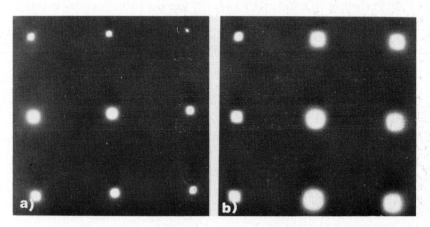

Fig. 44. Transmission electron diffraction patterns from CuAu thin film. (a) Sharp diffraction spots characteristic of the parent phase at 600°C; (b) Broadened and streaked diffraction spots at 350°C due to lattice oscillations (and before CuAu II formation) [73].

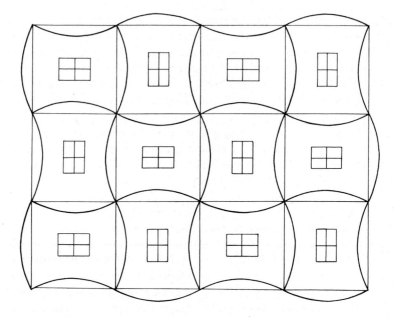

Fig. 45. Schematic interpretation of observed lattice oscillations [73].

terms of displacement waves as shown in fig. 45. Unextended regions defined by planes made up of nodal points evidently give rise to the streaking in the diffraction patterns.

The observations just mentioned are highly recent in nature, and present interpretation must of necessity be provisional because of their qualitative nature. It does seem, however, that a pretransformation lattice instability is indicated from transmission electron microscopy. Further analysis must await more quantitative observations. This is presently being done; electron multiplication measurements are now being made to determine the amplitude and frequency of the LO as a function of temperature and will be reported in course [73].

Some of the findings described have resulted from research sponsored by the U.S. Army Research Office (Durham), the U.S. Atomic Energy Commission, and the National Science Foundation. The support of these Offices is gratefully acknowledged. I am also indebted to Drs. I. Cornelis, R. Oshima and H.C. Tong for many helpful discussions.

References

[1] J.W.Christian, in: Mechanism of Phase Transformations in Crystalline Solids, No. 33 (Institute of Metals Monograph, London, 1969) p. 129.
[2] C.M.Wayman, in: The Crystallography of Martensitic Transformations in Alloys of Iron, Vol. III, Advances in Materials Research, ed. H. Herman (Interscience Publishers, New York, 1968) p. 147.
[3] J.S.Bowles and C.M.Wayman, Met. Trans. 3 (1972) 1113.
[4] C.M.Wayman. J. Less Common Metals 28 (1972) 97.
[5] J.S.Bowles and D.P.Dunne, Met. Sci. J. (in press).
[6] J.Van Landuyt and C.M.Wayman, Acta Met. 16 (1968) 803, 815.
[7] R.Smith and J.S.Bowles, Acta Met. 8 (1960) 405.
[8] I.Cornelis and C.M.Wayman, Acta Met. 22 (1974) 301.
[9] J.S.Bowles, B.C.Muddle and C.M.Wayman, Acta Met. 25 (1977) 513.
[10] K.Shimizu and C.M.Wayman, Met. Sci. J. 6 (1972) 175.
[11] B.A.Bilby and J.W.Christian, Inst. Met. Monograph. 18 (1956) 121.
[12] D.S.Lieberman, M.S.Wechsler and T.A.Read, J. Appl. Phys. 26 (1955) 473.
[13] J.W.Christian, The Theory of Transformations in Metals and Alloys (Pergamon Press, Oxford, 1965).
[14] J.S.Bowles and A.J.Morton, Acta Met. 12 (1964) 629.
[15] A.J.Morton and C.M.Wayman, Acta Met. 14 (1966) 1567.
[16] E.J.Efsic and C.M.Wayman, Trans. AIME 239 (1967) 873.
[17] J.S.Bowles and D.P.Dunne, Acta Met. 17 (1960) 201, 677.
[18] S.Jana and C.M.Wayman, Met. Trans. 1 (1960) 2815, 2825.
[19] M.Watanabe and C.M.Wayman, Met. Trans. 2 (1971) 2221, 2229.
[20] A.B.Greninger and A.R.Troiano, Trans. AIME 185 (1949) 590.
[21] R.F.Bunshah and R.F.Mehl, Trans. AIME 197 (1953) 1251.
[22] E.C.Bain, Trans. AIME 70 (1924) 25.
[23] M.A.Jaswon and J.A.Wheeler, Acta Cryst. 1 (1948) 216.
[24] J.W.Christian, Iron and Steel Inst. Spec. Rept. 93 (1965) 1.
[25] C.Laird and H.I.Aaronson, Acta Met. 15 (1967) 73.
[26] M.S.Wechsler, D.S.Lieberman and T.A.Read, Trans. AIME 197 (1953) 1503.
[27] J.W.Christian, J.Inst. Met. 84 (1956) 386.
[28] K.A.Bywater and J.W.Christian, Phil. Mag. 25 (1972) 1249.
[29] J.S.Bowles and J.K.Mackenzie, Acta Met. 2 (1954) 129.
[30] J.K.Mackenzie and J.S.Bowles, Acta Met. 2 (1954) 138.
[31] J.S.Bowles and J.K.Mackenzie, Acta Met. 2 (1954) 224.
[32] R.Bullough and B.A.Bilby, Proc. Phys. Soc. B69 (1956) 1276.
[33] I.Tamura, Trans. Iron and Steel Inst. of Japan 6 (1966) 249.
[34] I.Tamura et al., Trans. Japan Inst. Metals 5 (1964) 47.
[35] R.L.Patterson and C.M.Wayman, Acta Met. 12 (1964) 1306.
[36] R.L.Patterson and C.M.Wayman, Acta Met. 12 (1966) 347.
[37] M.S.Wechsler and T.A.Read, On the Formation of Martensite in Low and Medium Carbon Steels, unpublished report Contract AF18(600)-951, Columbia University, 1954.
[38] M.S.Wechsler, T.A.Read and D.S.Lieberman, Trans. AIME 218 (1960) 202.
[39] A.G.Crocker and B.A.Bilby, Acta Met. 9 (1961) 678.

[40] J.S.Bowles and N.F.Kennon, J. Aust. Inst. Met. 5 (1960) 106.
[41] D.P.Dunne and C.M.Wayman, Met. Trans. 2 (1971) 2327.
[42] N.H.D.Ross and A.G.Crocker, Acta Met. 18 (1970) 505.
[43] A.G.Acton and M.Bevis, Mater. Sci. Eng. 5 (1969/70) 19.
[44] D.P.Dunne and C.M.Wayman, Acta Met. 19 (1971) 425.
[45] N.F.Kennon, Acta Met. 20 (1972) 5.
[46] M.Oka and C.M.Wayman, Trans. AIME 242 (1968) 337.
[47] D.P.Dunne and C.M.Wayman, Met. Trans. 4 (1973) 137, 147.
[48] T.Tadaki and K.Shimizu, Trans. Japan Inst. Met. 11 (1970) 44.
[49] M.Oka and C.M.Wayman, Trans. ASM 62 (1969) 370.
[50] J.M.Chilton, C.J.Barton and G.R.Speich, JISI 206 (1970) 184.
[51] A.G.Fitzgerald and M.Mannami, Proc. Roy. Soc. 293 (1966) 343.
[52] R.Gevers, J.Van Landuyt and S.Amelinckx, Phys. Stat. Sol. 18 (1966) 343.
[53] R.Oshima and C.M.Wayman, Trans. JIM 16 (1975) 73.
[54] G.V.Kurdjumov and A.G.Khachaturyan, Met. Trans. 3 (1972) 1069.
[55] R.Oshima and C.M.Wayman, Scripta Met. 8 (1974) 223.
[56] K.Shimizu, J. Phys. Soc. Japan 17 (1962) 508.
[57] M.Watanabe and C.M.Wayman, Scripta Met. 5 (1971) 109.
[58] R.Oshima and C.M.Wayman, Met. Trans. 3 (1972) 2163.
[59] I.Cornelis and C.M.Wayman, Scripta Met. 7 (1973) 579.
[60] H.C.Tong and C.M.Wayman, J. Crystal Growth 15 (1972) 211.
[61] H.C.Tong and C.M.Wayman, Acta Met. 21 (1973) 1381.
[62] A.M.Hunt and D.W.Pashley, J. Phys. Rad. 23 (1962) 846.
[63] D.W.Pashley, M.J.Stowell, M.H.Jacobs and T.J.Law, Phil. Mag. 10 (1964) 127.
[64] P.B.Hirsch, A.Howie, R.B.Nicholson, D.W.Pashley and M.J.Whelan, Electron Microscopy of This Crystals (Butterworths, London, 1965).
[65] A.Koreeda and K.Shimizu, J. Electron Microscopy 22 (1973) 159; A.Koreeda et al., Rev. Sci. Inst. 42 (1971) 1676.
[66] H.Kubo, Y.Uchimoto and K.Shimizu, Metal Sci. J. 9 (1975) 61.
[67] K.E.Easterling and P.R.Swann, Acta Met. 19 (1971) 117.
[68] K.Shimizu and H.Okamoto, Presented at Annual Fall Meeting, Japan Institute of Metals, Nagoya, October 1972.
[69] C.W.Allen, P.Delavignette and S.Amelinckx, Phys. Stat. Sol. (a) 9 (1972) 237.
[70] M.Oka, Y.Tanaka and K.Shimizu, Japan J. Appl. Phys. 11 (1972) 1073.
[71] K.Shimizu and Z.Nishiyama, Met. Trans. 3 (1972) 1055.
[72] I.Cornelis, R.Oshima, H.C.Tong and C.M.Wayman, "Observations of Lattice Oscillations which Precede Phase Transformations", presented at Annual Meeting, American Society for Metals, Chicago, October 1973.
[73] I.Cornelis, R.Oshima, H.C.Tong and C.M.Wayman, Scripta Met. 8 (1974) 133.

Diffraction and Imaging Techniques in Material Science,
eds. S. Amelinckx, R. Gevers and J. van Landuyt
© *North-Holland Publishing Company, 1978*

COMPUTED ELECTRON MICROGRAPHS AND THEIR USE IN DEFECT IDENTIFICATION *

P.HUMBLE

Commonwealth Scientific and Industrial Research Organization,
Division of Tribophysics, University of Melbourne,
Victoria, Australia

1. Introduction

An important advance in the quantitative electron microscopy of defects in crystals occurred with the introduction of the two-beam dynamical theory of electron diffraction by Howie and Whelan in 1961 [1]. Since that time, the theory has been used increasingly in the detailed identification of defects, especially in relation to dislocations and various forms of stacking fault. Most of the deductions and calculations using the theory have referred to defects in elastically isotropic crystals and have been mainly concerned with establishing general rules for the behaviour of the images of defects under different diffracting conditions. The simple invisibility rules ($g \cdot b = 0$ for a screw dislocation, for example) and the symmetry properties of stacking faults can be deduced directly from the Howie and Whelan equations, but many of the more sophisticated rules (for example, those concerning the contrast of dislocations bordering a stacking fault) require extensive numerical calculation.

---

* Since giving this lecture, the technique has been described in much greater detail in a monograph "Computed Electron Micrographs and Defect Identification", A.K. Head, P. Humble, L.M. Clarebrough, A.J. Morton and C.T. Forwood (North-Holland, 1973). The monograph contains the listings of the computer programmes and several important modifications, together with descriptions of how they work and the elements of diffraction and anisotropic elasticity theory necessary for their understanding. The experimental procedures for obtaining the data from the experimental micrographs and diffraction patterns are described in full and the monograph contains sufficient worked examples and illustrations of image matching collected from the authors' experience to give the reader an idea of how to use the technique to identify defects.

What I want to describe in the first part of this lecture is a method of doing the numerical contrast calculations for linear and planar defects which is much more efficient than previous methods. As a consequence, the results of the calculations have been employed in a way which was not possible with previous calculations. One of the main inovations has been to use the calculated intensities to form a complete two-dimensional image — a theoretical or computed micrograph. This method of presentation has the advantage that it is displayed in the same form as the experimental image and it is thus much easier for an observer to make a comparison between the theoretical and experimental situations. Previously, the theoretical results were presented in the form of intensity profiles: that is, as a plot of the variation of the intensity along a line traversing the defect. In this case, the observer has to mentally reconstruct a two-dimensional image from several of these profiles before making the comparison. In addition to the micrograph form of presentation, another innovation is the use of anisotropic elasticity to calculate the displacement fields around dislocations. Thus, although we use the same Howie and Whelan equations, the intensity calculations are more representative of dislocations in real crystals than previous calculations.

A short section of this lecture will concern some general rules for image contrast from various defects. It should be pointed out at this stage, however, that partly as a result of the use of anisotropic elasticity, but mainly because this fast method of computing has enabled us to examine many more cases than previously possible, it has become clear that there are, indeed, very few general rules of image contrast behaviour. This unfortunate situation is redeemed, however, by the speed of the method itself because it is this which allows us to produce, if we wish, a theoretical micrograph corresponding to each specific experimental micrograph. In many uses this makes the need for general rules largely redundant. On the other hand, general rules do have an important role to play in the prediction of image behaviour leading to quick recognition of broad classes of defect. One or two such rules will be illustrated.

Calculation of the contrast from defects for specific cases has led to a technique of defect identification which, because of the aspects of speed and presentation emphasised above, is both quick and easy to use. The technique consists of computing theoretical micrographs corresponding to a series of experimental micrographs of the unknown defect. The theoretical micrographs have the same diffracting conditions etc. as the experimental ones, but are scanned over all probable types of defect. The unknown defect is then identified as that defect for which a particular set of theoretical micrographs matches the experimental set. The last part of this lecture will describe several instances of this use of the theoretical micrographs. Most of the examples are particular applications which have occurred in recent work carried out at the Division of Tribo-physics, but they illustrate the general types of problem which can be attempted with the technique of image matching.

2. The computer programmes

The aim of this section of the talk is to describe the principles of the pro-grammes and to provide such additional information which, together with the information in the original references, will enable the reader to set up and run a programme of this sort. In this way it is hoped that he may have immediate access to the theoretical micrographs which suit his own particular needs.

Head [2] has described the general principles for producing the informa-tion necessary for a picture quickly, and has shown how it may be assembled into a half-tone micrograph using the computer line printer. Humble [3] has extended the ideas of Head to handle more complicated defects under situa-tions which are met with in routine microscopy. The theoretical micrographs are produced in about one minute by a CDC 3600 computer, most of this time being spent in the numerical integration of the Howie and Whelan dif-ferential equations. The programmes we have evolved will reproduce all the conditions met with in two-beam experimental electron microscopy (tilted foils, different exposure times, different magnifications etc.) and all the characteristics of the material (appropriate elastic constants, anomalous ab-sorption, crystallography etc.). Thus in every case a direct comparison may be made between computed and experimental micrographs.

Most of what follows refers specifically to dislocations and stacking faults, but in fact the descriptions hold good for any straight line or planar defect. Also the description is limited to two-beam calculations in foils of constant thickness. However, the principles also apply to multi-beam diffraction con-ditions and to cases where the foil tapers uniformly.

2.1. *The two basic principles*
The information necessary to compile a picture is essentially that contained in a large number of profiles across the dislocation image. The fact that makes computer pictures of dislocations a practical proposition is that about 65 pro-files, which is sufficient for one picture, can be computed in essentially the same time as 4 profiles using older methods. The reason for this lies in the simple form of the elastic displacements around a straight defect and the linearity of the Howie-Whelan differential equations.

The equations of Howie and Whelan that describe the interaction of beam and displacement field are a pair of first-order linear differential equations for T and S, the amplitudes of the transmitted and scattered beams. The equations are:

$$\frac{dT}{dZ} = -RT + QS$$

$$\frac{dS}{dZ} = QT + (-R+2iw+2\pi i\beta')S$$

where R = normal absorption, $Q = (i -$ anomalous absorption), $\beta' = d/dz(\mathbf{g} \cdot \mathbf{R})$ where $\mathbf{R}$ is the displacement field, w = dimensionless deviation from the Bragg condition and the units in the beam direction (Z) are π/ξ_g, ξ_g being the extinction distance corresponding to the diffracting vector, $\mathbf{g}$.

There can be only two independent solutions of these equations and if these are known, then all other solutions can be obtained by taking linear combinations of them. The programmes are designed to find the two solutions by integrating two independent beams (each of which splits into two beams of the two-beam approximation) concurrently through the crystal.

If we consider configurations consisting only of parallel straight dislocations (defects) with or without faults connecting them, and if no surface relaxations are allowed, then the elastic displacement field of the dislocations is constant along any line parallel to them. (This is true in either isotropic or anisotropic elasticity; as stated above, the programmes we have developed use anisotropic elasticity.) Under these conditions it is possible to reduce the problem to one in two dimensions by projection along the line of the dislocations, $\mathbf{u}$, onto a plane containing the electron beam direction, $\mathbf{B}$, which intersects the dislocations. For convenience, the plane we have chosen is normal to the vector defined by $(\mathbf{u} \times \mathbf{B}) \times \mathbf{B}$. On this plane, called the generalised cross-section, all the displacements due to the presence of the dislocations are unique and single valued. By moving a pair of lines of constant separation (equal to the foil thickness) across this plane, it is possible to sample the displacement field through which the electron beam passes during the formation of the entire micrograph. The linear combination of solutions referred to above are taken on the lower of this pair of lines in such a way that the boundary condition at the upper line is that for an electron beam entering the crystal from a vacuum.

2.2. *Application of the principles to the case of a single dislocation in an untilted foil*

Fig. 1a shows a dislocation sloping through an untilted foil. The dislocation enters the bottom surface of the foil on the line HG and leaves the top surface on the line LM. The vertical lines in fig. 1a are parallel to the beam direction. The generalised cross-section for this configuration is obtained by projection in a direction parallel to the dislocation onto the plane LMNO. This generalised cross-section is shown in fig. 1b. The dislocation is coming out of the paper but is not normal to it. The dashed letters in fig. 1b correspond to the undashed letters in fig. 1a. Note that the line HG projects into $H'G'$, which is coincident with $L'M'$, the projection of LM. Lines $E'F'$ and $H'G'$ represent the top and bottom surfaces of the foil respectively for the profile in which the dislocation is just entering the bottom of the foil; $L'M'$ and $O'N'$ represent the top and bottom surface of the foil for the profile in which the dislocation is just leaving the top of the foil. Intermediate profiles on, for example, the shaded plane shown in fig. 1a, are obtained by taking the portion of the displacement field between the two dashed lines on the generalised cross-section in fig. 1b.

The amplitudes T and S are integrated down columns in the cross-section parallel to the beam direction. An equal number of columns on either side of the dislocation is considered, care being taken not to integrate down a column that is within a small distance of the dislocation core. If columns close to the dislocation core are considered, the programme takes an excessive amount of time to integrate through the rapidly changing strain field.

Consider the jth column from the dislocation as shown in fig. 1b. The integration down this column is done in two main parts, the first part (A) from P to Q and the second part (B) from Q to R. Each part is divided into n

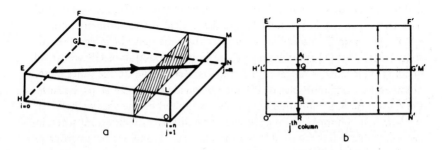

Fig. 1. The geometry and the generalised cross-section for a single dislocation in an untilted foil.

steps of equal size. Two beams, with independent initial amplitudes at the top of the cross-section are integrated down the column simultaneously, and the amplitudes (corresponding to the four beams) at the end of each step stored in the computer memory. The intensity of the image for the surfaces of the foil in the positions shown by the dashed lines in fig. 1b is obtained by combining the two solutions for the position B_i linearly and in such a manner as to give the correct boundary conditions for the top surface of the foil; that is, $T = 1$ and $S = 0$ at A_i.

By allowing i to run from 0 to n, we obtain $n + 1$ values of the intensity for the jth column in successive profiles running from the plane EFGH to the plane LMNO in fig. 1a. Thus we have $n + 1$ intensity values to establish the points on one row of the theoretical micrograph parallel to the dislocation line. By repeating the procedure for $j = 1$ to m, we obtain the m rows of the picture. In the present case, $n = 128$ and $m = 60$. In fact, for foils of the order of 5 extinction distances thick, the time to compute the micrographs is optimised if $n + 1 = 65$ and the other 64 points needed for each row of the picture are obtained by interpolation [2]. This has been found to introduce no serious error.

The geometry of projection, both onto the generalised cross-section and in the electron beam direction to produce the micrograph itself becomes more complicated for tilted foils containing more than one defect [3], but the theoretical micrographs are obtained using the same principles as outlined above.

In addition to simulating tilted foils and obtaining images of more complicated configurations, an important feature which it is necessary to be able to reproduce is that of variable magnification. This is important so that direct comparisons can be made with experimental images. In fact, the human eye seems to be much more sensitive to small differences in magnification when making a comparison than it is to the somewhat large differences in overall darkness which can occur between the theoretical and experimental micrographs. Magnification is obtained by restricting the range of integration to some fraction of PQ and the same, corresponding fraction of QR whilst still dividing these smaller ranges into 128 steps. Reduction, on the other hand, is obtained by using multiples of PQ and QR divided into 128 steps. Because the resolution in a computed micrograph is limited by the spacing between the rows (or columns), the magnification facility is also important when increased resolution is required. For example, figs. 2a and b show micrographs of the same defect (a complex Frank dislocation loop) under identical diffraction conditions imaged at two different magnifications. In fig. 2b a fine dark line can be seen running along the centre of the micrograph. This is not resolved in fig. 2a which is at about half the magnification of fig. 2b.

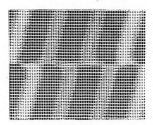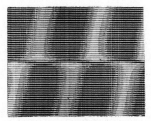

Fig. 2. Theoretical micrographs of a stepped Frank dislocation loop taken under identical conditions illustrating the increased resolution available at increased magnification.

After taking the linear combinations of the amplitudes for given levels, either the bright-field or dark-field intensities can be obtained by multiplying the appropriate amplitudes by their complex conjugates. Thus, one may obtain the dark-field micrograph at the same time as the bright-field one with the expenditure of only a few seconds spent in multiplication and printing the picture. All the micrographs shown here are bright-field micrographs.

2.3. The production of the half-tone micrograph

It was decided to use the line printer to produce the half-tone pictures because this is the piece of equipment most commonly used for computer output and so lends itself to easy routine use. More sophisticated ways of half-tone reproduction can be used (for instance, a television type display used with some form of photography [4]), but in most cases this increases the cycle time to produce a picture from the order of 1 min to the order of 5 min, is not in routine use in most computer networks and so increases the turn-round time and only a little more detail is available in the image.

A typical line printer picture of a dislocation is shown in fig. 3 together with the grey scale used. In order to get the blackest symbols it was found necessary to use over-printing. All combinations of printing and overprinting of the available symbols were examined and 11 different shades of grey could be distinguished, one of which was blank paper. The composition of the 10 printed shades chosen is shown in the grey scale. There are six lines of each symbol, the first and second columns being the individual characters and the third being the result when the first column is overprinted by the second. Most of the characters used are, of necessity, punctuation marks and other special symbols, since it is a characteristic of a good type face that letters and numerals do not have large differences in apparent blackness.

Fig. 3. Large magnification of a computed micrograph of a dislocation. The third column of characters at the left-hand side depicts the grey scale together with the intensity values (referred to background intensity) at which they begin to operate. The characters are obtained by overprinting column one with column two.

The standard picture size used is 60 lines of 129 symbols, which in the original form is 10 by 13 in. It is usually reduced by about a factor of 10 for journal reproduction so that the individual characters lose their identity. The dislocation runs from left to right, intersecting the bottom surface of the foil at the left-hand margin of the picture and the top surface at the right margin. The line of the dislocation is located midway between the rows of the picture indicated by the letters D on the right-hand margin. Due account is taken of the different spacings of characters along a line and between lines so that angles are true and linear scales are equal in all directions. The actual scale of the picture will depend on the foil thickness and the angle at which the dislocation slopes through the foil as well as the chosen range of integration.

The correspondence between value of intensity and shade of grey was determined by photometric measurements of the reflectivity R of large areas of the 11 shades. The corresponding intensity values I are then given by

$$\log I = \gamma^{-1} \log (R/E) \,,$$

where the chosen values of the constants E and γ correspond to the photographic variables of exposure and contrast. Unless otherwise stated, the 10 boundary values indicated on the grey scale in fig. 3 were used for all of the present pictures. These values are not intensities as such but are the ratios of intensity to background. This means that all the pictures have the same contrast but each exposure is adjusted so that the background is always the first shade of grey. This appears a suitable choice for bright-field pictures of dislocations, for which most of the information is in the regions darker than background and one shade, full white, is sufficient to represent those areas that are significantly lighter than background. The contrast was chosen so that the values at which the background symbol changes (0.93 and 1.15) are approximately the experimental visibility limits for deviations from background.

Different choices for the exposure and contrast are necessary for dark-field pictures, for defects which produce very faint images or when comparisons are being made with unusually exposed experimental micrographs. The computer programmes which we have been using contain nine calibrations of the grey scale representing the combinations of three values of exposure with three values of contrast. In practice, however, the calibration of the grey scale shown in fig. 3 is the one which has been most used; two or three others have been used occasionally.

2.4. The parameters needed to run the programme and their evaluation

The quantities needed to produce a theoretical micrograph of a single dislocation are: the elastic stiffnesses (for cubic crystals, C_{11}, C_{12}, C_{44}); the anomalous absorption constant* (this may be measured using the image matching technique itself [5]: for most cases, this has been taken as 0.1); the Burgers vector, b (this is usually the quantity to be determined); the direction of the dislocation line, u; the reflecting vector, g; the electron beam direction, B; the foil normal, FN; the dimensionless deviation from the Bragg condition, w; and the thickness of the foil, t, in units of the extinction distance.

The elastic constants for many materials may be found in standard references on anisotropic elasticity (e.g. Huntington [6]), and u may be obtained by stereographic analysis of three or more micrographs taken when the differences in the foil tilt are large. g can be found by indexing the diffraction patterns, and B, FN and w can all be evaluated using Kikuchi line patterns. These are standard techniques, which, together with methods for measuring t, may be found in [7].

---

* Since intensities are normalised to background intensity, the other absorption constant which appears in the equations, the real absorption constant, divides out and its precise value is never needed.

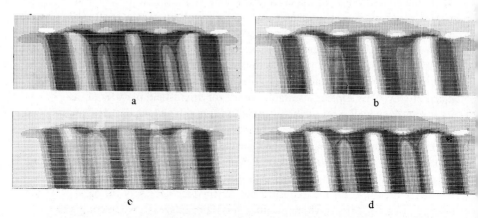

a   b

c   d

Fig. 4. Examples of the change in image character of an intrinsic stacking fault on (111) together with its bounding Shockley dislocation ($\mathbf{b}=\frac{1}{6}[11\bar{2}]$) for small changes in foil thickness. The reflecting vector is $1\bar{1}1$, the value of w is 0.15 and in (a) and (b) the anomalous absorption is 0.07 and in (c) and (d) 0.05. t/ξ_g is 3.1 for (a), 3.2 for (b), 3.0 for (c) and 3.15 for (d).

Providing due account is taken of the rotations of the image when going to the diffraction pattern, $\mathbf{g}$ can be determined exactly, but the evaluation of the other quantities is subject to experimental error. Moreover, it has been our experience that in a certain small number of cases the images of defects are sensitive to the values of these quantities. For instance, at small values of any one of anomalous absorption, w or t, the images are often sensitive to small variations in the values of the other two. Fig. 4 shows the images of a Shockley dislocation ($\mathbf{b}=\frac{1}{6}[11\bar{2}]$), bordering an intrinsic stacking fault (on (111)) taken with $\mathbf{g} = \bar{1}\bar{1}1$ at a w of 0.15. Figs. 4a and b have a value of anomalous absorption of 0.07; t is 3.1 ξ_g for fig. 4a and 3.2 ξ_g for fig. 4b. Although this represents a change in thickness of only 25Å the difference in the fringe number and contrast is obvious. Figs. 4c and d have an anomalous absorption constant of 0.05 and t for fig. 4c is 3.0 ξ_g and for fig. 4d is 3.15 ξ_g. This change of thickness of about 36Å produces a change in the dislocation contrast which is so marked that the dislocation could be said to be "out of contrast" in fig. 4c but "in contrast" in fig. 4d. For this particular example similar image sensitivity has been observed to occur at other combinations of w, t and anomalous absorption.

The "shearing" effect on an image of a dislocation due to the non-coincidence of $\mathbf{FN}$ and $\mathbf{B}$ has been discussed elsewhere [3], but in general large

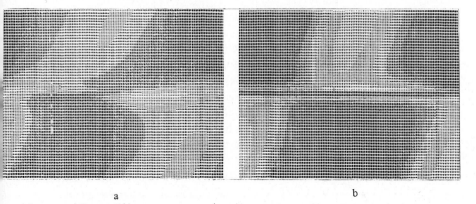

a   b

Fig. 5. Theoretical micrographs of a step in a complex Frank dislocation loop taken under identical diffraction conditions but with slightly different beam directions. The beam direction is [011] in (a) and [057] in (b).

differences in **FN** and **B** are necessary before the change in the image becomes large. The angle which fault fringes make to the line of the terminating dislocation, on the other hand, can be extremely sensitive to the value of **FN** under certain circumstances, and the images of composite defects which have interacting displacement fields are often sensitive to the electron beam direction, **B**. Fig. 5 shows an example of this last effect. It contains two micrographs of a region of a complex Frank loop [8] where two dislocations and three stacking faults are in close proximity. The narrow stacking fault (180 Å wide) separating the two dislocations is vertical, and the dislocations are on top of each other in fig. 5a (**B**=[011]), but this is not the case in fig. 5b (**B**=[057]). In going from **B** = [011] to a **B** of [057] (a rotation of $9\frac{1}{2}°$) a strong dark line has appeared in the image. A rotation of $9\frac{1}{2}°$ in the opposite sense from [011], however, produces virtually no change in the image shown in fig. 5a. [057] is typical of the sort of beam direction it is necessary to use in the vicinity of [011] in order to get good two-beam conditions, and in examples of the type described above, therefore, it is necessary to use the exact beam direction and not the nearest low index direction.

Unfortunately, it is usually impossible to predict if large variations in the image will result from small variations in the parameters. Commonly, therefore, for the purpose of image matching to be described later, each parameter is varied over two or three values within the experimentally determined error range to see if the images are sensitive. It is largely because of this unpredictable degree of sensitivity that it is extremely difficult to formulate any meaningful rules for image behaviour.

3. Illustrations of the use of computed micrographs

Since the introduction of the programmes, we have used the theoretical micrographs in three ways. The first of these concerns computations to distinguish quickly between different types of defect without resort to specific and detailed computing. The aim has been the compilation of a few simple properties of several types of defect so that an observer may rapidly select the defects of interest from the images he sees in situ on the microscope screen. This use is equivalent to that of the general rules established previously. The second way in which the theoretical micrographs have been used is to establish a range of diffraction conditions in which images are most characteristic or most suitable for detecting small changes in a particular defect parameter. With such information, an observer may set up the specimen in the microscope to these optimised conditions and examine the image for the features of interest. The third way in which the computed micrographs have been employed is in the detailed image matching of experimental images in order that defects may be identified. The sequence of events in this case is that the observer takes experimental micrographs of the defect to be identified under as many different diffracting conditions as possible. Theoretical micrographs are then computed for each of the experimental images, the Burgers vector or the fault shear (for example) being scanned until a matching set of computed micrographs is obtained. The defect is then identified.

3.1. *The symmetry properties of images and the classificiation of defects*

As an example of the first type of use, consider the symmetry properties of three defects: a dislocation, a line of dilation and a dislocation dipole. The basic types of symmetry of a dislocation image are well known (see [7]). The image of a dislocation may have no symmetry (fig. 6a), may be symmetrical on either side of a line along its length (fig. 6b), or symmetrical on either side of a line about mid-foil (fig. 6c). It can be shown, however [9], that the image of a dislocation has a centre of inversion symmetry when w is zero and anomalous absorption is zero (fig. 7). Since this is the only known case, the images of dislocations in real materials probably never have such symmetry. However, there are two defects whose images always possess such symmetry and this may be used as a test to distinguish them from dislocations. One of these defects is a dislocation dipole [10,11] and the other is a line of dilation [12]. Figs. 8 and 9 show the experimental and theoretical micrographs of a dislocation dipole taken under five different reflecting conditions and fig. 10 shows the theoretical micrographs of a line of dilation. (The displacements around the line of dilation are calculated on isotropic elasticity.)

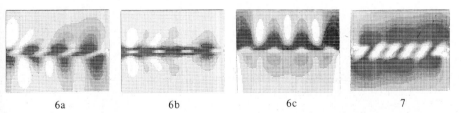

6a   6b   6c   7

Fig. 6. Computed micrographs of dislocations illustrating the three possible types of symmetry this defect may possess for non-zero values of anomalous absorption.

Fig. 7. Illustrating the centre of inversion symmetry of a dislocation image when anomalous absorption and w are both zero.

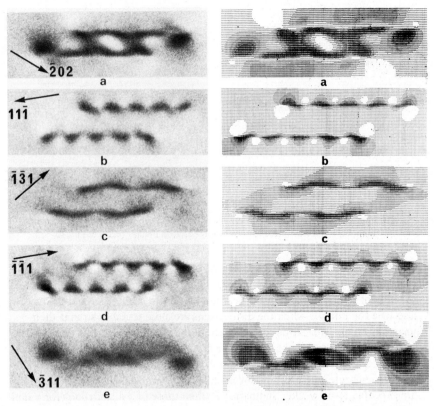

Fig. 8. Experimental micrographs showing the images of a dislocation dipole in nickel taken under five different diffracting conditions.

Fig. 9. Theoretical micrographs of a dislocation dipole in nickel which match the experimental micrographs in fig. 8. Note that the micrographs all have centre of inversion symmetry.

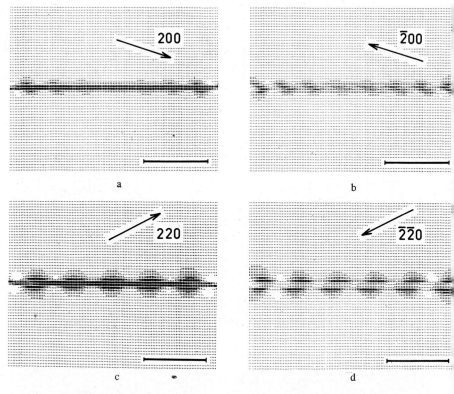

Fig. 10. Four images of a line of dilation. Note that they also have centre of inversion symmetry and that there is no relation between images taken with ± **g**.

On reversing the reflecting vector, the bright-field image of a dislocation becomes the 180° rotation of the original image. In general, however, the images of a line of dilation taken on ± **g** bear no relation to each other and this is also true for a dipole when the dislocations are close together so that their images overlap. Thus, although it is easy to instantly distinguish a dislocation from the other two defects, it is not easy to find a way to distinguish between a line of dilation and a dislocation dipole and to the author's knowledge there is no general rule which can be invoked. However, images of a line of dilation are expected to be weaker and narrower than those of a dislocation (for a similar displacement at the cores of the two defects [12]), and this may enable a distinction to be made. Also a reflecting vector along the line of the defect will produce a weak image for a line of dilation (no image at all in isotropic elasticity) but would produce a weak image in the case of a dipole only if the dislocations were of edge character.

3.2. *Pre-computation to determine favourable experimental conditions*

The recent work of Clarebrough and Morton [13,14] contains examples of the use of computed micrographs in determining the optimum conditions for observing a given defect. They were interested in trying to detect the separation of two dislocations at the edge of a Frank dislocation loop. Figs. 11 and 12 consist of computed micrographs of this defect taken on $02\bar{2}$ and $0\bar{2}0$ reflect-

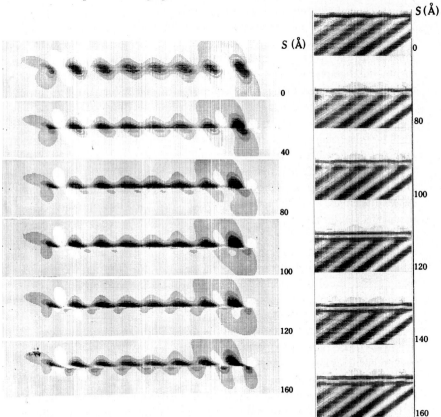

Fig. 11. Six computed micrographs of a Frank dislocation dissociated into a Shockley and a stair-rod dislocation separated by a distance S. The reflecting vector is $02\bar{2}$ so that the stacking fault is out of contrast. Note that the images change most rapidly for values of S in the range 0 to 40 Å.

Fig. 12. Seven computed micrographs of the same defect as in fig. 11 but with a **g** of $0\bar{2}0$. The images in this set change most rapidly for values of S in the range 80 to 120 Å.

ing vectors respectively for various separations, S (in Å) of the Shockley and stair-rod dislocations. It is apparent from fig. 11 that the diffracting conditions chosen for these micrographs are suitable for identifying separations in the range 0 to 40Å since there is a marked change of image in this range. However, there is little change in the images for separations in the range 80 to 160Å. On the other hand, it can be seen from the differences in the images for values of S from 80 to 120Å in fig. 12, that these diffraction conditions would be suitable for detecting dissociations of this magnitude.

3.3. *Image matching and defect identification*

Whilst theoretical micrographs prove useful in many cases for predicting the type of experimental image to be expected, the problems have usually been approached the other way round. Commonly, one already has a set of experimental micrographs of a defect of interest and theoretical micrographs are computed which correspond to the conditions of the experiment. The sets of theoretical images are then compared with the experimental set of micrographs until a match is obtained.

Before describing several cases of such identification, it is perhaps necessary to define what is meant by a "match" in this context and what criteria are used in comparing the computed and experimental micrographs. In general it is only the topology of the images which is compared and not their absolute intensities. First, the broad features of the image are noted and compared, e.g. whether it is double or single, dotted or continuous, one-sided or symmetrical, fine or wide and so on. In many cases these broad features are sufficient to enable a match to be made, but in some cases one has to take note of finer detail such as the shape of a dark dot, the occurrence of small light areas or the slight offset of prominent features etc. Although no account is taken of absolute intensities, in general, use is sometimes made of the fact that one image is much fainter than another. When we first began to use the image matching technique, we placed little reliance on features of the image which occurred close to the surface of the foil. This is because the programme does not allow for surface relaxations in the neighbourhood of the emerging dislocations which presumably occur in practice. However, experience with the technique has shown that the detail in the image close to a surface is remarkably well reproduced and since distinctive images usually occur at these places, we have often used this detail when making comparisons.

The process of matching a set of computed micrographs to an experimental set usually begins as one of rejection. The experimental image with the most

character* is selected first and the images of all the probable defects computed
for this case. The gross mis-matches, judged on the criteria outlined above, are
immediately rejected. The next most characteristic experimental image is then
compared with the theoretical micrographs computed for the remaining possibilities. After comparison with two or three experimental micrographs in
this way one is usually left with two or three likely defects. At this stage,
theoretical micrographs for these defects are computed corresponding to the
diffraction conditions of all the available experimental micrographs. A process of selection and rejection then ensues until the final match is chosen.

As a specific example of image matching, consider the four images of an
unknown dislocation in beta-brass shown in fig. 13. Because of the large elas-
tic anistropy of this material, the $\mathbf{g} \cdot \mathbf{b} = 0$ type of rule for the invisibility of
dislocations does not apply in general and it is necessary to devise some other
method of Burgers vector determination [15,16]. Fig. 14 shows the theore-
tical micrographs corresponding to the image in fig. 13a for all the $\frac{1}{2} \langle 111 \rangle$,
$\langle 111 \rangle$, $\langle 100 \rangle$ and $\langle 110 \rangle$ Burgers vectors possible in beta-brass. The image in fig.
13a may be characterised as being double, dotted, having a region at back-
ground intensity along the centre of the image, an "arrow head" at one end
and a light area at the other. Scanning through the micrographs shown in fig.
14 the reader may choose figs. 14a, c, e, g and i as being possible matches to
the experimental image. Some are obviously better matches than others, but
it may be agreed that all the images rejected are gross mis-matches. Fig. 15
shows the micrographs computed for the dislocations depicted in figs. 14a,
c, e, g and i but with diffracting conditions appropriate to fig. 13b. The image
in fig. 13b may be characterised as being double and dotted, the dots being
much larger on one side of the line than the other. It also has a region at background intensity along the centre. Only the theoretical micrographs in figs.
15a and c match this description, the others are mis-matches. Distinction
between the possiblities represented by these two micrographs may be made
by comparing fig. 13c with figs. 16a and b. The image in fig. 16a is not sufficiently one-sided and it is therefore concluded that fig. 16b is the match in
this case. Further confirmation may be obtained by computing the theoretical micrograph for the dislocation in fig. 16b but for the diffraction conditions of fig. 13d. This is shown in fig. 17.

---

* By "the image with most character" we usually mean (at least in the case of a dislocation image) one which differs most from a featureless straight line. Images of "good
  character" (and thus most suitable for the image matching technique) may often be obtained by setting a small value of the deviation parameter, w.

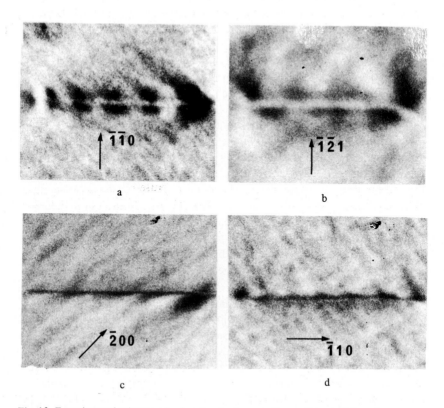

Fig. 13. Experimental micrographs showing the images of an unknown dislocation in beta-brass taken under four different reflecting vectors which are marked. The dislocation line direction, **u**, is close to $[\bar{1}11]$ and **FN** is close to $[001]$. **B** is close to $[001]$ for (a), (c) and (d) and to $[113]$ for (b). w is about 0.5 for (a), (c) and (d) and 0.7 for (b). The foil thickness is about 5.0 ξ_{110}.

In summary, the theoretical micrographs which match the experimental images in figs. 13a–d are figs. 14e, 15c, 16b and 17 respectively. The Burgers vector for these micrographs is $[\bar{1}11]$ and since the dislocation line is also along $[\bar{1}11]$ the dislocation in question is identified as being a pure screw superlattice dislocation of Burgers vector $[\bar{1}11]$. It is noteworthy that figs. 13a and b which have $\mathbf{g \cdot b} = 0$ show more contrast than figs. 13c and d which have $\mathbf{g \cdot b} = 2$. Although this is an exaggerated example, since the elastic anisotropy of beta-brass is unusually large, similar effects also occur in materials of lesser

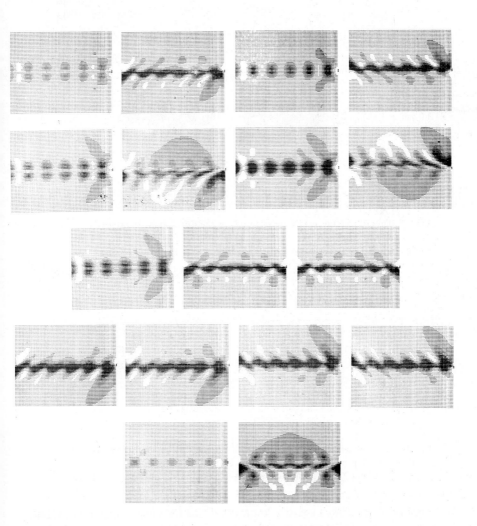

Fig. 14. Theoretical micrographs computed for the diffraction conditions of fig. 13a for dislocations of all Burgers vectors probable in beta-brass. Reading from a to q the Burgers vectors are: $\frac{1}{2}[\bar{1}11]$, $\frac{1}{2}[111]$, $\frac{1}{2}[1\bar{1}1]$, $\frac{1}{2}[\bar{1}\bar{1}1]$, $[\bar{1}11]$, $[111]$, $[1\bar{1}1]$, $[\bar{1}\bar{1}1]$, $[001]$, $[010]$, $[1\bar{0}0]$, $[01\bar{1}]$, $[101]$, $[0\bar{1}1]$. $[\bar{1}01]$. $[\bar{1}10]$ and $[110]$.

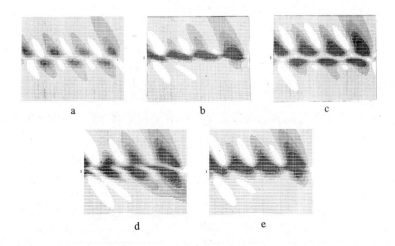

a   b   c

d   e

Fig. 15. Theoretical micrographs computed for the diffraction conditions of fig. 13b for the remaining possible Burgers vectors after comparing fig. 13a with fig. 14. Reading from a to e the Burgers vectors are $\frac{1}{2}[\bar{1}11]$, $\frac{1}{2}[1\bar{1}1]$, $[\bar{1}11]$, $[1\bar{1}1]$ and $[001]$.

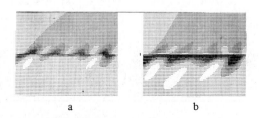

a   b

Fig. 16. Theoretical micrographs computed for the diffraction conditions of fig. 13c for the remaining possible Burgers vectors after comparing figs. 13a and 14 and figs. 13b and 15. The Burgers vector for a is $\frac{1}{2}[\bar{1}11]$ and for b is $[\bar{1}11]$.

anisotropy. In many cases it is known that true invisibility cannot occur, but the extent of the contrast can only be determined by computation. This is an instance, therefore, in which a previously established rule breaks down. It can be re-established only on a very restricted basis for pure edge or pure screw dislocations which lie normal to mirror planes in the crystal [16,17].

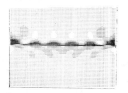

Fig. 17. A theoretical micrograph computed for the diffraction conditions of fig. 13d with a Burgers vector of [$\bar{1}11$].

Before leaving this particular example, consider the sets of intensity profiles shown in figs. 18a—d. These are computed for the same conditions as the micrographs in figs. 14e, 15c, 16b and 17 and correspond to about every third column of the micrographs, starting at the right-hand side. It will be noted that although they contain the same information as the theoretical micrographs they are much more difficult to compare with the experimental images and such features as the "arrow head" in fig. 14e tend to be missed in the profiles (fig. 18a).

Another case in which an established approximation was shown to be inaccurate by the use of theoretical micrographs was that of the contrast from three overlapping stacking faults [18]. In low stacking fault energy materials, the glide dislocations are widely split into Shockley partial dislocations connected by ribbons of stacking fault. Since slip often takes place on closely spaced planes in the crystal, there are usually many regions of overlapping stacking faults. An example which is believed to be one such region is shown in fig. 19. This is an electron micrograph of a thin foil of a Cu-8 at% Si alloy which has been deformed about 1%. It was taken under two-beam conditions and the reflecting vector 0$\bar{2}$0 is indicated. If the fault fringes at A are assumed to be due to a single stacking fault, then it can be shown that the fault is intrinsic. The fringes at B are apparently those typical of an extrinsic fault. However, following the interpretation of Whelan and Hirsch [19,20] the contrast from this area is probably due to the presence of a second closely overlapping intrinsic fault. In region C faint fringe contrast may be seen. It was proposed that in this area a third intrinsic fault is present, and the faint fringe contrast is due to three overlapping intrinsic stacking faults. Another separate and fainter example of this type of contrast can be seen running from D to E.

It can be seen from fig. 19 that the set of fringes at C is asymmetrical about mid-foil and that at DE symmetrical. The fringes at C are more intense than those at DE. Microdensitometer traces across the fringes showed that the maximum intensity of the fringes at C is about 18% below background intensity and the fringes at DE are only about 5% below background intensity.

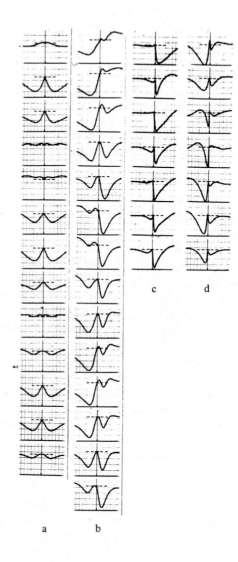

Fig. 18. Sets of profiles computed for the diffraction conditions of fig. 13 with a Burgers vector of $[\bar{1}11]$.

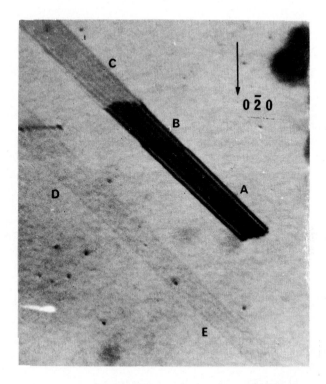

Fig. 19. Experimental micrograph of a lightly deformed specimen of a Cu-Si alloy showing faint fringe contrast at C and at DE.

Figs. 20 and 21 contain theoretical micrographs showing the contrast to be
expected from three overlapping stacking faults for several spacings of the
faults. The spacing of the faulted planes, x and y, in units of the slip plane
spacing are

<table>
<tr><td></td><td></td><td>a</td><td>b</td><td>c</td><td>d</td><td>e</td><td>f</td></tr>
<tr><td>for fig. 20</td><td>x</td><td>1</td><td>1</td><td>2</td><td>1</td><td>2</td><td>3</td></tr>
<tr><td></td><td>y</td><td>1</td><td>2</td><td>1</td><td>3</td><td>2</td><td>1</td></tr>
</table>

<table>
<tr><td></td><td></td><td>a</td><td>b</td><td>c</td><td>d</td><td>e</td></tr>
<tr><td>for fig. 21</td><td>x</td><td>1</td><td>2</td><td>3</td><td>4</td><td>5</td></tr>
<tr><td></td><td>y</td><td>5</td><td>4</td><td>3</td><td>2</td><td>1</td></tr>
</table>

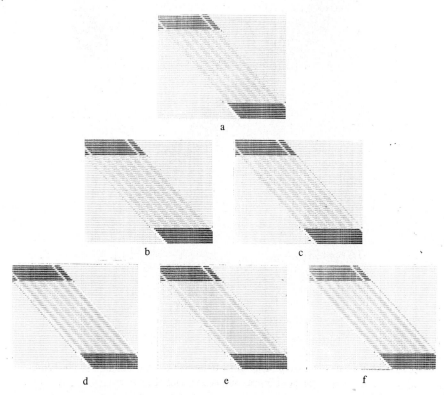

Fig. 20. Theoretical micrographs showing the contrast from three parallel overlapping intrinsic stacking faults computed for the diffraction conditions of fig. 19 and for the separations given in the text.

Since the contrast from these defects is everywhere weak, this is one case
where a special calibration of the grey scale has been used when printing the
theoretical micrographs. In fact, the visibility limits for these micrographs are
5% above background intensity and 2% below background intensity rather than
the commonly used ones of 15% above and 7% below. Moreover, this is one
case where the absolute intensity of the images had to be taken into account
when image matching.

It can be seen from these theoretical micrographs that whenever $x = y$ a set
of fringes which is symmetrical about mid-foil results. When $x \neq y$ the fringes
are asymmetrical about mid-foil. It is also apparent that the set of fringes for

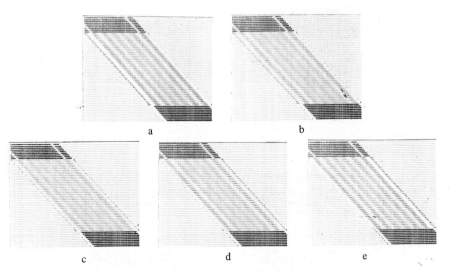

Fig. 21. Theoretical micrographs showing the contrast from three parallel overlapping intrinsic stacking faults computed for the diffraction conditions of fig. 19 and for the separations given in the text.

$x = n$, $y = m$ (where n and m are integers) become the set of fringes for $x = m$, $y = n$ by a 180° rotation. The fringes increase in intensity as the sum $(x+y)$ increases.

By noting both the symmetry and the intensity, it is possible to choose the theoretical micrograph in fig. 20a as the only one which will match the contrast at DE in the experimental micrograph. Thus the defect giving rise to this contrast may be identified as three overlapping intrinsic stacking faults on neighbouring slip planes (spaced about 2.1 Å apart). Similarly, the contrast at C may be identified as that due to three overlapping faults spaced 1 and 5 slip planes apart (fig. 21a).

It should be mentioned that since (to a good approximation) stacking faults do not have any strain field associated with them, elasticity theory plays no part in the image forming process, so that the success of the image matching technique in this case is independent of isotropic or anisotropic elasticity.

A more recent problem in which image matching has been used is that of identifying the precise nature of large faulted Frank loops formed on quenching low stacking fault energy materials (Ag and CuAl alloys [8,13,14]). When metals are quenched rapidly from close to the melting point down to ≈0°C the large supersaturation of vacancies trapped in the lattice can aggregate

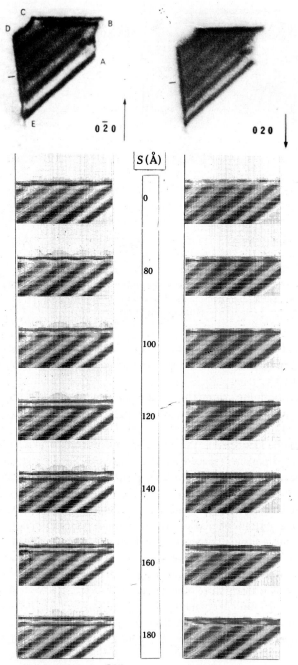

Fig. 22. Two images of a Frank dislocation loop together with the corresponding theoretical micrographs computed for the edge CB with various separations, S, of the Shockley and stair-rod dislocations.

either as planar defects (dislocation loops) or as three dimensional defects (voids or stacking fault tetrahedra). In low stacking fault energy materials, however, many of the Frank loops which are formed have features which run across the plane of the loop. In some well developed examples, it could be seen that this feature was, in fact, a step in the plane of the fault. It was thought that the explanation of this might lie in the fact that the Frank dislocations bounding the loop are dissociated (into Shockley and stair-rod dislocations connected by a ribbon of stacking fault), so that during growth vacancies cannot add on at the edge of the loop but have to add on to the plane of the loop. In order to test this it was necessary to determine if Frank dislocations are dissociated in these materials and whether the steps in the loop are consistent with the fault climb mechanism.

Fig. 22 shows two experimental images of a Frank loop in a quenched Cu 15.6% Al alloy and the corresponding theoretical images for edge CB of this loop (which lies along [$\bar{1}01$]) computed for various separations of the Shockley and stair-rod dislocations. It may be seen by inspection that the best match between theory and experiment occurs at a separation of 160 Å. This is in agreement with the stacking fault energy of this alloy measured by other methods. It should be noted that the edges DC and BA which do not lie along a ⟨110⟩ direction and, therefore, cannot be dissociated, have images which are matched by the computed micrographs for zero separation.

For the alloys examined [13,14] the width of the dissociation varied from about 80 Å to 160 Å. Because the separation is so small, and because the {111} plane of dissociation was often shallowly inclined to the electron beam, the two dislocations and the ribbon of stacking fault could not be resolved as separate entities. Image matching, however, left no doubt as to the actual physical situation.

The problem of identifying the nature of the step was also one in which the dislocations and the stacking fault could rarely be separately resolved [8]. The quantities to be determined were the Burgers vectors of the two dislocations at the step, their relative orientation, whether the plane of the step was faulted and if so, intrinsically or extrinsically, and the height of the step. Fig. 23 shows an image of a stepped (complex) loop in Cu 9.4% Al, together with theoretical micrographs for 6 of the 36 probable physical configurations for this case. Although many other experimental micrographs were taken and compared with their corresponding theoretical micrographs, it happens that in this case this one $\bar{2}00$ image was sufficient to distinguish unambiguously between all 36 probabilities. By inspection of the fine detail in the images close to the step, it is possible to select the image in fig. 23b as the match to the experimental image. The step is, therefore, identified as consisting of low energy stair-rod disloca-

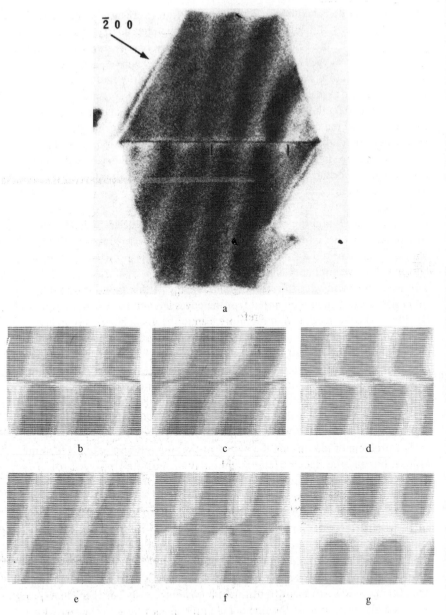

$\overline{2}\,0\,0$

Fig. 23. The image of a complex Frank dislocation loop in a quenched Cu 9.4% Al alloy with theoretical micrographs for 6 of the 36 probable configurations which could give rise to the contrast at the step.

tions of Burgers vector $\pm \frac{1}{6}$ [101] bounding a region of intrinsic fault on the {111} plane acutely inclined to the main plane of the loop. The step height is close to 180Å.

With information of this type obtained for many such loops, together with the information on the dissociation of Frank dislocations lying along ⟨110⟩ it was possible to show that fault climb by vacancy addition was the only way in which the occurrence of complex loops could be explained [8].

The last example of the image matching technique which will be given here concerns the detailed identification of the Burgers vectors and geometry of dislocation dipoles in nickel [10,11]. Although nickel is not very elastically anisotropic, calculation shows that the anisotropy is sufficient to affect the position of stable equilibrium (measured by the angle ϕ from the slip plane) of oppositely signed $\frac{1}{2}$ ⟨110⟩ dislocations.

Fig. 8 shows five experimental images of a dislocation dipole lying along the [$\bar{1}\bar{1}2$] direction in a nickel specimen, and fig. 9 shows the corresponding theoretical micrographs computed for dislocations of Burgers vector $\pm \frac{1}{2}$ [$\bar{1}01$] and $\phi = 60°$. It can be seen that these images match the experimental ones. The value of $\phi = 60°$ was obtained from anisotropic elasticity theory using the known elastic constants for nickel: using isotropic elasticity, such dislocations, being only 30° from screw orientation, would have an equilibrium position directly above each other, $\phi = 90°$. In several of the cases examined so far, it has been possible to determine ϕ to $\pm 5°$ and within this error, agreement between theory and experiment has been obtained in every case. In fact the image shown in fig. 9e is particularly sensitive to changes in ϕ and fig. 24 shows five images computed for this particular diffracting vector with ϕ running between 55° and 65° in steps of 2.5°. Inspection of these shows that mismatches are obtained for the two extreme values so that $\phi = 60° \pm 2.5°$. Thus in this example it was possible to illustrate a new type of interaction and stability for dislocations in moderately anisotropic materials.

4. Future developments in defect identification using electron microscopy

In the preceding examples of defect identification using theoretical micrographs, one is involved in computing all the probable physical situations and comparing them with experiment. Whilst this is sufficiently convenient and successful to be employed as a routine method, it is not the most direct or general way of defect identification. Head has recently shown [9,21] that the possibility exists, at least in principle and under certain conditions, of taking the intensity information present in the experimental micrographs and using it to

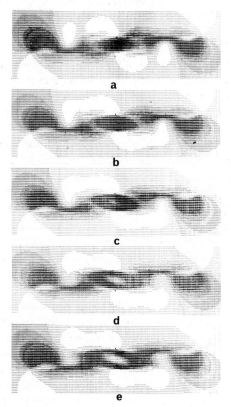

Fig. 24. Computed micrographs of a dislocation dipole in nickel corresponding to the diffraction conditions of fig. 8e. From a to e the equilibrium angle ϕ varies from $65°$ to $55°$.

reconstruct the displacement field of the defect producing the images. It is perhaps worthwhile, therefore, to spend a little time considering the principles behind this method of defect identification.

For two-beam diffraction conditions and for objects along which there is a direction in which the displacements are constant, Head has shown that the reconstruction may be done uniquely, even though all the phase information in the electron beams forming the image has been lost. Put another way, this theorem states that different defects produce different sets of electron diffraction images. This, of course, has been implicitly assumed in the "compute and match" method of defect identification discussed previously. Moreover, it follows from this theorem that a set of images from a defect will be unique to that defect for any degree of elastic anisotropy. Thus, a set of images from a dislocation (for example) even in an isotropic material will have detail in their topology etc. which will distinguish it from all other dislocations and defects.

The reconstruction method essentially rests on the fact that for defects for which there is a direction along which the displacements are constant, the displacements in one column (in the electron beam direction) in the crystal (at y) are related to those in the neighbouring column (at $y+\delta y$) by the addition and subtraction of the derivatives of the displacements $\beta'(y)$ and $\beta'(y-t)$ in small elements of material at the top and bottom surfaces of the foil. It follows that the scattering matrices for these columns are closely related. In fact, Head has shown that the scattering matrix for the column at y is related to the derivatives of the displacements in the small elements ($\beta'(y)$ and $\beta'(y-t)$) for a column at $y + \delta y$ through the second derivative of the intensity, I'', for the column at $y + \delta y$. By starting the reconstruction in undistorted crystal, where the scattering matrix is known and $I'' = 0$, it is possible to proceed along the direction in the image which is the projection of the line of constant displacement and determine either $\beta'(y)$ or $\beta'(y-t)$. For one direction of reconstruction, only one of these is unknown on moving to a neighbouring column (the other will have been determined for a column earlier in the reconstruction) and so by moving from undistorted crystal past the defect and back into undistorted crystal again one complete component (in the g direction) of the displacement field will be reconstructed. Thus, intensity information from three micrographs taken with non-coplanar diffracting vectors is sufficient to completely define the vector displacement field and hence identify the defect.

Obviously, this method of defect identification, if it is practically realized and put into routine use, is much to be preferred over the present one and would give the electron microscope an even greater role in the identification of defects in crystalline materials.

APPENDIX ADDED FOR THE SECOND EDITION

Since 1969 when the above lecture was prepared, the concepts of producing computed electron micrographs and using image matching have gained wide acceptance. Computed images have been used by France and Loretto [22], Jones and Edington [23,24], Strutt et al. [25] and Thölén [26] to identify

the Burgers vectors of isolated dislocations in various materials. Bullough et al.
[27] and Maher et al. [28] have computed the images of small dislocation
loops such as are formed in irradiated metals; Degischer [29] has investigated
the images of individual small coherent precipitates whilst Fillingham et al. [30]
have produced images of crystals containing random and periodic arrays of
such precipitates. Montheillet et al. [31] have investigated the images of dislocations which are decorated or surrounded by precipitate. Thölén [32] has
computed the images of arrays of dislocations and compared them with
moiré fringes and Easterling and Thölén [33] have looked at the strain at contact zones between small metal particles.

Several people have used multi-beam rather than two-beam theory to compute images. Spring and Steeds [34] and Steeds [35] have computed the
images to be expected at bend contours and compared them with images produced in high voltage electron microscopy to obtain values for the real lattice
potential of crystals and to investigate absorption parameters. Skalicky and
Papp [36], Nakahara and Thomas [37] and Humble [38] have computed
multi-beam theoretical micrographs of single dislocations and Allpress et al. [39]
and Allpress and Sanders [40] have published multi-beam Fourier lattice images
of ordered structures in complex mixed oxides.

Although in some of the work mentioned above multi-beam diffraction
theory was necessary, the theoretical micrographs we have been using to identify
defects in metals examined in the electron microscope at 100 kV are computed
using a two-beam theory. However, despite tilting the specimens so that only
two strong beams are present, the diffraction patterns always indicate the
presence of other weaker beams, usually in the systematic row defined by the
two strong beams. Thus, the experimental images are never taken exactly under
two-beam conditions and the question arises of how good an approximation
the theory is to the experimental case.

In practice we have found that, provided the experimental micrographs are
taken under conditions in which the diffraction patterns show just two strong
beams, the two-beam theoretical approximation to the experimental (n-beam)
image is entirely adequate for image matching. This is illustrated in fig. A1
which shows a set of four experimental images of a dislocation in aluminium *
(fig. A1(a)) and the matching set of theoretical micrographs computed on the
two-beam theory (fig. A1(b)). Although the experimental micrographs were
taken under good two-beam conditions, theoretical images were also computed
using four-beams (one extra systematic reflection on either side of the two

_____

* These images are slightly affected by the presence of another dislocation in the upper
  part of the field.

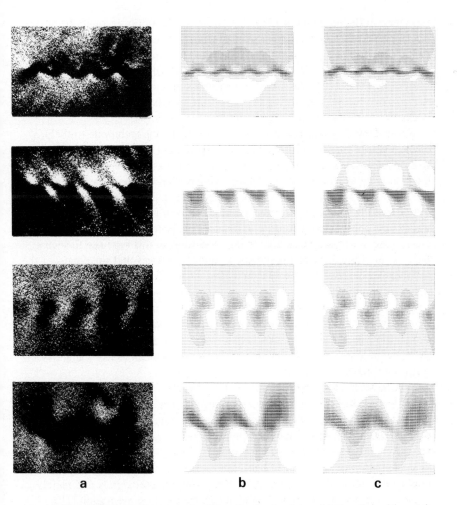

Fig. A1. Four experimental images of a dislocation in aluminium (a), together with matching sets of theoretical micrographs computed on a two-beam theory (b) and a four-beam systematic theory (c). The parameters used for computing (b) and (c) were substantially the same except the foil thickness for (b) was 1830 Å and for (c) was 1760 Å.

strongly diffracted beams) and these are shown in fig. A1(c). It can be seen that the two sets of computed micrographs are very similar and both are a good match to the experimental images. The only significant difference between the two sets is that the foil thickness for the set in fig. A1(b) was 1830 Å whereas that for fig. A1(c) was 1760 Å. This sort of result has led us to suggest in the monograph [38] that two-beam theory is adequate for image matching purposes, but a dimension change may be necessary, corresponding to the adoption of an "apparent" two-beam extinction distance (ξ_{ga}) rather then the use of the theoretical two-beam extinction distance (ξ_g). However, this is only necessary in cases where measurements are to be deduced from the matched images (e.g. the separation of the two dislocations in angstroms in fig. 22).

Recently we have been applying the image matching technique to the problem of identifying dislocations in grain boundaries (Humble and Forwood, to be published). This problem has become of increasing general interest lately and the usual experimental approach has been to orient the specimen so that one crystal is in good two-beam diffracting conditions whilst the other is not diffracting any beam strongly (i.e. it is acting more or less as an absorbing wedge) and then to use $\mathbf{g} \cdot \mathbf{b}$ rules to identify the Burgers vectors of the dislocations. We have found that diffracting conditions of this type rise to such a large range of intensity across the grain boundary fringes that the details of the dislocation image tend to be obscured. The diffracting conditions seem to be much more reproducible and the character of the images is much more visible if the specimen is oriented so that *both* crystals are simultaneously in good two-beam diffracting conditions. Moreover, since crystals are elastically anisotropic, the region where two elastic half spaces meet (a grain boundary is a most inappropriate place to try to apply $\mathbf{g} \cdot \mathbf{b}$ rules which refer to a single isotropic continuum.

Consequently, our approach has been to calculate the anisotropic displacement field for a dislocation at a grain boundary (Tucker* [41]), to use this to compute the theoretical micrograph for the simultaneous two-beam diffracting condition and then image match in the usual way. Figs. A2(a)–(e) show a matching set of theoretical and experimental micrographs of two dislocations in a coherent twin boundary in lightly deformed copper. The theoretical micrographs for each dislocation have been computed separately and merely arranged in the way shown in the figure for the sake of presentation. The dislocation at A is identified as a Shockley dislocation of $\mathbf{b} = \frac{1}{6} [\bar{1}2\bar{1}]$ and the dislocation at B has $\mathbf{b} = \frac{1}{2} [\bar{1}\bar{1}0]$, the Burgers vectors being indexed with respect to the upper crystal. The ends of the dislocations appear to be in close proximity at the upper surface of the specimen and it is possible that they are the products of a dislocation reaction occurring at the boundary. This suggestion is supported by the fact that the sum of their Burgers vectors is $\frac{1}{6} [\bar{4}\bar{1}1]$ which corresponds to $\frac{1}{2} [0\bar{1}\bar{1}]$ in the lower crystal. Moreover, dislocations with such

---

* We are grateful to Dr. Tucker (private communication) for correcting errors in the relevant formula in [41].

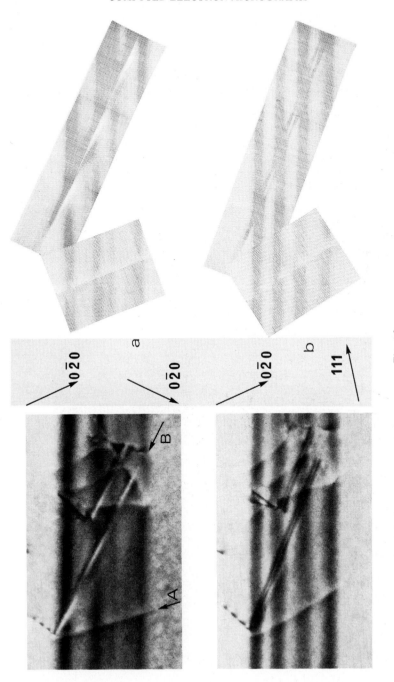

Fig. A2.

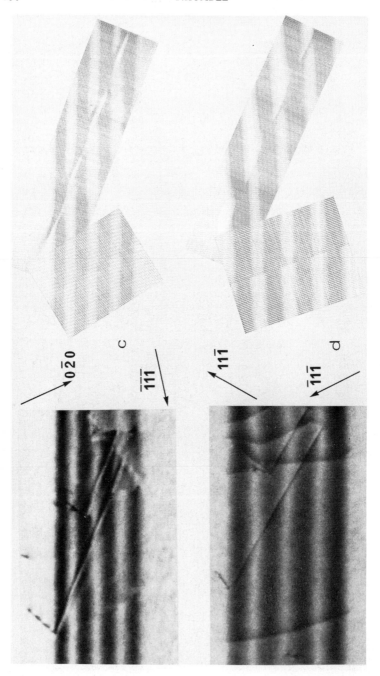

Fig. A2 (continued).

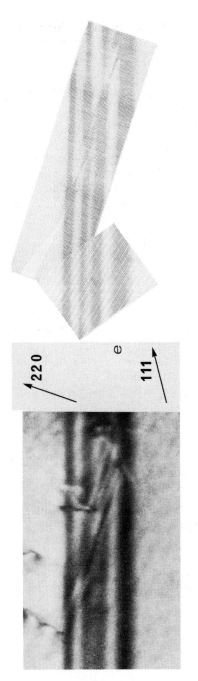

Fig. A2. Five experimental images taken under simultaneous two-beam diffraction conditions of a portion of a coherent grain boundary in lightly deformed copper together with the corresponding computed images which match the images of the dislocations at A and B.

Burgers vectors are glissile on the slip plane in the lower crystal which intersects the boundary along the line of B. Thus, it is possible that during deforma-
tion a dislocation with $\mathbf{b} = \frac{1}{2}\ [0\bar{1}\bar{1}]$ in the lower crystal slipped into the boundary and dissociated into A and B. Because the Burgers vector of B, $\frac{1}{2}\ [\bar{1}\bar{1}0]$,
does not lie in the boundary, (111), B would be sessile and constrained to stay
along the line of intersection. However, the boundary plane is a possible slip
plane for the Shockley dislocation A, $\mathbf{b} = \frac{1}{6}\ [\bar{1}2\bar{1}]$ and indeed it can be seen
that this dislocation has moved along the boundary in the course of taking the
set of micrographs (compare, for example, the positions of A in the experimental micrographs in figs. A2(b) and (d)).

It would appear, therefore, that the image matching technique combined
with micrographs taken under simultaneous two-beam conditions will be extremely useful in investigating the defect structure of boundaries.

It should be noted that all the methods of using computed images to identify
defects which have been developed follow the procedure of making guesses at
the identity of the defect and computing the corresponding images. When the
computed images for one guess match the experimental images, the defect is
identified. At the end of the lecture, mention was made of the possibility, for
generalised cross-section defects, of reconstructing the displacement field of a
defect directly from its experimental images and identifying the defect this
way. However, since the method of reconstruction is a step-wise one and involves
working from one end of the defect to the other, the errors tend to be cumulative. Because of this, in practice it has been found that the experimental reconstruction of the displacement fields of defects such as straight dislocations
cannot be carried out successfully (Head, private communication). However,
the uniqueness theorems which relate the displacement field of a defect to the
intensities in its image in the electron microscope are still invaluable in placing
the image matching technique as currently used on a firm basis.

In compiling the material for this lecture, the author has relied heavily on
the work of a number of his colleagues: L.M.Clarebrough, C.T.Forwood,
A.K.Head, M.H.Loretto and A.J.Morton. In some cases their arguments have
been followed closely, but in others the lack of space has restricted the discussion to only a brief summary of the work and thus does not do it full
justice. The author would like to thank these colleagues for permission to
discuss their work in this way and for much helpful criticism in preparing this
manuscript.

References

[1] A.Howie and M.J.Whelan, Proc. Roy. Soc. A263 (1961) 217.
[2] A.K.Head, Aust. J. Phys. 20 (1967) 557.
[3] P.Humble, ibid. 21 (1968) 325.
[4] R.Bullough, D.M.Maher and R.C.Perrin, Nature 224 (1969) 364.
[5] L.M.Clarebrough, Aust. J. Phys. 22 (1969) 559.
[6] H.B.Huntington, Solid State Phys. 7 (1958) 213.
[7] P.B.Hirsch, A.Howie, R.B.Nicholson, D.W.Pashley and M.J.Whelan, Electron Microscopy of Thin Crystals (Butterworths, London, 1966).
[8] A.J.Morton and L.M.Clarebrough, Aust. J. Phys. 22 (1969) 393.
[9] A.K.Head, ibid. 22 (1969) 43.
[10] C.T.Forwood and P.Humble, ibid., 23 (1970) 697.
[11] A.J.Morton and C.T.Forwood, Crystal Lattice Defects 4 (1973) 165.
[12] P.Humble, Austr. J. Phys. 22 (1969) 51.
[13] L.M.Clarebrough and A.J.Morton, ibid. 22 (1969) 351.
[14] L.M.Clarebrough and A.J.Morton, ibid. 22 (1969) 371.
[15] A.K.Head, M.H.Loretto and P.Humble, Phys. Stat. Sol. 20 (1967) 505.
[16] A.K.Head, M.H.Loretto and P.Humble, ibid. 20 (1967) 521.
[17] A.N.Stroh, Phil. Mag. 3 (1958) 625.
[18] P.Humble, Phys. Stat. Sol. 30 (1968) 183.
[19] M.J.Whelan and P.B.Hirsch, Phil. Mag. 2 (1957) 1121.
[20] M.J.Whelan and P.B.Hirsch, ibid. 2 (1957) 1303.
[21] A.K.Head, Aust. J. Phys. 22 (1969) 345.
[22] L.K.France and M.H.Loretto, Proc. Roy. Soc. A307 (1968) 83.
[23] P.J.Jones and J.W.Edington, Phil. Mag. 25 (1972) 729.
[24] P.J.Jones and J.W.Edington, Phil. Mag. 27 (1973) 393.
[25] P.R.Strutt, G.M.Rowe, J.C.Ingram and Y.H.Choo, in: Electron Microscopy and Structure of Materials, ed. G.Thomas (University of California Press, 1972) p. 722.
[26] A.R.Thölén, Phil. Mag. 22 (1970) 175.
[27] R.Bullough, D.M.Maher and R.C.Perrin, Phys. Stat. Sol. (b) 43 (1971) 689.
[28] D.M.Maher, R.C.Perrin and R.Bullough, Phys. Stat. Sol. (b) 43 (1971) 707.
[29] H.P.Degischer, Phil. Mag. 26 (1972) 1137.
[30] P.J.Fillingham, H.J.Leamy and L.E.Tanner, in: Electron Microscopy and Structure of Materials, ed. G.Thomas (University of California Press, 1972) p. 163.
[31] F.Montheillet, J.M.Haudin and G.Frade, Phys. Stat. Sol. (a) 17 (1973) 593.
[32] A.R.Thölén, Phys. Stat. Sol. (a) 2 (1970) 537.
[33] K.E.Easterling and A.R.Thölén, Acta Met. 20 (1972) 1001.
[34] M.S.Spring and J.W.Steeds, Phys. Stat. Sol. 37 (1970) 303.
[35] J.W.Steeds, Phys. Stat. Sol. 38 (1970) 203.
[36] P.Skalicky and A.Papp, Phil. Mag. 25 (1972) 177.
[37] S.Nakahara and L.E.Thomas, in: Electron Microscopy and Structure of Materials, ed. G.Thomas (University of California Press, 1972) p. 68.
[38] A.K.Head, P.Humble, L.M.Clarebrough, A.J.Morton and C.T.Forwood, Computed Electron Micrographs and Defect Identification (North-Holland, 1973) p. 298.
[39] J.G.Allpress, E.A.Hewat, A.F.Moodie and J.V.Sanders, Acta Cryst. A28 (1972) 528.
[40] J.G.Allpress and J.V.Sanders, J. Appl. Cryst. 6 (1973) 165.
[41] M.O.Tucker, Phil. Mag. 19 (1969) 1141.

Diffraction and Imaging Techniques in Material Science,
eds. S. Amelinckx, R. Gevers and J. van Landuyt
© *North-Holland Publishing Company, 1978*

DIRECT STRUCTURE IMAGING IN ELECTRON MICROSCOPY

D. VAN DYCK

Rijksuniversitair Centrum, Antwerpen, B-2020 Belgium

1. Introduction

The application of optical microscopy for studies at the atomic level was proved to be impossible when Ernst Abbe in 1873 showed that its theoretical resolution limit is restricted to the order of the wavelength of the "light" used.

Not until fifty years later, a new impulse was given to the problem by the hypothesis of Louis de Broglie, postulating the wave nature of particles, which was verified shortly thereafter for electrons by the famous experiments of Davisson–Germer and Thomson. Now the domain of the electromagnetic waves could be abandoned in favour of accelerated-particle optics.

The preliminary work of Hans Busch and Dennis Gabor on the focussing properties of electron lenses allowed Max Knoll and Ernst Ruska in 1931 to construct the first electron microscope, immediately followed by L. Marton in Brussels (1932) who underlined the importance of the new technique by reporting the first pictures of biological samples. Technical improvements followed each other so quickly that even before world war II, Ruska was able to convert his prototype into a commercial device with a remarkable resolving power of 20 Å. Stimulated by the development of new specimen preparation techniques in the fifties, electron microscopy increased his impact on materials science. Furthermore, the disposal of a real space image, supplemented by a simultaneous diffraction pattern offers an undeniable advantage for structural investigations. For this reason electron microscopy is complementary to other diffraction techniques and much more adapted to the study of complicated and disordered systems. However, in spite of the fact that the theoretical resolution limit of a 100 keV electron microscope reaches the order of 0.02 Å, the practically obtainable resolving power never exceeded 10 Å so that the early hope for imaging of atoms never became reality. As a direct consequence, the majority of experimental investigations was performed on large scale structures as crystal defects and domain structures.

The reason for this limitation has to be sought in the occurrence of inevitable aberrations peculiar to the use of magnetic lenses, as shown in section 2.3. Mainly as a result of steady technological improvements in the mechanical and electrical stabilities of modern electron microscopes, combined with the use of newly designed polepieces, higher acceleration voltages and point filaments, the attainable resolution has entered very recently the region of the interatomic distances. And indeed, registrations of single atom images have already been reported e.g. [1—3]. Needless to emphasize that this technique opens new perspectives for the investigation of structures of solids on an atomic scale. The experimental method for obtaining structure images in crystals is briefly described in section 4.1. According to their interpretability, high resolution images can usually be subdivided into three classes. In some favourable situations, direct structure images can be interpreted unambiguously in terms of the projected crystal structure. This is demonstrated in section 4.2 where it is even argued that minor deviations in the images can enhance the information about the real space group of the crystal. A second class contains the structure images that can be translated after the deduction of an "imaging code". Here some prior knowledge about the structure is required. Examples of such images in one as well as in two dimensions which confirm the power of this method, are given in section 4.3. Optical diffraction simulation has also proved to be a complementary tool. For the third class of images usually observed at very high resolution the interpretation is not always obvious and often impossible, particularly in the case of crystal structure images. The only way to overcome this difficulty lies in the comparison of the experimental images with those calculated for hypothetical crystal structures. The operation of the electron microscope is therefore briefly describe in section 2 in order to derive the mathematical formulae governing the image formation. The only missing link in the calculation of lattice images remains the description of the diffraction of electrons in the crystal foil, which requires an appropriate diffraction theory. Since hundreds of scattered beams can be involved in this process suitable diffraction formulations have to be searched for with care (section 5).

Section 6 finally shows the resulting structure images computed for some complex oxide represented as half-tone pictures; these can directly be compared with the experimentally observed images.

2. The transmission electron microscope

2.1. *Operation*
The working principle of the electron microscope differs in no means from

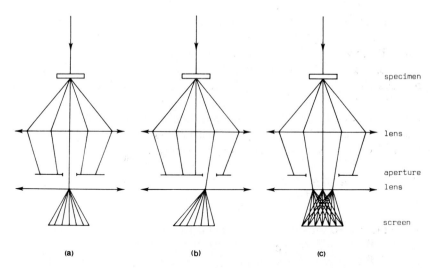

Fig. 1. Image formation in an electron microscope. (a) Bright field: only the transmitted beam contributes to the image. (b) Dark field: only one diffracted beam contributes to the image. (c) Structure imaging: the image is formed by a large number of diffracted beams.

its optical analogue. The specimen is illuminated by a monochromatic electron beam and a rotated and enlarged image is produced by the objective lens. This image is in turn projected onto a fluorescent screen by means of a combined system of intermediate and projector lenses. A second modus operandi exists in focussing the intermediate lenses onto the back focal plane of the objective lens thus generating the diffraction pattern on the fluorescent screen. In order to prevent them from contributing to the image formation, all the strongly inclined electron beams that are severely affected by the spherical aberration, are eliminated by an aperture placed in the back focal plane of the objective lens. For modern electron microscopes with reduced spherical aberration, a larger aperture can be used so that in contrast with the currently used bright- and dark field techniques, where only the transmitted respectively one diffracted beam are selected, a large number of beams can contribute to the image enhancing also the resolving power as shown in fig. 1. The structure image thus obtained is generated by superposition of the corresponding Fourier components.

2.2. Theory of image formation

Guided by the fact that a diffraction pattern can always be generated, simultaneously it is obvious that the Abbe-theory of image formation is appropriate for the description of the imaging proces. The incident electron beam is described as a plane wave diffracting by the object that can be represented by a two dimensional transmission function $q(x, y)$.

According to the Huyghens principle, the exit plane of the object acts in turn as a set of point sources for spherical waves, generating the diffracted wavefront. Since the dimensions of the lenses are macroscopic as compared to the electron wavelength, and the diffraction is paraxial, the amplitude of the diffracted wave in the direction (u, v) is adequately given by the Fraunhofer expression which is the Fourier transform of the object function.

$$Q(u, v) = \mathcal{F}_{u,v} \, q(x, y),\tag{1}$$

where the angular variables (u, v) are defined as:

$$u = \beta_x/\lambda, \qquad v = \beta_y/\lambda,\tag{2}$$

with β_x, β_y the angles of diffraction and λ the electron wavelength. As the principal property of an ideal lens is to focus parallel beams into a point of the back focal plane, the amplitude in the back focal plane of the objective

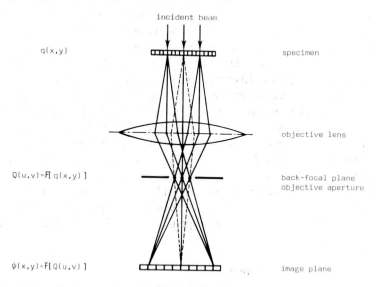

Fig. 2. Schematic representation of the image formation by the objective lens in a transmission electron microscope. The corresponding mathematical operations are indicated (see text).

lens represents the Fourier transform (diffraction pattern) of the wave function at the exit plane of the object.

For the second part in the image formation this back focal plane can be considered as a Huyghens source generating spherical waves that, possibly influenced by aberration phase shifts, interfere in the image plane. The total imaging process can thus be described as a double Fourier transform from the object to the back focal plane where the diffraction pattern is formed and from this plane to the image plane where an enlarged reproduction of the object is reconstructed (fig. 2).

2.3. Deviations from the ideal image formation

2.3.1. Aperture

The objective aperture which eliminates electron beams with inclination exceeding β_A restricts the obtainable resolution by the Abbe limit:

$$\rho_A = 0.61\lambda/\beta_A . \tag{3}$$

2.3.2. Spherical aberration

In the equation describing the motion of an electron in a magnetic lens, the inclination β always appears in the Lorentz expression as $\sin \beta$ which can be expanded as:

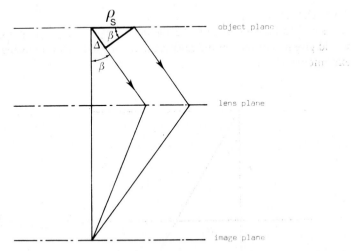

Fig. 3. Schematic representation of an inclined beam influenced by the spherical aberration. The phase shift can be deduced from the figure.

$$\sin \beta = \beta - \frac{\beta^3}{3!} + \frac{\beta^5}{5!} - \cdots . \tag{4}$$

In the paraxial ray description where $\sin \beta \approx \beta$ it can be shown that a faithful point-to-point imaging can be obtained in the so-called "gaussian plane". However in the strongly excited objective lens, third order aberrations always occur causing inclined beams to be deflected more strongly.

Hence points in the neighbourhood of an object point can contribute to the same image point giving rise to a disc of confusion in the object plane whose resolution limiting radius can proved to be

$$\rho_s = C_s \beta^3 . \tag{5}$$

β is the aperture angle and C_s is the spherical aberration coefficient of the instrument with a typical value between 1 and 10 mm. The aberrated electron suffers a phase shift whose magnitude can be roughly estimated from fig. 3 as:

$$\chi_s = 2\pi \frac{\Delta}{\lambda} = 2\pi \frac{\rho_s \beta}{\lambda} = 2\pi \frac{C_s \beta^4}{\lambda} . \tag{6}$$

More careful calculations based on spherical waves would only give one fourth of this result as pointed out by Scherzer [4].

2.3.3. Defocus

As will be shown in section 3.3 the ideal image of a perfect phase object would give no contrast in the gaussian plane so that exact focussing becomes extremely difficult.

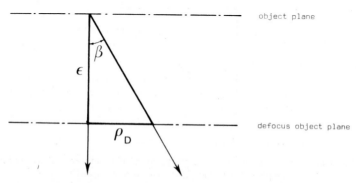

Fig. 4. Schematic representation of the ray geometry caused by defocus.

Defocussing the electron microscope by an amount ϵ while leaving the plane of observation unchanged, with the object situated near the first focal plane results in an apparent displacement of the object plane over the same amount ϵ.

From fig. 4 it follows that here also a disc of confusion is generated with a resolution limiting radius:

$$\rho_D = \epsilon\beta , \tag{7}$$

whereas the corresponding phase shift is given by:

$$\chi_D = 2\pi \frac{\Delta}{\lambda} = \frac{2\pi}{\lambda} [\tfrac{1}{2}\rho_D \beta] = \frac{\pi}{\lambda} \epsilon\beta^2 . \tag{8}$$

2.3.4. Chromatic aberration

As its optical analogue, chromatic aberration arises from the relative spread on the wavelength of the incident electron due to instabilities in the accelerating potential and inelastic scattering in the specimen $(\Delta V/V)$ or from variations in the lens currents $(\Delta I/I)$. The netto effect on the image formation can be shown to be a spread on the focus distance given by:

$$\Delta f = C_c \sqrt{(\Delta V/V)^2 + 2(\Delta I/I)^2} , \tag{9}$$

corresponding to a radius of confusion similar to a defocussing:

$$\rho_C = \Delta f \beta . \tag{10}$$

C_c is the chromatic aberration constant whose value for modern electron microscopes can be reduced below 10 mm with the relative instabilities $\Delta V/V$ and $\Delta I/I$ reaching the order of 10^{-6} so that Δf takes a typical value of 100 Å.

2.3.5. Beam divergence

As a consequence of the finite dimensions of electron source and condensor lens aperture, a slight divergence of the incident beam, combined with a decrease in its lateral coherence is inevitable.

The apex angle of the illuminating cone can even increse to 2×10^{-3} radians when higher beam intensities are required as in the case of direct structure imaging.

Fortunately Hibi [5] has shown experimentally that the influence of this effect on the image can be described by a continuous superposition of independent image intensities, each corresponding to another angle of the divergence cone so that this effect can, at least qualitatively, be accounted for the calculations.

2.3.6. Other deviations

Other deviations such as astigmatism, coma, distortion, curvature, specimen drift and mechanical instabilities are either unimportant or can satisfactorily be compensated or eliminated in modern electron microscopes and will not be further discussed here.

2.4. *Ultimate resolution*

As already discussed, mainly three independent factors: aperture, spherical and chromatic aberration can restrict the resolving power so that the resultant resolution limit is given by:

$$\rho = \sqrt{\rho_A^2 + \rho_S^2 + \rho_C^2}\,,\tag{11}$$

with ρ_A, ρ_S, ρ_C respectively expressed by (3), (5), (10).

In fig. 5 ρ, ρ_A, ρ_S, ρ_C are graphically expressed as a function of the aperture half angle β for the practical case of the 100 keV electron microscope used for the experimental work in sections 4.2 and 4.3 with aberration constants $C_s = 8.2$ mm and $C_c = 3.9$ mm.

It follows from this diagram that the chromatic aberration has only minor

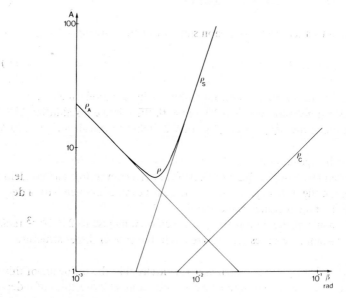

Fig. 5. Graphic representation of ρ, ρ_A, ρ_C, ρ_S as a function of the aperture angle β. The aberration constants are respectively $C_s = 8.2$ mm and $C_c = 3.9$ mm.

influence on the resolving power and that an optimal aperture angle of 5×10^{-3} radians exists corresponding to a point resolution of 5 Å.

2.5. Mathematical formulation of the real image formation

As shown in section 2.2 the amplitude in the back focal plane of the objective lens is given by the Fourier transform of the wave function at the exit plane of the object:

$$Q(u, v) = \mathcal{F}_{u,v} \, q(x, y) . \tag{12}$$

During the second step of the image formation, which is also described by a Fourier transform, the electron suffers a phase shift $\chi(u, v)$ caused by spherical aberration and defocus as shown in section (2.3). The final image amplitude is then given by the expression:

$$\mathcal{U}(x, y) = \mathcal{F}_{x,y} \, A(u, v) \, e^{-i\chi(u,v)} \, Q(u, v) , \tag{13}$$

with for the phase shift $\chi(u, v)$ from (6) and (8) using (2):

$$\chi(u, v) = \tfrac{1}{2}\pi C_s \lambda^3 (u^2 + v^2) + \pi\epsilon\lambda(u^2 + v^2) . \tag{14}$$

$A(u, v)$ represents the aperture function selecting the admitted electron beams. The image intensity is finally obtained as $|\Psi(x, y)|^2$. As mentioned earlier in section 2.3 the influence of beam divergence and chromatic aberration can properly be introduced by adding up image intensities corresponding respectively to various angles from the cone of incidence or to different focus values. Very recently [6] however it is shown that the blurring effect of either beam divergence and chromatic aberration on image quality is quite similar and can to a first approximation be taken into account in the calculations by simply reducing the effective radius of the aperture and so eliminating the most strongly affected electron beams.

3. Direct interpretation of structure images

3.1. Phase grating

The wavelength of an electron accelerated by a potential E is known to be:

$$\lambda = \frac{h}{\sqrt{2meE}} , \tag{15}$$

with h: the Planck constant; m: the electron mass; e: the electron charge.

During the motion through an object with local potential $V(x, y, z)$ the wavelength will vary with the position of the electron as:

$$\lambda'(x, y, z) = \frac{h}{\sqrt{2me[E + V(x, y, z)]}} .$$ (16)

For thin phase objects and high accelerating potentials the assumption can be made that the electron keeps travelling along the z-direction so that by propagation through a slice dz the electron suffers a phase-shift.

$$d\chi(x, y, z) = 2\pi \frac{dz}{\lambda'} - 2\pi \frac{dz}{\lambda}$$

$$= 2\pi \frac{dz}{\lambda} \left(\frac{\sqrt{E + V(x, y, z)} - 1}{\sqrt{E}} \right) \simeq \sigma V(x, y, z)\, dz$$ (17)

with:

$$\sigma = \pi/\lambda E .$$

So that the total phaseshift is given by:

$$\chi(x, y) = \sigma \int V(x, y, z)\, dz = \sigma\varphi(x, y)$$ (18)

where $\varphi(x, y)$ represents the potential of the specimen projected along the z-direction.

Under this assumption the specimen acts as a pure phase grating with transmission function:

$$q(x, y) = e^{i\sigma\varphi(x,y)} .$$ (19)

The effect of all processes, prohibiting the electrons from contributing to the image contrast, including the use of a finite aperture can in a first approximation be represented by a projected absorption function [7] in the exponent of (19) so that:

$$q(x, y) = e^{i\sigma\varphi(x,y) - \mu(x,y)} .$$ (20)

3.2. *Image interpretation in the optimal "Scherzer defocus"*

Where the phase object is very thin or weakly scattering, the exponential in (20) can be expanded to the first power as:

$$q(x, y) \simeq 1 + i\sigma\varphi(x, y) - \mu(x, y), \tag{21}$$

so that the Fourier transform, yielding the amplitude in the back focal plane becomes:

$$Q(u, v) = \delta(u, v) + i\sigma\phi(u, v) - M(u, v), \tag{22}$$

with the Dirac function $\delta(u, v)$ representing the transmitted beam.
Substitution in (13) yields for the image amplitude:

$$\psi(x, y) = \underset{x,y}{\mathcal{F}} Q(u, v) e^{-i\chi(u,v)}$$

$$= \underset{x,y}{\mathcal{F}} [\delta(u,v) + \sigma\phi(u, v) \sin \chi(u, v) - M(u, v) \cos \chi(u, v)$$

$$+ i\sigma\phi(u, v) \cos \chi(u, v) + iM(u, v) \sin \chi(u, v)]. \tag{23}$$

An ideal image of the phase function $\varphi(x, y)$ should be obtained in case $\sin \chi(u, v) \approx \pm 1$ for all contributing diffracted beams, a technique which finds his analogue in the quarter wavelength plate in optical phase contrast microscopy.

Unfortunately, due to spherical aberration and defocus, $\sin \chi(u, v)$ appears to be a rapidly oscillating function of the diffraction angle β so that this requirement can never be fulfilled exactly.

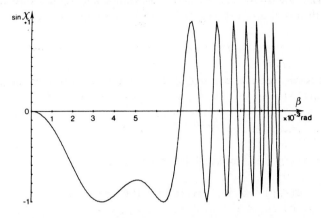

Fig. 6. $\sin \chi$ as a function of the diffraction angle β at the Scherzer underfocus of -2100 A. The spherical aberration constant is 8.2 mm.

However, a careful examination of the expression (14) for $\chi(u, v)$ learns that for a proper negative choice of the defocus value ϵ called the "Scherzer defocus" the phase contribution from spherical aberration is canceled by the defocus for a relatively large range of diffraction angles. And indeed from fig. 6 where $\chi(u, v)$ is sketched as a function of the diffraction angle β for the explicite case of section 2.4 it follows clearly that for an optimal Scherzer defocus value of -2100 Å, $\sin \chi \approx -1$ for the range of diffraction angles corresponding to a point resolution of 5 Å in agreement with the results of section 2.4.

Now (23) becomes:

$$\psi(x, y) \approx \mathcal{F}_{x,y} \left[\delta(u, v) - \sigma\phi(u, v) - iM(u, v) \right]$$

$$= 1 - \sigma\varphi(x, y) - i\mu(x, y) ,$$

and the image intensity to the first order:

$$I(x, y) \approx 1 - 2\sigma\varphi(x, y) .$$

In the Scherzer defocus, the image contrast of a thin object is thus proportional to its projected potential $\varphi(x, y)$ along the direction of incidence as confirmed by the observations (see section 4.2).

The value of this theory, that can even be generalised for larger phase changes [8] lies in the fact that it describes the image formation in a real electron microscope by taking spherical aberration and defocus into account.

Nevertheless its application remains restricted to thin objects.

3.3. *Image interpretation for small defocus values: The projected charge density approximation*

In the absence of apertures and spherical aberration, the image amplitude is given from (13) as:

$$\psi(x, y) = \mathcal{F}_{x,y} \, e^{-i\pi\epsilon\lambda(u^2 + v^2)} Q(u, v) \tag{24}$$

which can be expanded for small defocus values ϵ as:

$$\psi(x, y) = \mathcal{F}_{x,y} \left[1 - i\pi\epsilon\lambda(u^2 + v^2) \right] Q(u, v)$$

$$= q(x, y) - i\pi\epsilon\lambda \, \mathcal{F}_{x,y} \, (u^2 + v^2) Q(u, v)$$

or explicitly:

$$= q(x, y) - i\pi\epsilon\lambda \int e^{2\pi i(xu+yv)}(u^2 + v^2) Q(u, v)\, du\, dv .$$

This expression can be transformed elegantly as:

$$\psi(x, y) = q(x, y) + \frac{i\pi\epsilon\lambda}{4\pi^2}\left(\frac{\delta^2}{\delta x^2} + \frac{\delta^2}{\delta y^2}\right)\int e^{2\pi i(xu+yv)} Q(u, v)\, du\, dv$$

$$= \left[1 + \frac{i\epsilon\lambda}{4\pi}\left(\frac{\delta^2}{\delta x^2} + \frac{\delta^2}{\delta y^2}\right)\right] q(x, y) , \qquad (25)$$

which for a phase grating, where $q(x, y) = e^{i\sigma\varphi(x,y)}$ becomes:

$$\psi(x, y) = \left\{1 - \frac{\epsilon\lambda\sigma\Delta\varphi(x, y)}{4\pi} \right.$$

$$\left. - \frac{i\epsilon\lambda\sigma^2}{4\pi}\left[\left(\frac{\delta\varphi(x, y)}{\partial x}\right)^2 + \left(\frac{\delta\varphi(x, y)}{\partial y}\right)\right]^2\right\} e^{i\sigma\varphi(x,y)} . \quad (26)$$

So that the image intensity $\psi(x, y)\psi^*(x, y)$ is given to the first order by:

$$I(x, y) = 1 - \frac{\epsilon\lambda\sigma\Delta\varphi(x, y)}{2\pi} . \qquad (27)$$

Since the potential $\varphi(x, y)$ is of electrostatic origin it obeys the Poisson equation:

$$\Delta\varphi(x, y) = -4\pi\rho(x, y) , \qquad (28)$$

so that finally:

$$I(x, y) = 1 + 2\epsilon\lambda\sigma\rho(x, y) . \qquad (29)$$

The image contrast is thus proportional to the projected charge density; it disappears in the gaussian image plane ($\epsilon = 0$) as already mentioned and reverses with the sign of the defocus.

Although this theory remains valid for a larger range of specimen thicknesses as shown in [9,10] and can be generalised to account for spherical aberration [11], its applicability remains restricted to resolutions for which this spherical aberration is less important.

Nevertheless the great value of the charge density and the Scherzer defocus methods lies in the fact that they permit a straightforward interpretation of structure images in cases (e.g. biological) where no diffraction calculations can be carried out.

4. Experimental structure imaging of crystals

4.1. *Technique*

The transmission function of a crystalline object is periodic so that the diffraction pattern consists of a regular array of spots corresponding to the diffracted beams allowing both identification and proper orientation of the crystal foil. Unit cells with two large and one small lattice parameter are most appropriate for direct structure imaging since their reciprocal lattice consists of largely separated dense planes. Such crystals can be oriented with their short axis parallel to the incident beam causing the nearly plane Ewald sphere to touch the dense plane through the origin (fig. 7) so that a large number of beams are simultaneously excited whereby maximal information can contribute to the image (fig. 8). In this situation the electrons propagate parallel to the atom rows making an interpretation in terms of the projected structure meaningful. For this reason, the use of a goniometer stage with tilting possibilities is required. In practice, specimens are usually prepared by grinding the crystals in an agate mortar, suspending the powder in methanol and depositing a drop of this suspension on a perforated supporting film. Thin wedge shaped crystal flakes, partly covering the holes of the film are searched for at low magnification and serve to obtain the best crystal structure images. In some cases grinding has to be carried out at liquid nitrogen temperature where the material is more brittle and cleavage along a required plane can be favoured. Since exact focusing is impossible pictures are usually taken at different focus values regularly spaced at about 100 Å: a so called "through focus series". Current exposure times amount to a few seconds at a primary magnification of approximately 300,000X.

4.2. *Structure images with a straightforward interpretation*

According to sections 3.2 and 3.3 the image of very thin specimens can often be interpreted in terms of the projected crystal structure.

This can be clearly demonstrated for the mineral dumortierite, a nesosubsilicate with formula $(Al,Fe)_7 [O_3 | BO_3 | (SiO_4)_3]$ consisting of isolated SiO_4 tetrahedra with BO_3 triangles as additional complex anions held together by Al ions in sixfold coordination (fig. 9).

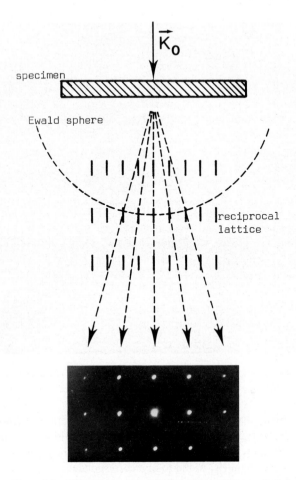

Fig. 7. Formation of the diffraction pattern. The simultaneously excited electron beams
can be used for the image formation.

The mineral is orthorhombic with space group $D_{2h}^{16}-P_{cmn}$ with unit cell
parameters a = 11.79 Å, b = 20.21 Å, c = 4.70 Å which makes it especially
suitable for structure imaging. Viewing down the [001] direction (fig. 9) the
crystal can be considered as consisting of channels with distorted face-sharing
AlO_6 octahedra(A channels) and channels with BO_3 triangles (B channels).
The A and B channels are in a 6/3 coordination, every A channel being surrounded by 6 B channels and evert B channel by 3 neighbouring A channels.
Fig. 10 shows a large magnification of the structure image, taken at the

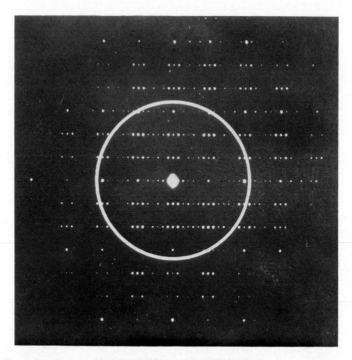

Fig. 8. Typical diffraction pattern as used for structure imaging. The aperture, selecting the contributing beams is also indicated.

Scherzer undefocus and consisting of white spots on a dark background. From the intensities, two types of spots can be clearly distinguished. According to their configuration the white spots can be identified as the A channels and the grey spots as the B-channels. A one-to-one correspondence with the real structure becomes obvious when comparing the lattice image with the X-ray structure as shown at the same scale in the inset. The channels are represented schematically by circles. The projections of the crystal structure into a plane perpendicular to a crystal axis may acquire additional symmetry elements as compared to the spatial crystal structure seen along the same zone. If the projected charge density or the thin phase grating approximations were correct as well the image as the diffraction pattern should show the higher symmetry of the projected crystal structure, however since they are in fact produced by an admittedly thin but nonetheless three dimensional crystal, deviations may be expected.

According to Wyckoff [12] the projection of the dumortierite structure

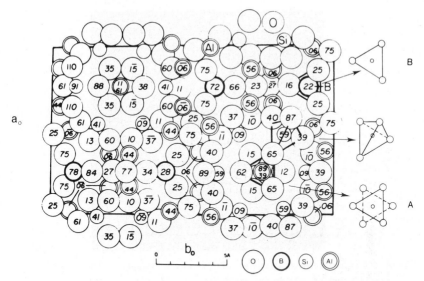

Fig. 9. Structure of dumortierite projected along the c-axis. The relative height of the atoms is indicated (after Wyckoff [12]). The polyhedral configurations are shown separately.

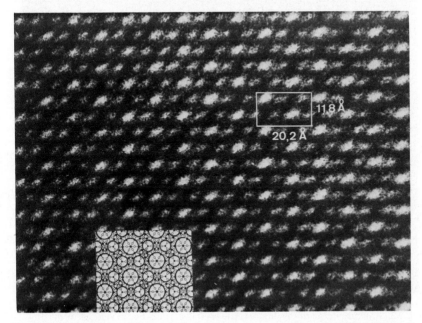

Fig. 10. Structure image of dumortierite seen along the c-axis. The unit cell is outlined. For comparison a projection of the crystal structure is inserted.

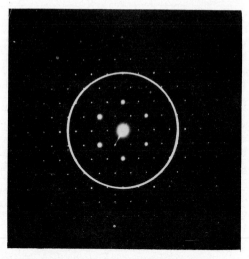

Fig. 11. The electron diffraction pattern of dumortierite, showing the (hko) reflections. The objective aperture including the imaging beams is also indicated.

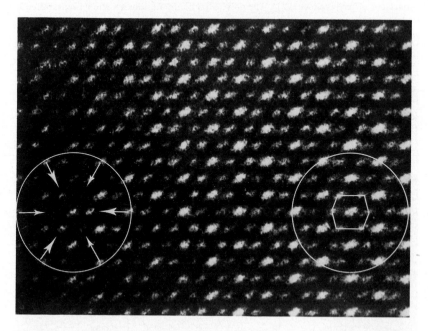

Fig. 12. Structure image of the dumortierite crystal showing two deviations of the projected structure (see text).

along the c-axis shows a pseudo 6 mm symmetry which at first sight was also observed in the diffraction pattern (fig. 11) and in the direct image of the thinnest crystal parts (fig. 10 right). However a closer examination of the lattice image shows two deviations from this symmetry. First the hexagon formed by the B channels surrounding an A channel seems to be flattened in the B-direction, secondly, according to minor intensity differences, two types of B channels can be observed in the thicker crystal areas as shown in fig. 12. This deviation of the projected crystal structure can be due to the different vertical positions and orientations of the BO_3 triangles in the B-channels. These effects should reduce the possible two-dimensional space group to pm or cm. No further distinction can be made since no deviations can be observed for the A channels.

4.3. Structure images that can be interpreted using an imaging code

4.3.1. Structure images showing one-dimensional periodicities [13]

As an example of crystals showing one dimensional periodic images, the hexagonal ferrites form a remarkable series of materials differing as well in structure as in composition. Their c-parameter can be as large as 1600 Å. The discussion here will be restricted to the so called $M_p Y_q$ series [14] although a MS_n series exists as well. The hexagonal structure of the pure M material as pointed out by Braun [14] is represented in fig. 13. Its composition is $BaFe_{12}O_{19}$ and its stacking sequence:

$$caCac|baBab|caCac,$$

with the small letters representing the oxygen layers and the capitals the oxygen-barium layers. The structure can be described as consisting of two M blocks M_1 and M_2 11.6 Å in width and rotated with respect to each other over 180° along the c-axis. The barium—oxygen layer forms a mirror plane. The rhombohedral Y structure with composition $Ba_2ZnFe_{12}O_{22}$ contains three Y-blocks in the unit cell of 14.52 Å with stacking sequence.

$$\begin{array}{ccc} Y_1 & Y_2 & Y_3 \end{array}$$
$$acACac|baBAba|cbCBcb|.$$

In appropriate conditions crystals can be grown with intermediate compositions, consisting of a mixture of M and Y blocks.

Fig. 14 shows a direct image of such crystal. The diffraction spots used for the imaging are shown in the inset. The line pattern clearly shows two spacings

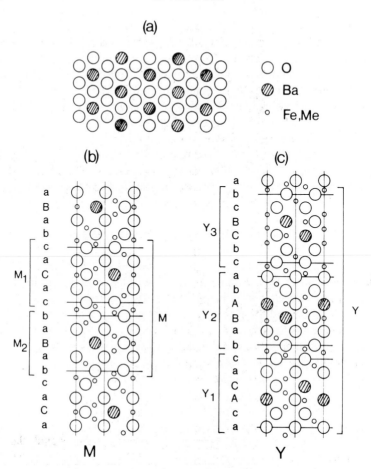

Fig. 13. Structure of the hexagonal ferrites. (a) Structure of the O−Ba layers. (b) The M-structure. (c) The Y-structure (after Braun [15]).

$d_1 = 11.6$ Å and $d_2 = 14.52$ Å respectively corresponding with the thickness of the M and Y blocks. It seems obvious to associate with two lines separated by a distance d_1 an M block and with d_2 an Y block. This simple imaging code can however only be used for certain diffraction conditions and crystal thicknesses. Imaging with non-central row spots can also give rise to an interpretable imaging code as shown in fig. 15 where it is apparent that successive Y bands are imaged with different contrast.

By this technique the stacking as determined by X-ray diffraction methods could be confirmed and moreover a number of new stacking variants could be

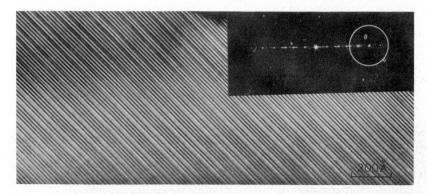

Fig. 14. One dimensional structure of an hexagonal ferrite. The insert shows the diffracted beams used of the image formation.

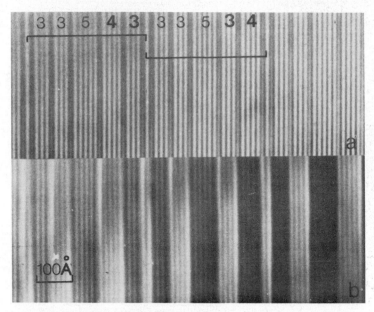

Fig. 15. Correspondance between images formed by central and non-central diffraction rows.

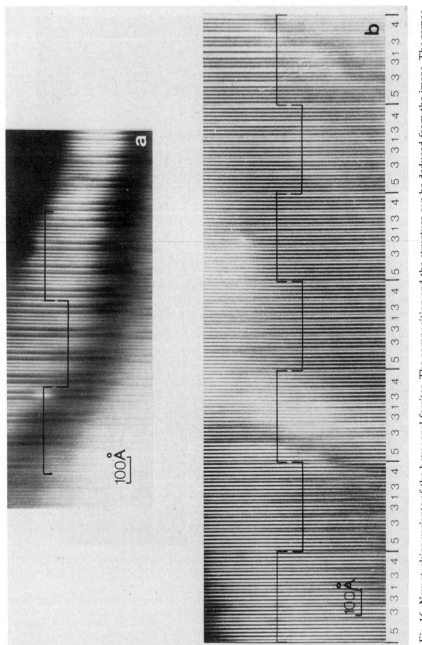

Fig. 16. New stacking variants of the hexagonal ferrites. The composition and the structure can be deduced from the image. The respective number of Y-layers separated by an M-layer are also indicated.

discovered and identified as shown in fig. 16. It could be concluded that M blocks always occur isolated whereas Y blocks always appear as alternating crystallographically differing "bands" as follows from the contrast differences of fig. 15.

The structure can simply be described as derived from the pure Y structure by non-conservative periodic twinning on a very fine scale in order to compensate for compositional deviations. The M blocks act hereby as twin boundaries.

4.3.2. Two dimensional structure images [16]

In the course of a systematic study of lanthanide compounds with two different anions by means of X-ray diffraction techniques, Dragon [17] demonstrated the existence of a very characteristic polytypism in YSeF. Eight different polytypes could be distinguished. Their unit cell parameters obey simple geometrical relations according to which they can be subdivided into orthorhombic and a monoclinic class with the same a and c parameters. Nguyen Huy-Dung was able to determine the crystal structure for three of these polytypes [18] using Patterson analysis refined by a least squares method. These polytypes were found to be built up by the periodic stacking of two types of unit blocks, called S and T hereafter. Corresponding to the number n of blocks in the repeated stacking, the polytypes can be characterised by the notation nO or nM whether they belong to the orthorhombic or monoclinic group. The projection on the (a, b) plane of the structure of one of this polytypes, the orthorhombic 6 O is represented in fig. 17. According to the slope of their Y planes two types of unit blocks, S and T can be distinguished, as schematically indicated in the right part of the figure. They can be deduced from each other by a glide mirror operation (a, c) with translation vector $a/2$ along [100] as consistent with the space group of this polytype. Notice also that the type of Y plane interchanges on passing through as ST boundary but remains the same through an SS or TT boundary. The polytype 6 O can thus be characterised by the stacking sequence SSSTTT. Similarly the two other polytypes 2 O and 4 M were respectively identified as ST and SSST. It was postulated in general that all the YSeF polytypes should be constructed by a repeated stacking of the two types of blocks in agreement with the simple geometrical relations of their unit cell parameters. However the application of the X-ray techniques for testing this model by determining the structure of the remaining polytypes failed due to the fact that their preparation in the form of pure monocrystals is almost impossible. Besides, this techniques is less adapted to the study of the longer and more complicated sequences.

As opposed to X-ray diffraction, high resolution electron microscopy is much more suitable for the study of compounds with large unit cells and can

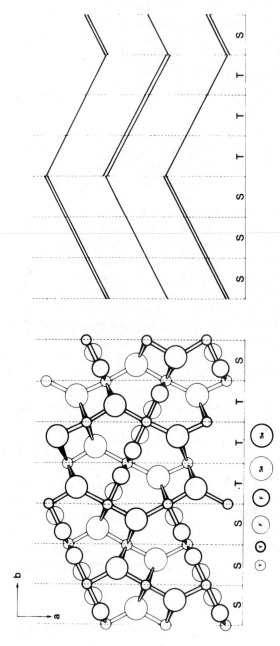

Fig. 17. Projection of the unit cell of the polytype 6 O on the (a, b) plane. The YF planes are schematically represented by double lines and the Y-planes by single lines.

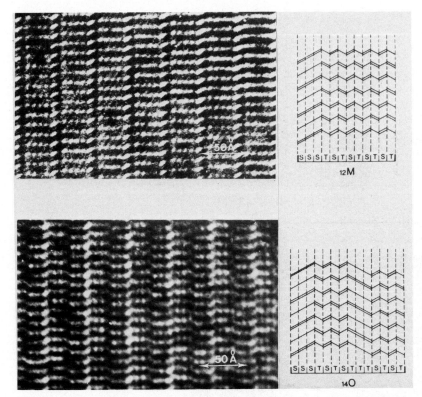

Fig. 18. Comparison of the structure images of the polytypes 12 M and 14 O with their proposed ST stackings as derived from the imaging code.

also be applied to the investigation of less pure an polycrystalline materials. For these reasons structure imaging could be used as a complementary tool for the study of the more complicated polytypes and of irregular sequences and defects. In order to translate the images into the corresponding structures, an imaging code had to be deduced. This could be obtained by comparing the structures of the three known polytypes with the images obtained viewing down the c-axis in the thinnest crystal parts at the optimal Scherzer defocus (~ −2000 Å). From the images thus obtained it could be concluded that an S block should be imaged as a (mostly bright) parallelogram with a slope corresponding to its Y-planes whereas a T block is imaged as a (mostly darker) parallelogram also having the same slope as its Y-planes. The alternation of S and T blocks can be clearly resolved but due to the resolution limit of the

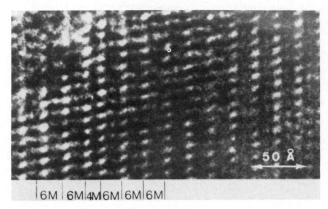

Fig. 19. Examples of a polytypic defect occurring as an intergrowth in a regular matrix.

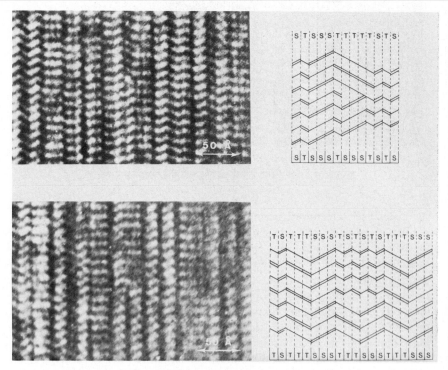

Fig. 20. Two examples of "frozen-in" defects associated with the polytype growth. The schematized structure and the stacking sequence can be read from the images.

instrument, the SSS and TTT blocks are imaged as a single parallelogram of triple length. Using the contrast features revealed by this imaging code, the images of the other five more complicated polytypes could be directly translated in terms of S and T blocks as shown in fig. 18 for the types 12 M and 14 O together with their schematised stacking model. Similarly three new polytypes could be discovered and characterised in syntaxy with other polytypes. Polytypic defects and frozen-in defects associated with their growth could be identified as e.g. respectively shown in figs. 19 and 20. Optical diffraction simulations with a laser beam on periodically arranged and photographically reduced schematical drawings of the polytype models showed a remarkable resemblance with the electron diffraction patterns as e.g. shown in fig. 21 and could be used for the identification of polytypes for which no high quality images could be obtained.

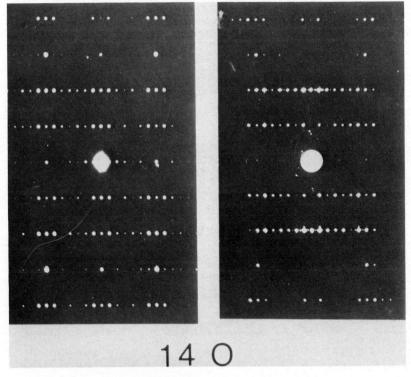

Fig. 21. Comparison between the simulated (right) and the electron diffraction pattern (left) obtained for the polytype 14 O.

Finally it could be concluded that the high-temperature formed polytypes
are all monoclinic and can be described by the repeated occurrence of an SSS
triad in an ST matrix as if T block is transformed into a S block at periodic
distances inversely proportional to the formation temperature. If associated
with a slight compositional change this might suggest a shear-structure like
mechanism of incorporating deviations from the stoichiometric so that descriptions in terms of polytypism should become questionable. And indeed a
recently performed accurate Patterson synthesis seems to give evidence for the
substitution of a small fraction of fluorine atoms by oxygen confirming also
this hypothesis [19]. This technique of structure imaging is thus complementary to classical X-ray diffraction techniques, from which it requires some
prior knowledge of the structure in order to deduce an imaging code which in
turn can be used to study the more complicated and disordered structures.

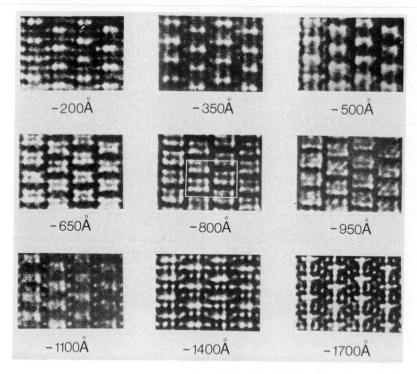

Fig. 22. Through focus series of structure images from the complex oxide $Ti_2Nb_{10}O_{29}$.
Notice that the contrast can change drastically with the defocus (courtesy Dr. Iijima).

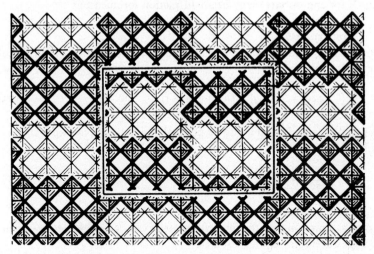

Fig. 23. Schematic representation of the unit cell of $Ti_2Nb_{10}O_{29}$ consisting of corner-
sharing NbO_6 octahedra with the Ti-atoms in tetrahedral sites.

4.4. *Structure images requiring calculations for the interpretation*

When no obvious imaging code is available, the interpretation of structure
images often becomes a precarious problem since especially at very high resolutions, the image contrast can vary drastically with the focus distance. As a
typical example, structure images obtained by Iijima for the complex oxide
$Ti_2Nb_{10}O_{25}$ with a point resolution of approximately 3.5 Å are shown in
fig. 22. The structure as reproduced schematically in fig. 23 consists of a
stacking of corner- or face-shearing NbO_6 octahedrons with the titanium atoms
in tetrahedral positions [20]. Structure images are taken at different focus
values, causing the contrast to change drastically as follows from fig. 22. The
best resemblance with the X-ray structure can be obtained near the optimum
Scherzer defocus which is −900 Å in this particular case. However the interpretation of such high resolution images never appears to be trivial. The only
way out remains in the comparison of the experimental images with those
calculated for the proposed crystal model, with the aid of the image formation
formulae derived in section 2. For this purpose the description of the diffraction in the crystal foil is the only missing link. In the next section a detailed
investigation is carried out in order to search for many beam diffraction formulations that are most adapted for the treatment of this problem.

5. Search for appropriate many beam diffraction formulations

5.1. *General expression*

The Schrödinger equation, describing the motion of an electron in a local potential is given by:

$$\Delta\psi(\mathbf{r}) + \frac{2me}{\hbar^2}[E + U(\mathbf{r})]\,\psi(\mathbf{r}) = 0 \ . \tag{30}$$

The crystal potential, assumed to be perfectly periodic can be expanded in a Fourier series as:

$$\frac{2me}{\hbar^2}U(\mathbf{r}) = \sum_{\mathbf{g}}V_{\mathbf{g}}e^{2\pi i\mathbf{g}\cdot\mathbf{r}} \ , \tag{31}$$

with $\mathbf{g}$ a reciprocal lattice vector.

In the assumption that the incident electron can be represented by a plane wave with wavevector $\mathbf{k}_0$ one also has:

$$2meE/\hbar^2 = 4\pi^2\mathbf{k}_0^2 \ . \tag{32}$$

The wave function $\psi(\mathbf{r})$ can now be written as a Bloch wave with wavevector $\mathbf{k}_0$ and z dependent Fourier coefficients:

$$\psi(\mathbf{r}) = \sum_{\mathbf{g}}\varphi_{\mathbf{g}}(z)e^{2\pi i(\mathbf{k}_0+\mathbf{g})\cdot\mathbf{r}} \ . \tag{33}$$

The wavefunction is thus a superposition of diffracted waves in directions $\mathbf{k}_0 + \mathbf{g}$ with corresponding amplitudes $\varphi_{\mathbf{g}}$ as in agreement with the Bragg law. Substitution of (31), (32) and (33) in (30) yields the following system of linear coupled differential equations.

$$\frac{d^2\varphi_{\mathbf{g}}(z)}{dz^2} + 4\pi i(\mathbf{k}_0+\mathbf{g})_z\frac{d\varphi_{\mathbf{g}}(z)}{dz} + 4\pi^2[\mathbf{k}_0^2 - (\mathbf{k}_0+\mathbf{g})^2]\varphi_{\mathbf{g}}(z)$$

$$+ 4\pi^2\sum_{\mathbf{g}'}V_{\mathbf{g}-\mathbf{g}'}\,\varphi_{\mathbf{g}'}(z) = 0 \ . \tag{34}$$

As pointed out in [21] the second order derivative terms, originating mainly from the backscattered electrons, can be neglected for high energy electron diffraction in a thin crystal foil.

Hence (34) becomes:

$$\frac{d\varphi_{\mathbf{g}}(z)}{dz} = i\pi \left(\frac{k_0^2 - (\mathbf{k}_0 + \mathbf{g})^2}{(\mathbf{k}_0 + \mathbf{g})_z} \right) \varphi_{\mathbf{g}}(z) + i\pi \sum_{\mathbf{g}} \frac{V_{\mathbf{g} - \mathbf{g}'} \varphi_{\mathbf{g}'}(z)}{(\mathbf{k}_0 + \mathbf{g})_z} \qquad (35)$$

which can be written in matrix notation as:

$$\Phi'(z) = i\pi S \Phi(z) , \qquad (36)$$

$\Phi(z)$ is the column vector with components $\varphi_i(z) = \varphi_{\mathbf{g}_i}(z)$ and $\mathbf{g}_1 = \mathbf{0}$. S is the dynamical matrix defined by:

$$i\pi S = T + V \qquad (37)$$

where:

$$T_{\mathbf{g},\mathbf{g}'} = 2\pi i s_{\mathbf{g}} \delta_{\mathbf{g},\mathbf{g}'} \qquad (38)$$

a diagonal matrix describing the propagation of the diffracted beams with:

$$s_{\mathbf{g}} = \frac{k_0^2 - (\mathbf{k}_0 + \mathbf{g})^2}{2(\mathbf{k}_0 + \mathbf{g})_z} , \qquad (39)$$

the excitation error, approximately equal to the distance from the reciprocal point $\mathbf{g}$ to the Ewald sphere, measured along z and:

$$V_{\mathbf{g},\mathbf{g}'} = \frac{i\pi V_{\mathbf{g} - \mathbf{g}'}}{(\mathbf{k}_0 + \mathbf{g})_z} , \qquad (40)$$

the matrix describing the scattering from $\mathbf{g}$ into $\mathbf{g}'$.

The linear system of coupled differential equations (36) usually called system of Howie and Whelan [22] was independently derived by Tournarie [23]. Its formal solution which is in fact Sturkeys expression [24] can be written as:

$$\Phi(z) = e^{i\pi S z} E_0 , \qquad (41)$$

with:

$$E_0 = \begin{pmatrix} 1 \\ 0 \\ \cdot \\ \cdot \\ \cdot \\ 0 \end{pmatrix} , \qquad (42)$$

expressing the boundary condition of continuity.

As pointed out in [25] and [26] by means of Feynman's path integral formalism, all dynamical high-energy electron diffraction formulations are in fact expansions or approximations of expression (41), so that the search for optimal formulations has to be concentrated on this relation. It is obvious that all expansions for the exponential matrix alone, are, although independent from the boundary condition, useless for structure image calculations since they require a computer memory proportional to the square of the number of beams involved with a calculation time proportional to the fourth power. Appropriate diffraction formulations therefore have to carry out the calculations with one vector, starting from the boundary condition. A discussion of possible formulations is given in the next sections.

5.2. The multislice formulation

Although derived from physico-optical instead of quantum mechanical principles, the multislice formulation can also be proved to be an expansion of the basic expression (41) (e.g. [25] and [27]). The crystal foil is divided into N slices with thickness Δz so that (41) becomes:

$$\Phi(z) = e^{i\pi S z} E_0 = e^{(T+V)z} E_0 = [e^{(T+V)\Delta z}]^n E_0 . \tag{43}$$

According to a theorem of Zassenhaus (e.g. [28]) one can expand:

$$e^{A+B} = e^A e^B e^{-1/2 [A,B]} \dots , \tag{44}$$

so that for small slice thicknesses:

$$e^{[T+V] \Delta z} \approx e^{T\Delta z} e^{V\Delta z} ,$$

and hence:

$$\Phi(z) = e^{T\Delta z} e^{V\Delta z} e^{T\Delta z} e^{V\Delta z} \dots e^{T\Delta z} e^{V\Delta z} E_0 . \tag{45}$$

The scattering through the crystal foil can thus be described by scattering in a slice, represented by the phase grating matrix $e^{V\Delta z}$ followed by a propagation $e^{T\Delta z}$ to the next slice and so on. Good convergence can be obtained in practice for slice thicknesses of about 2 Å. The method is cumulative so that the diffracted amplitudes can be simultaneously calculated for a range of crystal thicknesses. Furthermore, due to its relatively low computer requirements it was until recently, the only full dynamical many-beam diffraction theory that could be used successfully for the computation of structure images [10, 29–31]. However for very thin crystals where single scattering is dominant, this formulation is less economical since the time consuming calculation of the phase grating, has always to be carried out completely. Furthermore multiple ($\leqslant n$) times scattered electrons are always taken into account even if their amplitude contributes negligibly to the final result. Also when upper-layer-lines (higher dense planes in reciprocal space) are excited this method becomes less adapted since the slice thickness has to be decreased.

5.3. The path scattering approximation (PSA)

Guided by the knowledge that the very simple kinematical theory with almost no computer requirements, applies for very thin crystals ($\leqslant 5$ Å) it can be expected that a formulation, expanding (41) in powers of V (number of scatterings) would converge much faster for thin crystals and/or high acceleration voltages.

Hence the column vector is expanded as:

$$\Phi(z) = \sum_{n=0}^{\infty} \Phi_n(z). \tag{46}$$

Substitution into the system of Howie and Whelan:

$$\Phi'(z) = (T + V)\,\Phi(z), \tag{47}$$

and identifying equal powers of V (which is treated as a perturbation) gives:

$$\Phi'_n(z) = T\Phi_n(z) + V\Phi_{n-1}(z), \tag{48}$$

with solution:

$$\Phi_n(z) = e^{Tz} \int_0^z e^{-Tz}\,V\Phi_{n-1}(z)\,dz, \tag{49}$$

and:

$$\Phi_0(z) = E_0. \tag{50}$$

The subsequent terms in the convergent series (46) can thus be calculated using the recurrence relation (49) giving explicitly for the diffraction amplitudes:

$$\varphi_{n_{i_n}}(z) = \sum_{i_1 i_2 \cdots i_{n-1}} V_{i_n, i_{n-1}} \cdots V_{i_1, i_0}$$

$$\times \sum_{m=0}^{n} \frac{\exp(T_{i_m} z) - 1}{(T_{i_m} - T_{i_0}) \cdots (T_{i_m} - T_{i_{m-1}})(T_{i_m} - T_{i_{m+1}}) \cdots (T_{i_m} - T_{i_n})} \tag{51}$$

Notice that in case $T_i - T_j = 0$ the limit has to be taken.

Physically expression (51) means that an electron, incident with wavevector $\mathbf{k}_0 + \mathbf{g}_{i_0}$ is successively diffracted into directions $\mathbf{k}_0 + \mathbf{g}_{i_1}, \ldots \mathbf{k}_0 + \mathbf{g}_{i_{n-1}}$ and ends finally in the beam $\mathbf{k}_0 + \mathbf{g}_{i_n}$. Its history can be represented by a path in reciprocal lattice vectors $\mathbf{g}_{i_0}, \ldots \mathbf{g}_{i_n}$.

Summation over all possible paths yields the total diffraction amplitude $\varphi_{\mathbf{g}_{in}}$. In practice best convergence can be obtained by counting of all the different paths in order of their importance and adding up their calculated amplitudes (51). Upper-layer-lines can easily be taken into account [26].

5.4. The iterative method

According to the definition of the exponential matrix function, solution (41) can be expanded in a power series of the dynamical matrix as:

$$\Phi(z) = e^{i\pi Sz} E_0 = \sum_{n=0}^{\infty} \frac{(i\pi Sz)^n}{n!} E_0 , \tag{52}$$

No serious attention has ever been paid to this expansion for dynamical diffraction computations due to the slow convergence of the required full $N \times N$ matrix operations. However this objection falls if one suceeds in carying out the calculation with the vector starting from the boundary condition. This can be performed in the following way: expanding

$$\Phi(z) = \sum_{n=0}^{\infty} \Phi_n(z) , \tag{53}$$

where the column vectors are defined as:

$$\Phi_n(z) = \frac{(i\pi Sz)^n E_0}{n!} \tag{54}$$

then the recurrence relation holds:

$$\Phi_n(z) = \frac{i\pi Sz}{n} \Phi_{n-1}(z) \tag{55}$$

with:

$$\Phi_0(z) = E_0 . \tag{56}$$

Successive terms of the expansion (53) can thus be obtained by iteration using the recurrence relation (55) and starting from (56). Due to the low computer requirements the technique was proved to be very fast and adequate for many beam diffraction calculation with the possibility to include upper-layer-line interactions with relatively small excitation errors [26].

5.5. The direct integrating method

The system of Howie and Whelan [36] can be split from [37] into:

$$\Phi(z) = (T + V)\Phi(z) . \tag{57}$$

Treating V as a perturbation matrix e^{Tz} represents the unperturbed solution so that a solution can be tried of the form:

$$\Phi(z) = e^{Tz}\theta(z) . \tag{58}$$

Substitution in (57) yields the following system of coupled differential equations:

$$\theta'(z) = Q(z)\,\theta(z) , \tag{59}$$

with

$$Q(z) = e^{-Tz} V e^{Tz} , \tag{60}$$

or:

$$Q_{ij}(z) = V_{ij} e^{(T_j - T_i)z} . \tag{61}$$

This system can be solved with classical methods starting from the boundary condition $\theta(0) = E_0$. Nevertheless, classical integration procedures usually require a large computer memory and are thus less adapted for many beam situations. However a careful analysis of the available integration techniques

[26] allowed us to select the fourth order Runge Kutta $(\frac{1}{6}, \frac{1}{3}, \frac{1}{3}, \frac{1}{6})$ method as very appropriate, since for the special linear system (59) it can be modified into a form requiring only very few storage and time facilities.

Furthermore the computation is cumulative so that it can be carried out simultaneously for a range of crystal thicknesses and allows upper-layer-lines as well as deviations from the periodicity along the z direction to be taken into account.

5.6. *Discussion of the methods*

It was our aim to search for diffraction formulations that are capable of calculating the dynamical diffraction amplitudes for the many-beam situations occurring in structure imaging techniques on a small (16 K) desk computer. Only four formulations were found, all of them being expansions of (41) or solutions of (36), starting from the boundary condition, so that only one vector has to be carried through the calculations. Fig. 24 shows a very crude schematical comparison of their respective calculation times as function of the crystal thickness. At first sight it can be concluded that for very thin ($\leqslant 30$ Å) crystals and/or high acceleration potentials (e.g. 1 MeV) the PSA method with a capacity of treating 800 beams upper layers included, is mot appropriate because of the kinematical character of most diffracted beams and the possibility to exploit the crystal symmetry.

For thicker crystals its calculation time increases exponentially so that other

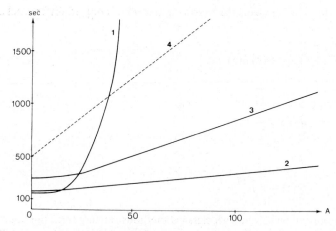

Fig. 24. Comparison of the calculation times as required by the different computation techniques: (1) PSA method (2) iterative method (3) direct integrating method (4) multi-slice method (roughly estimated).

techniques are to be used. If the calculations have to be carried out for one fixed crystal thickness, the very simple iterative method is preferred with a capacity of about 600 beams and a very high speed. The direct integrating method on the other hand can handle 450 beams simultaneously for a range of crystal thicknesses at a comparable speed. The calculation time of both methods, roughly proportional to the square of the number of beams and to the crystal thickness is shorter than that of the multislice procedure.

Furthermore they are more capable of treating upper-layer-lines. Deviations from the crystal symmetry normal to the direction of incidence can be introduced by artificially constructing a very large unit cell and thus sampling the Fourier integral of (1) by a large sum. Defects in the direction of incidence can be introduced most easily in the multislice- and direct integrating methods. The listing of the computer program for the iterative method is given in the appendix. Listings for the PSA and the cumulative methods (Fortran) and for the program, generating the halftone structure images (basic) can be received on request.

6. Calculation of structure images for the complex oxide $Ti_2Nb_{10}O_{29}$

The wave function at the exit plane of the crystal foil is given by:

$$\psi(\mathbf{r}) = \sum_{\mathbf{g}} \phi_{\mathbf{g}}(z) \exp\{2\pi i(\mathbf{k}_0 + \mathbf{g}) \cdot \mathbf{r}\},$$

so that substitution in (13) yields for the image amplitude:

$$U(x, y) = \sum_{\mathbf{g}}' \phi_{\mathbf{g}}(z) \exp\{2\pi i(\mathbf{k}_0 + \mathbf{g}) \cdot \mathbf{r}\}$$

$$\times \exp\{i\tfrac{1}{2}\pi C_s\lambda^3(\mathbf{k}_0 + \mathbf{g})_{\parallel}^4 + i\pi\epsilon\lambda(\mathbf{k}_0 + \mathbf{g})_{\parallel}^2\},$$

where Σ' means that the summation extends over all reciprocal points with the component $\mathbf{g}_{\parallel}$ parallel to the surface lying inside the aperture. Complete dynamical calculations for the diffracted amplitudes $\phi_{\mathbf{g}}(z)$ were preformed for the complex oxide, described in (4.4) [29] using the PSA, interactive and cumulative methods with a normalisation of 0.99. The final image amplitudes were calculated for the parameters $C_s = 1.8$ mm $\lambda = 0.037$ Å and for a range of defocus values corresponding to those of the experimental images (section 4.4). In order to account for chromatic aberration and the combined effect of beam divergence and spherical aberration, an effective objective aperture of

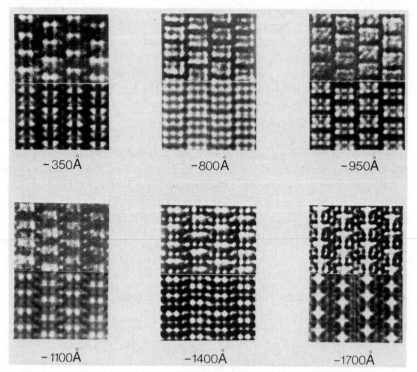

Fig. 25. Comparison of the calculated with the experimental structure images for
$Ti_2Nb_{10}O_{29}$ as a function of the defocus. Notice that a good resemblance can be obtained.

0.263 Å^{-1} instead of the experimental 0.33 Å^{-1} were used as suggested by
[6]. The final image $|U(x, y)|^2$ was presented as a halftone picture on a memory
oscilloscope, using a technique described in [32]. Photographic reproduction
of this image with a slightly defocussed lens appeared to be an elegant simulation of the beam divergence. The results are shown in fig. 25. It is clear that a
good agreement between the experimental (upper) and computer (lower)
images can be obtained.

Appendix

```
C THIS PROGRAM CALCULATES THE STRUCTURE AMPLITUDES FOR A CRYSTAL WHOSE   RUCA0010
C PROJECTION ALONG THE C AXIS IS CENTROSYMMETRIC(STATEMENT1-16),FOLLOWED RUCA0020
C BY THE CALCULATION OF THE DIFFRACTED BEAM AMPLITUDES WITH THE (HKO)    RUCA0030
C ZONE EXCITED(STATEMENT16-140).THE PROGRAM CAN EVEN BE CARRIED OUT ON A RUCA0040
C 16K COMPUTER(FORTRAN) FOR UP TO 600 BEAMS,WHERE THE UNIT CELL MAY      RUCA0050
C CONTAIN UP TO 9 DIFFERENT ATOM TYPES AND 40 ATOMS OF EACH .            RUCA0060
C THE PROGRAM CAN EASILY BE ADAPTED FOR OTHER COMPUTER SIZES BY          RUCA0070
C CHANGING ONLY THE DIMENSION STATEMENT                                  RUCA0080
      DIMENSION A(3),AL(3),CO(3),SI(3),SYM(9),P(9,9),X(9,40),Y(9,40),    RUCA0090
     1Z(9,40),NP(9),FR(600),B(3),CB(3),AR(600),AI(600),XR(600),XI(600)  RUCA0100
      EQUIVALENCE (AR(1),X(1,1)),(AI(1),Y(1,1)),(XR(1),Z(1,1)),(XI(1),   RUCA0110
     1P(1,1))                                                            RUCA0120
C CALCULATION OF THE STRUCTURE AMPLITUDES FOR THE (HKO) ZONE             RUCA0130
C NR AND NW ARE THE LOGICAL UNIT NUMBERS OF CARDREADER AND PRINTER       RUCA0140
C AND HAVE TO BE SPECIFIED                                               RUCA0150
      NR=2                                                               RUCA0160
      NW=3                                                               RUCA0170
C INPUT AND PRINTING OF THE DATA                                         RUCA0180
C INPUT OF THE LATTICE PARAMETERS A,B,C (IN ANGSTROM),ALPHA,BETA,GAMMA   RUCA0190
C (IN DEGREES)(6F8.4),TOTAL NUMBER OF ATOMS(I3),RESP.NUMBER OF EACH(9I3) RUCA0200
C C IS ALWAYS CHOSEN AS THE SHORT AXIS                                   RUCA0210
      READ(NR,1) A,AL,NA,NP                                              RUCA0220
    1 FORMAT(6F8.4,10I3)                                                 RUCA0230
      WRITE(NW,101) A,AL,NA,NP                                           RUCA0240
  101 FORMAT(1H1,'A1  =  ',F8.4,'   A2  =  ',F8.4,'   A3  =  ',F8.4,     RUCA0250
     1'   ALPHA1 =  ',F8.4,'   ALPHA2 =  ',F8.4,'   ALPHA3 =  ',F8.4,///,RUCA0260
     2' NUMBER OF DIFFERENT ATOMS  =  ',I2,5X,'NUMBERS OF EACH  =  ',9I3)RUCA0270
      DO 3 I=1,NA                                                        RUCA0280
C INPUT OF ATOM SYMBOL(A5) +8 PARAMETERS(8F8.4) FOR THE ANALYTIC FITTING RUCA0290
C OF THE ELECTRON FORM FACTOR AS A SUM OF 4 GAUSSIANS (SEE INT.TABLES)   RUCA0300
C THIS CARD HAS TO BE FOLLOWED BY THE INPUT OF THE COORDINATES OF ALL    RUCA0310
C THE ATOMS OF THIS TYPE,4 ATOMS PER CARD(12F6.4)                        RUCA0320
      READ(NR,2) SYM(I),(P(I,J),J=1,8)                                   RUCA0330
      WRITE(NW,201) SYM(I),(P(I,J),J=1,8)                                RUCA0340
  201 FORMAT(/1H0,'ATOM = ',A5,'         SCATTERINGPARAMETERS   = ',8F8.4)RUCA0350
    2 FORMAT(A5,8F8.4)                                                   RUCA0360
      N=NP(I)                                                            RUCA0370
      READ(NR,4) (X(I,J),Y(I,J),Z(I,J),J=1,N)                            RUCA0380
    4 FORMAT(12F6.4)                                                     RUCA0390
      WRITE(NW,401)                                                      RUCA0400
  401 FORMAT(1H ,'ATOM POSITIONS  = ')                                   RUCA0410
    3 WRITE(NW,402) (X(I,J),Y(I,J),Z(I,J),J=1,N)                         RUCA0420
  402 FORMAT(1H+,18X,3F8.4,2X,3F8.4,2X,3F8.4,2X,3F8.4,/)                 RUCA0430
C INPUT OF THE MAXIMAL NUMBER OF BEAMS TO BE USED(I3)                    RUCA0440
      READ(NR,5) IDIM                                                    RUCA0450
    5 FORMAT(I3)                                                         RUCA0460
      WRITE(NW,501) IDIM                                                 RUCA0470
  501 FORMAT(1H0,/,' MAXIMAL NUMBER OF BEAMS  = ',I3,///)                RUCA0480
C CALCULATION OF THE UNIT CELL PARAMETERS                                RUCA0490
      DO 6 I=1,3                                                         RUCA0500
      XX=.0174533*AL(I)                                                  RUCA0510
      CO(I)=COS(XX)                                                      RUCA0520
    6 SI(I)=SIN(XX)                                                      RUCA0530
      SX=SQRT(1.+2.*(CO(1)*CO(2)*CO(3))-(CO(1)**2+CO(2)**2+CO(3)**2))    RUCA0540
      VOL=A(1)*A(2)*A(3)*SX                                              RUCA0550
      DO 7 I=1,3                                                         RUCA0560
    7 B(I)=SI(I)/(A(I)*SX)                                               RUCA0570
      CB(3)=2.*(CO(1)*CO(2)-CO(3))/(SI(1)*SI(2))                         RUCA0580
```

```
C CALCULATION OF THE UPPER LIMITS FOR H AND K                               RUCA0590
      T=B(1)/B(2)                                                           RUCA0600
      S=SQRT((1.-T)**2+4.*T*FLOAT(IDIM))-1.-T                              RUCA0610
      IN1=IFIX(S/(4.*T))+1                                                  RUCA0620
      IN2=IFIX(S/4.)+1                                                      RUCA0630
      IM1=2*IN1-1                                                           RUCA0640
      IM2=2*IN2-1                                                           RUCA0650
      DO 10 I=1,IDIM                                                        RUCA0660
   10 FR(I)=0.                                                              RUCA0670
      DO 16 JH=1,IM1                                                        RUCA0680
      LH=JH-IN1                                                             RUCA0690
      XH=.5*FLOAT(LH)*B(1)                                                  RUCA0700
      DO 16 JK=1,IM2                                                        RUCA0710
      LK=JK-IN2                                                             RUCA0720
      XK=.5*FLOAT(LK)*B(2)                                                  RUCA0730
C CALCULATION OF THE SQUARE OF THE RECIPROCAL LATTICE VECTOR                RUCA0740
      G=-XH*XH-XK*XK-XH*XK*CB(3)                                            RUCA0750
C DELETE OF THE (0,0,0) SCATTERING AMPLITUDE                                RUCA0760
      IF(G)11,16,16                                                         RUCA0770
   11 XFR=0.                                                                RUCA0780
      DO 12 I=1,NA                                                          RUCA0790
      N=NP(I)                                                               RUCA0800
C CALCULATION OF THE ATOM FORM FACTOR USING THE ANALYTIC REPRESENTATION     RUCA0810
      F=(P(I,1)*EXP(P(I,2)*G)+P(I,3)*EXP(P(I,4)*G)+P(I,5)*EXP(P(I,6)*G)     RUCA0820
     1+P(I,7)*EXP(P(I,8)*G))*.0140823/VOL                                   RUCA0830
C CALCULATION OF THE TOTAL STRUCTURE AMPLITUDE                              RUCA0840
      DO 12 J=1,N                                                           RUCA0850
      R=6.2831853*(X(I,J)*FLOAT(LH)+Y(I,J)*FLOAT(LK))                       RUCA0860
   12 XFR=XFR+F*COS(R)                                                      RUCA0870
      I=(JH-1)*IM2+JK                                                       RUCA0880
      TG=1./(ABS(XFR)+1.E-12)                                               RUCA0890
C OUTPUT OF THE STRUCTURE AMPLITUDES AND EXTINCTION DISTANCES               RUCA0900
      WRITE(NW,13) I ,LH,LK,XFR,TG                                          RUCA0910
   13 FORMAT(1H ,I3,') H   K   = ',2I3,10X,'F(HKO)  = ',E13.5,10X,          RUCA0920
     1'TG   = ',F8.1,' ANGSTROM')                                          RUCA0930
      FR(I)=XFR                                                             RUCA0940
   16 CONTINUE                                                              RUCA0950
C START OF THE MANY-BEAM DIFFRACTION CALCULATION                            RUCA0960
C INPUT OF NORMALISATION PRECISION(F8.6),CRYSTAL DEPTH(F8.4) IN A,AND       RUCA0970
C NON-NORMAL COMPONENTS KOX,KOY,OF THE INCIDENT WAVEVECTOR IN A-1(2F8.5)    RUCA0980
   18 READ(NR,20) EPS,DEP,XKH,XKK                                          RUCA0990
   20 FORMAT(F8.6,F8.4,2F8.5)                                               RUCA1000
      WRITE(NW,21) EPS,DEP,XKH,XKK                                          RUCA1010
   21 FORMAT(1H1,'NORM. PRECISION =',E13.5,5X,'DEPTH =',F8.1,'ANGSTROM',    RUCA1020
     1/,'  NON-NORMAL COMPONENTS      KOX = ',F8.5,'    KOY = ',F8.5)       RUCA1030
      DEP=3.141593*DEP                                                      RUCA1040
      XPI=-.037*DEP                                                         RUCA1050
      IMAX=IM1*IM2                                                          RUCA1060
      DO 30 I=1,IMAX                                                        RUCA1070
      FR(I)=FR(I)*DEP                                                       RUCA1080
      AR(I)=0.                                                              RUCA1090
      AI(I)=0.                                                              RUCA1100
      XR(I)=0.                                                              RUCA1110
   30 XI(I)=0.                                                              RUCA1120
      I=(IN1-1)*IM2+IN2                                                     RUCA1130
      XR(I)=1.                                                              RUCA1140
      AR(I)=1.                                                              RUCA1150
      N=0                                                                   RUCA1160
```

```
C START OF A NEW ITERATION                                          RUCA1170
   40 N=N+1                                                         RUCA1180
      WRITE(NW,45) N                                                RUCA1190
   45 FORMAT(1H ,///////,I4,' TH ITERATION',//)                    RUCA1200
      ERROR =1.                                                     RUCA1210
      DO 100 JH=1,IM1                                               RUCA1220
      NH=JH-IN1                                                     RUCA1230
      XH=FLOAT(NH)*B(1)                                             RUCA1240
      YH=XH*XKH                                                     RUCA1250
      DO 100 JK=1,IM2                                               RUCA1260
      NK=JK-IN2                                                     RUCA1270
      XK=FLOAT(NK)*B(2)                                             RUCA1280
      YK=XK*XKK                                                     RUCA1290
      I=(JH-1)*IM2+JK                                               RUCA1300
C TEST IF REQUIRED DYNAMICAL MATRIX ELEMENT OUT OF RANGE           RUCA1310
      DO 80 IH=1,IM1                                                RUCA1320
      IF(IABS(JH-IH)+1-IN1) 60,60,80                                RUCA1330
   60 DO 80 IK=1,IM2                                                RUCA1340
      IF(IABS(JK-IK)+1-IN2) 70,70,80                                RUCA1350
   70 J=(JH-IH+IN1-1)*IM2+JK-IK+IN2                                 RUCA1360
      K=(IH-1)*IM2+IK                                               RUCA1370
      IF(MOD(N,2)) 75,75,76                                         RUCA1380
C MULTIPLICATION BY THE DYNAMICAL MATRIX                           RUCA1390
   75 XR(I)=XR(I)-FR(J)*XI(K)                                       RUCA1400
      GO TO 80                                                      RUCA1410
   76 XI(I)=XI(I)+FR(J)*XR(K)                                       RUCA1420
   80 CONTINUE                                                      RUCA1430
C CALCULATION OF THE DIAGONAL ELEMENTS (EXCITATION ERRORS)         RUCA1440
      SEX=XPI*(XH*XH+XK*XK+XH*XK*CB(3)+YH+YK)                       RUCA1450
      IF(MOD(N,2)) 85,85,86                                         RUCA1460
C MULTIPLICATION BY THE DIAGONAL ELEMENTS                          RUCA1470
   85 XR(I)=XR(I)-SEX*XI(I)                                         RUCA1480
C ACCUMULATION OF DIFFRACTION AMPLITUDES                           RUCA1490
      AR(I)=AR(I)+XR(I)                                             RUCA1500
      XR(I)=XR(I)/FLOAT(N+1)                                        RUCA1510
      GO TO 90                                                      RUCA1520
   86 XI(I)=XI(I)+SEX*XR(I)                                         RUCA1530
      AI(I)=AI(I)+XI(I)                                             RUCA1540
      XI(I)=XI(I)/FLOAT(N+1)                                        RUCA1550
C CALCULATION OF THE NORMALISATION ERROR                           RUCA1560
   90 ERROR=ERROR-AR(I)*AR(I)-AI(I)*AI(I)                           RUCA1570
  100 CONTINUE                                                      RUCA1580
      WRITE(NW,110) ERROR                                           RUCA1590
  110 FORMAT(1H0,5X,'NORMALISATION ERROR  = ',E13.5,//)            RUCA1600
      DO 115 I=1,IMAX                                               RUCA1610
      IF(MOD(N,2)) 111,111,112                                      RUCA1620
  111 XI(I)=0.                                                      RUCA1630
      GO TO 115                                                     RUCA1640
  112 XR(I)=0.                                                      RUCA1650
  115 CONTINUE                                                      RUCA1660
C TEST ON THE NORMALISATION ERROR OF THE TOTAL INTENSITY           RUCA1670
      IF(ABS(ERROR)-EPS) 120,120,40                                 RUCA1680
  120 DO 140 I=1,IMAX                                               RUCA1690
C OUTPUT OF THE DIFFRACTION AMPLITUDES                             RUCA1700
      WRITE(NW,130) I,AR(I),AI(I)                                   RUCA1710
  130 FORMAT(1H ,I3,'    ATOTR = ',E13.5,5X,'ATOTI = ',E13.5)      RUCA1720
      FR(I)=FR(I)/DEP                                               RUCA1730
  140 CONTINUE                                                      RUCA1740
      GO TO 18                                                      RUCA1750
      END                                                           RUCA1760
```

References

[1] D.Dorignac and G.Jouffrey, in: Proc. 6th European Congress on Electron Microscopy Jerusalem, 1976.

[2] H.Hashimoto, A.Kumao, K.Hino, H.Yotsumoto and A.Ono, Jap. J. Appl. Phys. 10 (1971) 1115.

[3] H.Formanek, M.Müller, M.H.Hahn and T.Koller, Naturwissenschaften 58 (1971) 339.

[4] O.Scherzer, J. Appl. Phys. 20 (1949) 20.

[5] T.Hibi, in: 5th International Congress for Electron Microscopy, Vol. 1 (Academic Press, New York, 1962) paper KK1.

[6] P.L.Fejes, Acta Cryst. A33 (1977) 109.

[7] G.R.Grinton, and J.M.Cowley, Optik 34 (1971) 221.

[8] J.M.Cowley and S.Iijima, Z. Naturforsch. 27a, 3 (1972) 445.

[9] D.F.Lynch and M.A.O'Keefe, Acta Cryst. A28 (1972) 536.

[10] M.A.O'Keefe, Acta Cryst. A29 (1973) 389.

[11] D.F.Lynch and A.F.Moodie, A31 (1975) 300.

[12] R.W.G.Wyckoff, Crystal Structures, Vol. 4 (J.Wiley, New York, 1968) p. 213.

[13] J.Van Landuyt, S.Amelinckx, J.A.Kohn and D.W.Eckart, J. Solid State Chem. 9 (1974) 103.

[14] P.B.Braun, Philips Res. Rep. 12 (1957) 491.

[15] D.Van Dyck, J.Van Landuyt, S.Amelinckx and Nguyen Huy-Dung, C.R. Acad. Sci. Paris, ser. C 282 (1976) 233.

[16] D.Van Dyck, J.Van Landuyt, S.Amelinckx, Nguyen Huy-Dung and C.Dagron, J. Solid. State Chem. 19 (1976) 179.

[17] C.Dagron, C.R. Acad. Sci. Paris, ser. C 275 (1972) 817.

[18] Nguyen Huy-Dung, Acta Cryst. B29 (1973) 2096;
Nguyen Huy-Dung, C. Dagron and P.Laruelle, Acta Cryst. B31 (1975) 514;
Nguyen Huy-Dung, C.Dagron and P.Laruelle, Acta Cryst. B31 (1975) 519.

[19] Nguyen Huy-Dung, private communication.

[20] A.D.Wadsley, Acta Cryst. 14 (1961) 664.

[21] D.Van Dyck, Phys. Stat. Sol. (b) 77 (1976) 301.

[22] A.Howie and M.J.Whelan, Proc. Roy. Soc. A263 (1961) 217.

[23] M.Tournarie, in: Actes du 5e Congress International de Crystallographie (1960).

[24] L.Sturkey, Proc. Phys. Soc. 80 (1962) 321.

[25] D.Van Dyck, Phys. Stat. Sol. (b) 72 (1975) 321.

[26] D.Van Dyck, Ph. D. thesis UIA Antwrp (1977).

[27] P.Goodman and A.F.Moodie, Acta Cryst. A30 (1974) 280.

[28] W.Magnus, Comm. Pure Appl. Math. 7 (1954) 649.

[29] J.M.Cowley and A.F.Moodie, Acta Cryst. 10 (1957) 609.

[30] J.G.Alpress, E.Hewat, A.F.Moodie and J.V.Sanders, Acta Cryst. A28 (1972) 528.

[31] D.F.Lynch and M.A.O'Keefe, Acta Cryst. A28 (1972) 536.

[32] C.Billington and N.R.Kay, Australian J. Phys. 27 (1974) 73.

PARTICULAR ASPECTS
OF ELECTRON DIFFRACTION

Diffraction and Imaging Techniques in Material Science,
eds. S. Amelinckx, R. Gevers and J. van Landuyt
© *North-Holland Publishing Company, 1978*

KIKUCHI ELECTRON DIFFRACTION AND APPLICATIONS

G.THOMAS

Inorganic Materials Research Division, Lawrence Radiation Laboratory,
Department of Materials Science and Engineering, College of Engineering,
University of California, Berkeley, California, USA

1. Geometry and orientations

1.1. *Geometry of formation*

The name Kikuchi electron diffraction is given to the patterns of lines that are observed from fairly thick crystals after their discovery in 1934 by Kikuchi [1]. The mechanism of formation is as follows: The electron beam, on entering a specimen, suffers inelastic and incoherent scattering by interaction with the atoms. These electrons can be subsequently rescattered coherently when Bragg's law is satisfied at a suitable set of reflecting planes.

Cones of radiation are emitted and if the incident waves are symmetrically impinging on the plane AB, cones of equal intensity are scattered, with semi-vertex angles of $(90-\theta)$ (fig. 1a), to each side and bisecting the reflecting plane AB. If, however, the waves impinge on an inclined reference plane AB (fig. 1b), then most of the electrons are initially scattered into the direction K_1 and relatively few into the forward direction K_2. Under normal conditions and on a positive print, one then observes a bright line corresponding to K_1 near the Bragg spot and a dark line corresponding to K_2 near the origin. Since for most applications a knowledge of the geometry is sufficient, a discussion of the dynamical behavior [2] and intensities of the Kikuchi lines [3] will not be given here.

The intersection of the cones of Kikuchi radiation with the reflecting sphere produces slightly hyperbolic lines due to the small angles θ and large radius of the sphere for fast electrons. These lines are actually straight on the photographic plate for the usual angles recorded in a pattern ($\approx 9°$ at 100 kV for $\lambda L = 2\text{Åcm}$). Each reflection (hkl) thus gives rise to a pair of Kikuchi lines hkl

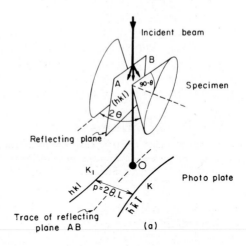

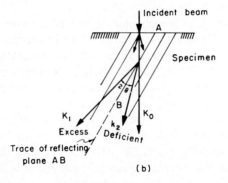

Fig. 1. Geometry of formation of Kikuchi lines. a. Incident beam is inelastically scattered; inelastic electrons are then rescattered coherently by plane AB to produce cones of radiation which intersect the reflecting sphere as slightly curved lines, which bisect the reflecting plane. Each Kikuchi pair corresponds to a unique reflecting plane. b. Diffraction representation for crystal oriented for Bragg diffraction. In this case, more electrons are scattered into the diffracting direction so that the Kikuchi lines K_1 are bright, and K_2 dark.

and $\overline{hkl}$ whose respective intensities depend principally upon the orientation, perfection, and thickness of the crystal. Figs. 2a, b show the geometry for crystals oriented symmetrically and at the exact Bragg condition. These are really the only two orientations that are needed during electron microscopy applications; case (b) should be used when crystallographic data is needed and case (a) is the two-beam situation necessary for contrast analysis.

It should be noted that in the case of rescattering of inelastic beams, the specimen acts as a monochromator, i.e., the planes (hkl) reflect electrons which are satisfied by Bragg's law for the wavelengths involved: $2d \sin(\theta)'$ $= n\lambda'$. Since typically the characteristic energy losses are of the order of tens of volts, then $\lambda' \approx \lambda$ (incident), and the same reflecting sphere-reciprocal lattice construction describing the spot pattern can be used for the Kikuchi pattern (figs. 2a, b).

Kikuchi patterns are always produced even in thin crystals, but the specimen must be thick enough in order that a sufficiently intense Kikuchi cone to be observed on the photo plate is produced. Furthermore, the specimen should be relatively free from long range internal strains (e.g., elastic buckling, a high dislocation density), otherwise, the Kikuchi cones will be incoherently scattered and may become too diffuse to be observed. The absence of observable Kikuchi lines or the appearance of very broad diffuse lines from heavily dislocated structures, e.g., ferrous martensite, is due to incoherent scattering. As the thickness of the foil increases, the diffraction pattern changes from spots, to Kikuchi lines and spots, to Kikuchi lines or bands, until finally complete absorption within the foil occurs. The thickness limits for these events increase with increasing voltage, due to enhanced penetration.

It can be seen from figs. 2a, b, that on tilting the specimen in one sense, the Kikuchi lines sweep across the pattern in the opposite sense. In fig. 2a the crystal has been tilted by θ_{hkl} anti-clockwise so as to excite the first order (hkl) relfection. The Kikuchi origin is fixed in the crystal so that as the crystal is tilted, the cones sweep across the pattern as if rigidly "fixed" to the specimen. Thus, the Kikuchi pattern is extremely useful in determining the precise orientation, as well as for calibrating tilt angles, etc. Since each Kikuchi line in a pair bisects the reflecting plane, then the angle subtended by each pair is always 2θ independently of crystal orientation*. Furthermore, the Kikuchi pattern represents the traces of all reflecting planes in the crystal and can thus be directly compared to the appropriate stereographic projection. The Kikuchi lines are also parallel to the Bragg extinction contours. Applying Bragg's law and the appropriate structure factor rules enables one to plot the complete Kikuchi pattern. Fig. 3 is derived to scale for the first order Kikuchi reflections for Al at 100 kV. This can be compared to the actual patterns shown in figs. 9–11, and the Bragg contour pattern of a bent foil in fig. 4. Further applications are described in sect. 1.4.

---

* Special situations arise when this rule is not strictly correct; and is important for large angle reflections (see Tan et al., ref. [3]).

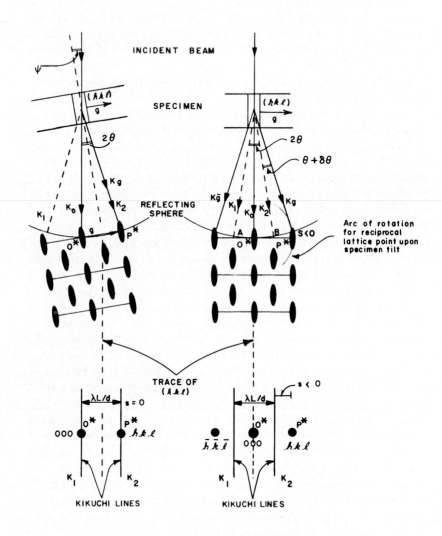

Fig. 2. Reciprocal lattice – reflecting sphere construction showing relation of Kikuchi pattern to spot pattern for, (a) exact Bragg two-beam orientation, and (b) the symmetrical orientation. The spacing of Kikuchi lines is independent of crystal orientation. (Courtesy of Physica Stat. Solidi.)

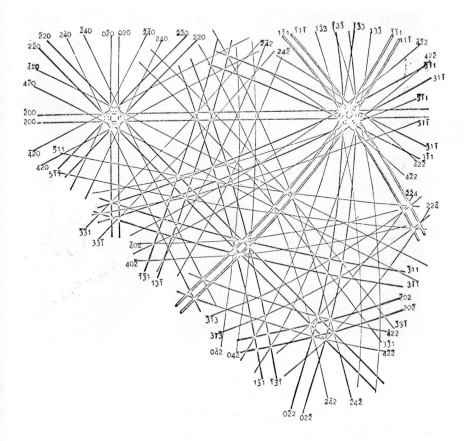

Fig. 3. Stereographic projection of first order Bragg contours (and Kikuchi pairs) drawn to scale for 100 kV electrons in aluminum up to $(h^2+k^2+l^2) = 27$. (After K. Ashbee and J. Heavens, University of California, UCRL Report No. 17614.).

Tilting the crystal tilts the reciprocal lattice in the same sense and magnitude. The spot pattern thus translates only slightly on tilting since each spot rotates on tilting about an arc of radius $|g|$ centered at the origin (fig. 2b). The Kikuchi pattern, however, shifts in an easily observable manner (≈ 1 cm per $1°$ tilt for $\lambda L \approx 2$ Å cm).

The Kikuchi lines associated with a particular reflection hkl always lie perpendicular to $g(hkl)$, i.e., on a line through the origin and normal to the Kikuchi pair.

Fig. 4. a. Bragg extinction contours in copper foil symmetrically deformed about [011]. Compare to [011] region of figs. 3 and 11. (Courtesy W.L.Bell.)

The centers of symmetry of the spot pattern and Kikuchi pattern thus coincide only in symmetrically oriented foils. For accurate determinations of orientation relationships the foil can be tilted until the symmetrical situation appears on the screen.

1.2. Relation to spot pattern and determination of deviation parameter

The Bragg deviation parameter s is important in contrast analysis. Both the sign and magnitude of s can be readily obtained by noting the orientation of the Kikuchi pattern to that of the spot pattern [4].

Since by definition $s > 0$ occurs when the reciprocal lattice point lies inside the reflecting sphere, then the Kikuchi line lies outside its corresponding diffraction spot (fig. 2). Thus, in a symmetrical orientation, $s < 0$ (fig. 2a). The sense of tilt of a foil is thus immediately apparent from the relation between the Kikuchi and spot patterns.

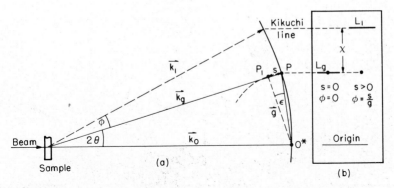

Fig. 5. Sketch showing shift in Kikuchi lines produced by a tilt ϵ. Position of Kikuchi lines at L_g and L_1 correspond to the cases $s = 0$, $s > 0$, respectively. The tilt ϵ moves the Kikuchi line through a and the spot through distance s about the radius O*P. (Courtesy J. Appl. Phys., ref. [4]).

In fig. 5 is shown the effect of tilting the foil to produce an $s > 0$ orientation (such as is required for maximum bright-field contrast in absorbing crystals). As the foil is tilted from the exact Bragg condition by an angle ϵ the Kikuchi lines move outwards a distance χ along g_{hkl} whereas the spot moves inside the sphere on the arc $O*PP_1$. In the pattern the Kikuchi line now lies outside the corresponding spot as shown in (b).

Since the Bragg angles are small, we can write

$$\phi = \chi/L = \chi\lambda/rd$$

where L is the camera length.

Since χ can be measured on the plate and since r and d are known from the indexed pattern, ϕ is calculated. Also

$$\phi = s/g .$$

Hence

$$s = \chi g/L = \chi/Ld$$

for a given Kikuchi band of separation p_1, $2\theta_1 \cong p_1/L = \lambda/d_1$ hence

$$s = \chi/Ld = \chi\lambda/d(p_1d_1) .$$

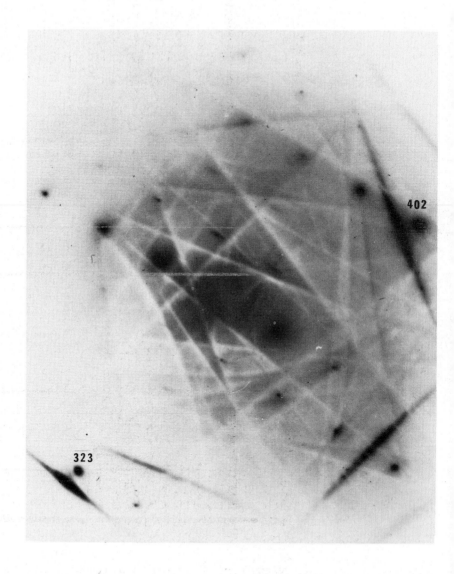

Fig. 6. Kikuchi pattern from molybdenum. For the 402 $s < 0$ and for $\overline{3}2\overline{3}$ $s > 0$. The orientation is 0.3° from [$\overline{3}\overline{3}5$]. (Courtesy, J. Appl. Phys., ref. [4].)

For example, for the 402 reflection in fig. 6, s is negative and has the value $0.0073(\text{Å})^{-1}$.

1.3. *The precise determination of orientations*

The general method of solving a Kikuchi pattern and determining the precise foil orientation is similar to the method for solving spot patterns. Since the spacing of each Kikuchi pair is proportional to 2θ (fig. 1a), then we have for different sets of Kikuchi pairs of spacings, $p_1 p_2$, etc.,

$$p_1 = K 2\theta_1 , \qquad p_2 = K 2\theta_2 , \qquad p_n = K 2\theta_n$$

where K is the effective camera length L.

Thus if the reflections $h_1 k_1 l_1 --- h_n k_n l_n$ are identified, the pattern can be calibrated in terms of distances on the plate and corresponding angles.

The identification of the Kikuchi reflections is done as follows. Suppose in fig. 7 there are three sets of intersecting Kikuchi lines at angles α, β, γ, the points of intersection A, B, C are zone axes (Kikuchi poles). If the crystal is cubic, then since $p_1 \propto 1/d_{h_1 k_1 l_1}$, etc., we have $p_1 d_1 = \lambda L, p_2 d_2 = \lambda L --- p_n d_n = \lambda L$, or

$$\frac{p_1}{p_2} = \frac{\sqrt{h_1^2 + k_1^2 + l_1^2}}{\sqrt{h_2^2 + k_2^2 + l_2^2}} \quad \text{and} \quad \frac{p_1}{p_3} = \frac{\sqrt{h_1^2 + k_1^2 + l_1^2}}{\sqrt{h_3^2 + k_3^2 + l_3^2}}$$

and so on.

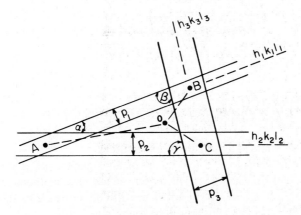

Fig. 7. Sketch to illustrate indexing of any Kikuchi pattern. If the poles A, B, C do not appear on the plate, use tracing paper to extend the Kikuchi lines through points of intersection.

Measure the spacings $p_1 p_2 p_3$, take their ratios and then, by using either tables of d-spacing ratios or a slide rule, the tentative indices $h_1 k_1 l_1$, etc., are assigned. The correctness of the assignment is then made by measuring the angles α, β, γ, and comparing them to the calculated values based on $h_1 k_1 l_1$, $h_2 k_2 l_2$, etc.

$$(\cos\alpha = (h_1 h_3 + k_1 k_3 + l_1 l_3)/(\sqrt{h_1^2 + k_1^2 + l_1^2} \cdot \sqrt{h_3^2 + k_3^2 + l_3^2}) \,.$$

This process can be time consuming, as it is often a question of trial and error in order to obtain the correct solution. The results can be checked by measuring other Kikuchi lines in the pattern.

Once the lines are indexed, the poles A, B, C are obtained by taking the respective cross products, e.g. $A = [h_1 k_1 l_1] \times [h_2 k_2 l_2]$. Let these poles be $p_1 q_1 r_1, p_2 q_2 r_2$ and $p_3 q_3 r_3$. The indices of the direction of the beam through the crystal (i.e., where the transmitted beam intersects the pattern at O) can be found either by calculation or by stereographic analysis. Both require measurement of the angles $\hat{O}A$, $\hat{O}B$, $\hat{O}C$ (fig. 7). Measure the distances OA, OB and convert to angles using either the calibration $p_1 = K2\theta$, or by measuring the distances AB-BC-CA and converting into angles since the angles $\hat{A}B$, $\hat{A}C$, $\hat{B}C$ can be calculated once, A, B, C are indexed*. Let $[uvw]$ be the axis O, then if $\theta_1 \theta_2 \theta_3$ are the angles $\hat{O}A$, $\hat{O}B$, $\hat{O}C$

$$\cos\theta_1 = \frac{u p_1 + v q_1 + w r_1}{\sqrt{u^2 + v^2 + w^2} \cdot \sqrt{p_1^2 + q_1^2 + r_1^2}}$$

$$\cos\theta_2 = \frac{u p_2 + v q_2 + w r_2}{\sqrt{u^2 + v^2 + w^2} \cdot \sqrt{p_2^2 + q_2^2 + r_2^2}}$$

$$\cos\theta_3 = \frac{u p_3 + v q_3 + w r_3}{\sqrt{u^2 + v^2 + w^2} \cdot \sqrt{p_3^2 + q_3^2 + r_3^2}}$$

and uvw is determined by solving these equations.

The solution can also be found by use of stereographic projection as described in detail elsewhere [5]. The reader can use these methods to check that the orientation of fig. 8 is [419] which can also be verified from the Kikuchi map of fig. 9, at A. The solution can be found in ref. [6].

* E.g. for the Siemens Elmiskop 1 at 100 kV and projector pole piece 3, 1 cm $\equiv 1°$.

Fig. 8. Symmetrical orientation of a Kikuchi pattern from silicon corresponding to point A of fig. 9. (Courtesy of J. Appl. Phys., ref. [6].)

For patterns containing one Kikuchi pole or none the solution can only be obtained by reference to the appropriate Kikuchi map.

1.4. Kikuchi maps

The solution of a Kikuchi pattern when there are no Kikuchi poles present can be obtained by comparing an unknown pattern with standard Kikuchi projections, called Kikuchi Maps [6,7]. The most usual case when no Kikuchi poles occur is when one works in two-beam orientations. However, in general the Kikuchi map is suitable and convenient for solving any unknown pattern

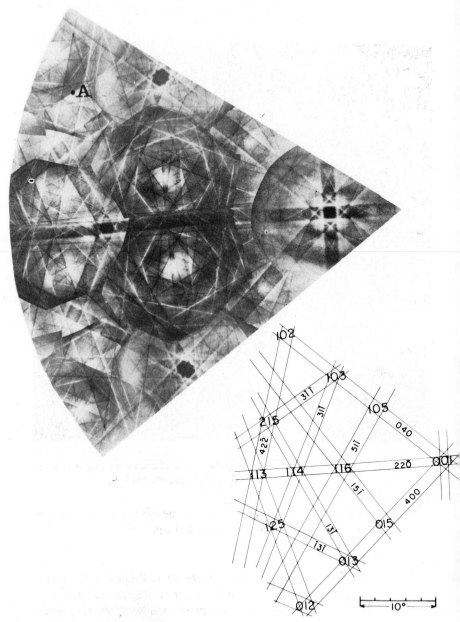

Fig. 9. a. Part of the Kikuchi map for silicon corresponding to area near [001] of reciprocal space. b. Indexing of (a) together with scale factor. (Courtesy J. Appl. Phys. ref. [6].)

since the maps eliminate the three-pole (or two-pole) solutions described above. The maps also eliminate the usual trial and error procedures involved in indexing.

If one is working with a particular crystal system all one needs is a Kikuchi map of that system. The maps are obtained so as to cover completely the standard triangle of the appropriate stereographic projection. In order to do this either single crystals or large randomly oriented polycrystalline specimens should be used. The specimen is then tilted into a symmetrical low index orientation, and by tilting outwards successively along principal Kikuchi lines, successive photographs are obtained so that some overlap of the pattern occurs from one plate to the next. After all the plates are printed, they can be glued onto a board so that successive photographs are matched. It is necessary to completely cover the area of reciprocal space in order to complete the map. If a complete [001] - [011] - [111] map is plotted, the curvature of the Kikuchi lines causes some distortion of the map. The distortion is not noticeable if one works with regions of about $20°$ around a principal pole. Further details are to be found in refs. [6] and [7].

Maps can also be obtained by utilizing the stereographic projection to obtain traces of reflecting planes, as is shown in fig. 3 to scale for aluminum at 100 kV.

Figs. 9–13 show composite maps for diamond cubic, BCC and HCP crystals. Figs. 9–11 can also be used for FCC crystals (compare to fig. 3) by allowing for the differences in structure factor (e.g., 200 is normally missing in diamond cubic). However, both the DC and HCP maps include reflections of zero structure factor which appear due to double diffraction [7]. In general, for non-cubic crystals separate maps need to be used for each material so that axial ratios and angles are identical.

Many difficulties can be avoided in the case of hexagonal crystals if the four index notation is used as described in detail by Okamoto and Thomas [8]. For example, any pole is determined from intersection of two Kikuchi bands $(h_1 k_1 i_1 l_1)(h_2 k_2 i_2 l_2)$ from the equation,

$$
uvtw = \left[\begin{vmatrix} l_1 k_1 i_1 \\ l_2 k_2 i_2 \\ 0\ 1\ 1 \end{vmatrix}, \quad \begin{vmatrix} h_1 l_1 i_1 \\ h_2 l_2 i_2 \\ 1\ 0\ 1 \end{vmatrix}, \quad \begin{vmatrix} h_1 k_1 l_1 \\ h_2 k_2 l_2 \\ 1\ 1\ 0 \end{vmatrix}, \quad \begin{vmatrix} h_1 k_1 i_1 \\ h_2 k_2 i_2 \\ 1\ 1\ 1 \end{vmatrix} \right].
$$

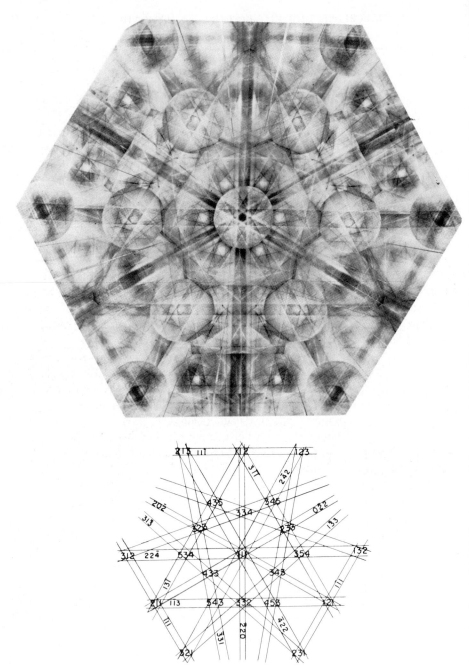

Fig. 10. a, b as fig. 9 for [111] region. (Courtesy J. Appl. Phys., ref. [6].)

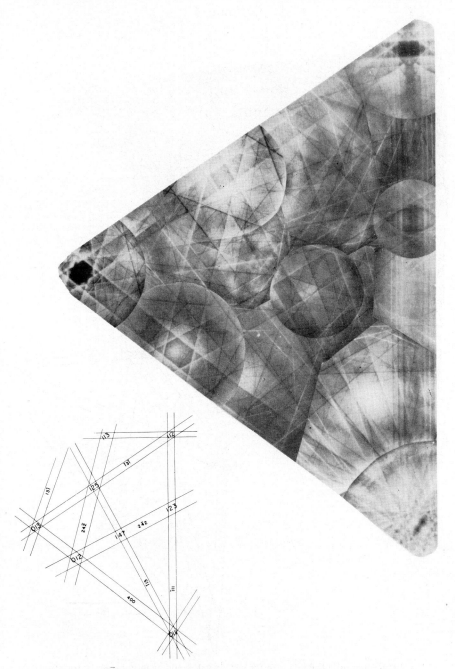

Fig. 11. a, b as fig. 9 for [110] region. (Courtesy J. Appl. Phys. ref. [6].)

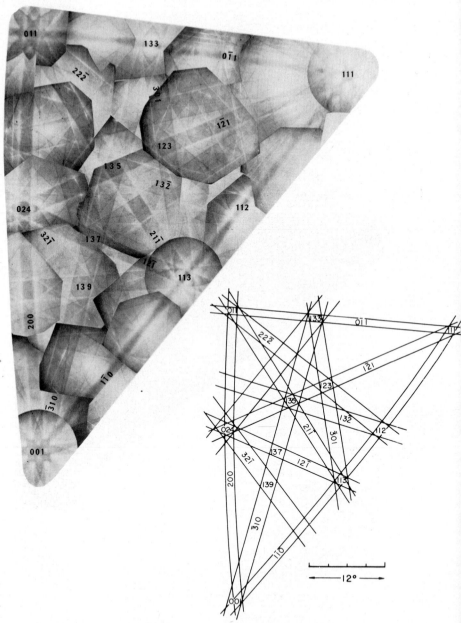

Fig. 12. a. Composite Kikuchi map for bcc crystal, b. indexing and scale factor. (Courtesy J. Appl. Phys. ref. [7].)

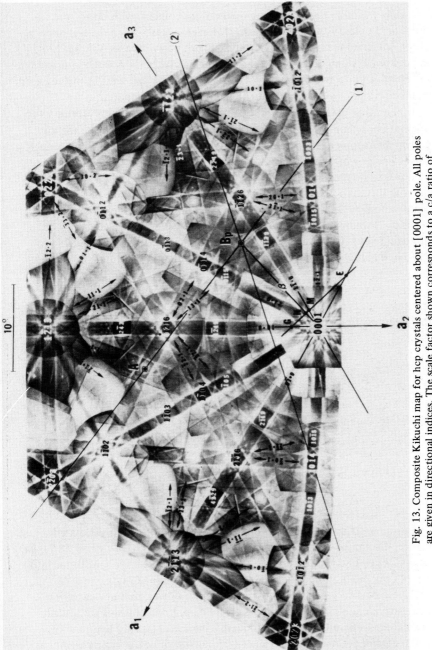

Fig. 13. Composite Kikuchi map for hcp crystals centered about [0001] pole. All poles are given in directional indices. The scale factor shown corresponds to a c/a ratio of 1.588 (e.g., Ag₂Al, Ti). (Courtesy Phys. Stat. Sol., ref. [8].)

As a rule, the more useful working orientations coincide with one of the prominent poles of the Kikuchi map. However, in cases when the foil orientation coincides with one of the less prominent poles, such as A in fig. 13 its indices $[u_A v_A t_A w_A]$ can be obtained immediately. Since A is the intersection of several Kikuchi bands, any two such as the $[02\bar{2}1]$ and $[\bar{3}121]$ may be used to obtain $[u_A v_A t_A w_A] = [5,\bar{7},2,18]$ from the above equation.

In the worst possible situation corresponding to a completely arbitrary foil orientation, a simple solution is still possible provided the center of the unknown diffraction pattern lies at the intersection of two lines passing through pairs of poles which are or can be indexed. In view of the large numbers of such poles, the probability of finding two suitable lines is large. For example, suppose the unknown diffraction pattern is compared with the map and its center found to lie at B_p in fig. 13. We find it lies at the intersection of lines (1) and (2) where line (1) passes through poles A and $[\bar{1}013]$, and line (2) through poles $[10\bar{1}4]$ and $[\bar{2}\bar{2}49]$. But these lines are themselves parallel to Kikuchi bands and if they can be indexed, the orientation of pole B_p can be determined as before.

Since $g \cdot r = 0$ for any Kikuchi band passing through the zone axis of r, any two such zones $r_1 = [u_1 v_1 t_1 w_1]$ and $r_2 = [u_2 v_2 t_2 w_2]$ will suffice for the determination of its indices. They are the solution to the system of equations

$$g \cdot r_1 = hu_1 + kv_1 + it_1 + lw_1 = 0 \, ,$$

$$g \cdot r_2 = hu_2 + kv_2 + it_2 + lw_2 = 0 \, ,$$

$$h + k + i = 0 \, .$$

Therefore, the indices of the unknown Kikuchi band can be written

$$(hkil) = \left(\begin{vmatrix} \bar{w}_1 v_1 t_1 \\ \bar{w}_2 v_2 t_2 \\ 0 \quad 1 \quad 1 \end{vmatrix} , \quad \begin{vmatrix} u_1 \bar{w}_1 t_1 \\ u_2 \bar{w}_2 t_2 \\ 1 \quad 0 \quad 1 \end{vmatrix} , \quad \begin{vmatrix} u_1 v_1 \bar{w}_1 \\ u_2 v_2 \bar{w}_2 \\ 1 \quad 1 \quad 0 \end{vmatrix} \quad \begin{vmatrix} u_1 v_1 t_1 \\ u_2 v_2 t_2 \\ 1 \quad 1 \quad 1 \end{vmatrix} \right) .$$

For our particular problem, using the orientation of pole A calculated earlier, the indices of lines of lines (1) and (2) are $(h_1 k_1 i_1 l_1) = (3,\bar{15},18,\bar{7})$ and $(h_2 k_2 i_2 k_2) = (11,\bar{14},3,\bar{2})$ respectively. When these indices are substituted into eq. (4), the orientation of pole B_p is found to be $[u_B v_B t_B w_B] = [\bar{1},\bar{1.85},2.85,11.7]$. It should be pointed out, however, that in view of the large angular range covered by the Kikuchi map, Kikuchi bands are actually curved lines. Therefore, in order to justify the use of straight lines, the two pairs of poles defining lines (1) and (2) should be chosen as close together as possible.

2. Some applications of Kikuchi patterns

2.1. *Introduction*

In the foregoing we have shown how Kikuchi patterns facilitate obtaining the precise orientation of the foil. If the Kikuchi pattern is sharp, the orientation may be obtained to within one hundredth of a degree and without the 180° ambiguity inherent in spot patterns. Thus the Kikuchi pattern is obviously very useful for obtaining crystallographic data, such as orientations, orientation relationships, trace analysis and habit planes, lattice parameters and axial ratios, identification of phases, detection of deviations from random solid solutions, etc. Kikuchi patterns also greatly simplify contrast analysis by facilitating selection of particular reflections and control of orientation and for obtaining stereoscopic images quickly and accurately. In addition, the Kikuchi pattern provides the most accurate method for calibrations, such as image rotation, electron wavelength, foil thickness, etc., and can provide information on non-isotropic elastic strains, and the angular misorientation across subgrains and dislocation walls.

Since space is limited, a comprehensive survey will not be attempted, but included in the following are representative examples of some of these applications. The details are to be found in the references listed.

2.2. *Some general applications of Kikuchi maps*

(a) Structure analysis. Since the Kikuchi patterns map out reciprocal space very accurately, they provide very useful means for structure analysis by electron diffraction. Examples have been described previously [11]. The maps can be constructed as described in the previous section. The main advantage of the Kikuchi pattern over the spot pattern is that the symmetry of the Kikuchi pattern is precisely that of the crystal giving rise to the pattern. This is not true of spot patterns at least if they are in symmetrical orientation or confined to a single Laue zone. This can be illustrated by fig. 14 which compares the symmetrical dc and hcp patterns from silicon and magnesium. Although both spot patterns show sixfold symmetry, the Kikuchi pattern of [111] silicon is threefold, but the [0001] pattern of Mg is sixfold. This ia particularly clear upon examinating the high order lines near the center of the patterns

(b) Contrast work. The Kikuchi map can be utilized in a similar way to a road map when one is operating the microscope. Examination of a low index pattern on the screen and comparison to the appropriate map (which can be placed in front of the operator) immediately locates the orientation. Once this is established suitable diffraction vectors via the shortest tilting paths can be quickly chosen to examine the contrast behavior of defects, e.g., determination

Fig. 14a. Symmetrical [111] silicon diffraction pattern.

Fig. 14b. Symmetrical [0001] magnesium diffraction.pattern. Notice 6 fold symmetry of spot pattern in cases but in (a) the Kikuchi symmetry is three-fold.

of Burgers vectors [6,7]. The map is particularly useful for studies of dislocations in non-cubic crystals where spot patterns are often difficult to analyse
by inspection at the microscope. Examples of the use of hexagonal maps have
been given for the system Ag-Al [10]. Contrast theory predicts that under
two-beam conditions and $s \approx 0$, a defect characterized by a displacement vector
R is invisible (or weakest) when $g \cdot R = 0$. Thus, any Kikuchi pair (g) which
converges at a pole R satisfies $g \cdot R = 0$ and the Kikuchi map indicates the sense
and amount of tilt needed to obtain that two-beam orientation (fig. 2a). For
example, fig. 12 is the appropriate map for bcc crystals; dislocations whose
Burgers vector are along [111] will thus be invisible for all reflections (Kikichi
lines) which pass through the [111] pole, e.g., $0\bar{1}1$, $1\bar{2}1$, $1\bar{1}0$ (fig. 6b). Similar
arguments apply to strain contrast images in general.

Fig. 15 illustrates an example where the map has been used to prove that
the loops in the slip bands in prismatically oriented Ag_2Al (hcp) have Burgers
vectors of the $\frac{1}{3} a$ [$1\bar{2}10$] type [10].

Such applications enable the somewhat tedious process of contrast analysis
to be done at the microscope in the minimum of time.

(c) Stereomicroscopy. The electron microscope image is a two dimensional
projection of the volume of the specimen being examined. The true three
dimensional image of the specimen can be obtained, however, by taking stereo
pairs (two pictures) of the same area without changing g (or s) by simply tilting along the Kikuchi band corresponding to g by about $10°$. Examples may
be found in refs. [13,14]. The Kikuchi map greatly simplifies and facilitates
this process, e.g., suppose one wanted a stereo image near the 0001 zone of a
hcp crystal, using $g = [0\bar{1}10]$. Reference to fig. 13 shows that a tilt from [0001]
to [$2\bar{1}\bar{1}9$] left along the $0\bar{1}10$ Kikuchi band shifts the viewing angle by about
$13°$ which is ample for stereo images. Although the scale factor for hcp (and
non-cubic in general) maps will depend on c/a, the tilt angle is not critical
merely for obtaining three dimensional information. Sometimes the tilt angle
does need to be known accurately, e.g., for accurate thickness measurements
or depth determinations such as in the analysis of small defects after irradiation [15]. The tilt angle is accurately measured by taking two diffraction patterns, one before and one after tilting, and after locating these on the map, the
tilt angle can be measured directly from the map using the appropriate scale
factor (figs. 9–13).

(d) Measurements from intensity distributions. Normally, diffraction patterns are obtained using a defocused condenser lens system in which the illumination is nearly parallel. When a fully focussed condenser lens system is
employed, a divergent beam pattern is obtained for the diffraction "spot" exhibiting the intensity fluctuations ("rocking curve") across the image of the

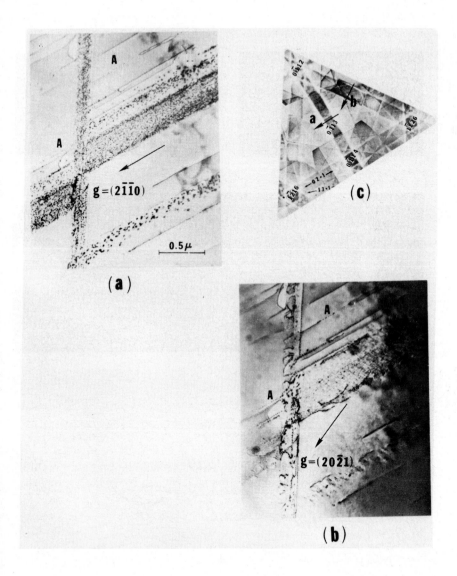

Fig. 15. a, b. Contrast experiment utilizing pre-determined **g** vectors with the aid of part of the map shown in (c). The prismatic loops in (a) go out of contrast in (b) showing that Burgers vector is $\frac{1}{3} a \,[\bar{1}2\bar{1}0]$.

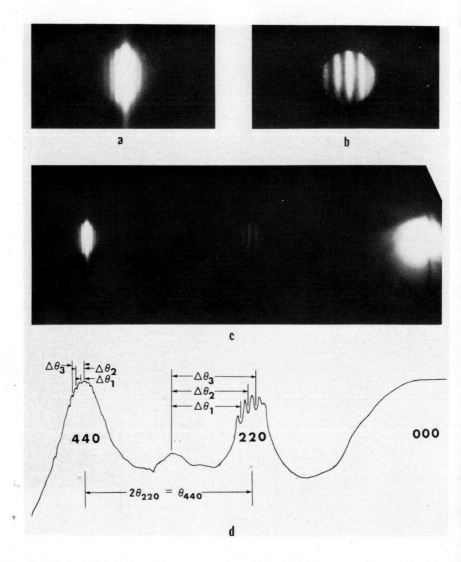

Fig. 16 a–c. Diverging beam photograph of the diffraction pattern of the 000, 220 and 440 maxima in silicon, (a), (b) are enlargements of the 220 and 440 reflections in (c). d. Microphotometer trace of (c).

condenser aperture. The control of orientation and unique indexing of the diffraction spot used for intensity measurements is facilitated by utilizing the Kikuchi pattern. For example, figs. 16 a–c show a divergent beam pattern for the 440, 220, and 000 reflections in silicon. The microphotometer traces corresponding to these are shown in fig. 16d.

Amelinckx's relation between foil thickness and intensity distribution is [12]

$$t = 2^{\frac{1}{2}} \{s_1^2 - 2s_2^2 + s_3^2\}^{-\frac{1}{2}}$$

where s_1, s_2, s_3 are the deviation parameters of three successive darkfield intensity minima in the dynamical intensity distributions.

For small angles this equation can be rewritten [16] as

$$t = \frac{2^{\frac{1}{2}}d^2}{\lambda} \left\{ \left[\frac{\Delta\theta_1}{2\theta_B} \right]^2 - 2 \left[\frac{\Delta\theta_2}{2\theta_B} \right]^2 + \left[\frac{\Delta\theta_3}{2\theta_B} \right]^2 \right\}^{-\frac{1}{2}}$$

where θ_B is the Bragg angle and $2\theta_B$ is the angle between diffraction "spots". Thus, $\Delta\theta_1$, $\Delta\theta_2$, $\Delta\theta_3$, $2\theta_B$ can be measured in any convenient units, and is independent of magnification. For fig. 16, the foil thickness is 2380Å using either the 220 or the 440 reflections.

Further applications of this method include determination of extinction distances [3] and magnification calibrations.

(e) Calibration of electron wavelength (and accelerating voltage). The wavelength of electrons is related to the magnification of the diffraction pattern through the camera constant equation

$$\lambda L = pd$$

where p is the measured width of the Kikuchi band in the pattern (fig. 7). In order to find λ it is necessary to known the value of L. This can be done by using the Kikuchi pattern as first indicated by Uyeda et al. [17]. Actually, by utilizing a known pattern which has been accurately calibrated as to the angle-distance scale factor (figs. 9–13), a simple method of analysis can be followed.

Suppose on a given Kikuchi pattern two poles, A and B, have been uniquely indexed e.g. by comparing to the appropriate map. Since the angle ϕ between these poles can easily be calculated or obtained from tables of angles, and the distance y between poles measured on the actual pattern, the scale factor is ϕ/y (rad. cm^{-1}). Now take any known low index (hkl) Kikuchi band of spacing p then since by Bragg's Law

$$2d \sin \theta = \lambda$$

or

$$\lambda \cong 2\theta \cdot d \quad \text{(for small angles)}$$

then

$$\lambda = (\phi/y) \, p \cdot d$$

which for cubic crystals is written

$$\lambda = \frac{\phi a p}{y \sqrt{h^2 + k^2 + l^2}} \, .$$

Hence, λ can be found without a knowledge of the plate-specimen distance L. For the Kikuchi map of silicon in fig. 9, $a = 5.142\text{Å}$, the scale factor is $2° \text{ cm}^{-1}$ so for the 400 reflection near [001] p is measured to be 0.8 cm, hence $\lambda = 0.0376\text{Å}$. The voltage is thus actually 97.2 kV and not 100 kV.

This map may be used as a standard to calibrate other voltage e.g. for high voltage microscopes. If λ_1 is the true wavelength determined for a given map for a single crystal pattern of identical orientation to a part of a map, the unknown

$$\lambda_2 = \lambda_1 \left(\frac{p_2}{p_1} \times \frac{y_1}{y_2} \right)$$

where p_1, y_1 and p_2, y_2 are measured on the map and pattern, respectively.

(f) Applications in studies of phase transformation. The Kikuchi pattern is helpful in identifying changes in microstructure produced by phase transformations, e.g., detecting modulations in composition (and/or structure) due to ordering, clustering and spinodal reactions. Two types of approach can be utilized, viz., (a) analysis of symmetrical patterns and (b) overlapping patterns in which line pairing from reflections of identical indices but different d spacings are examined [18]. Examples have been given in ref. [11], (see also ref. [19]). Also, since Kikuchi patterns enable orientations to be obtained very accurately, the Kikuchi pattern should always be used where possible for determining orientation relationships between phases and for measurements of orientation changes across boundaries.

APPENDIX ADDED FOR THE SECOND EDITION

Critical voltage measurements

The preceding chapter gives basic information on interpretation and applications of Kikuchi patterns. One further application worth noting is the measurement of critical voltage – the voltage at which second (or higher) orders of reflection go through a minimum in intensity (e.g. [20,21]). The effect is a consequence of many beam dynamical interaction, and values of the critical voltage can be easily measured (if a high voltage electron microscope is available) and calculated. For example, table A1 lists values of critical voltage using systematic interactions (see e.g. refs. [20–26]).

The critical voltage depends sensitively on the d-spacings of reflecting planes, Debye temperature and structure factors. Thus measurements of critical voltage provide data on local chemical composition, scattering factors, Debye temperature, improved contrast at lattice defects etc. (see e.g. ref. [20,21, 25–29]) and appears to be very promising in studies of phase transformations [26].

Experimentally, the two most accurate methods of measuring critical voltage are the converging beam method [23] and Kikuchi line method [20,24,29]. In the latter, the second order Kikuchi line disappears at critical voltage while other neighboring lines are unaffected. Calibration of the operating voltage is essential – this is done as described in section 2.2(e) of the chapter.

Measurements are made using a small field limiting aperture (e.g. 20–50 micron dia) with a fully focussed second condenser and a slightly off focus diffraction lens (this enables a converging beam to be observed). The specimen is tilted so that the Kikuchi pattern is at s slightly positive of $2g$ (so the Kikuchi intensity is more easily observed). There is an asymmetry in the intensity of the line occurring at the center of the second order Kikuchi band and which will pass close to the first order reflection. Below the critical voltage *on the plate or film negative*, the intensity is light towards the origin of the pattern (000) and above the critical voltage, the intensity is black towards (000). Thus, by inspection of this line, it is immediately recognized if the microscope voltage is above or below critical voltage. It is necessary to use high magnifications to see the asymmetry in the Kikuchi line and by carefully taking successive diffraction patterns at 5 kV intervals so as to pass through the reversal in intensity, accuracies of 1% or better can be achieved. Actual examples of this method have been published, e.g. refs. [20,26,28]. It is also possible to calculate the changes in Kikuchi line symmetry and display the results for ease of comparison to the actual experiments [24].

Table A1
Critical voltages for several elements.

Structure	Material	(B)	Reflection	Calculated 3-beam $V_c(kV)$[1]	Experimental $V_c(kV)$
Fcc	Al	0.85[2]	222	$-$, 465	425[3], 430[2]
			400	$-$, 1010	$-$
			440	$-$, 3700	$-$
	Cu	0.54[2]	222	130, 405	310[3], 325[2]
			400	380, 840	600[3]
			440	1530, 1900	$-$
	Ni	0.40[2]	222	145, 380	295[2]
			400	410, 670	610[4]
			440	1680, 1870	$-$
	Ag	0.58[5]	222	25, 75	$-$
			400	215, 230	225[3]
			440	1075, 910	$-$
			622	1770, 1500	$-$
	Au	0.62[5]	222	-110, $-$	$-$
			400	35, $-$	$-$
			440	630, $-$	715[6]
			622	1100, $-$	$-$
Bcc	Fe	0.36[2]	220	240, 390	305[2]
			400	1240, 1350	$-$
	W	0.20[5]	220	-80, -40	$-$
			400	520, 590	550[3]
			422	1175, 1280	$-$
Dia	Si	0.24[5]	440	$-$, 1440	1400[7]
	Ge	0.87[5]	440	680, 960	$-$

[1] Electron scattering data from International Tables (Ibers and Vainshtein). Values on the left obtained from the Thomas-Fermi-Dirac statistical model data. Values on the right obtained from self-consistent field data (W.L.Bell).
[2] Ref. [20].
[3] Ref. [21].
[4] Experimental observation, E.L.Bell.
[5] International Tables: Table 3.3.5, 1A (1962).
[6] Ref. [25].
[7] Ref. [30].

The continued support of the United States Atomic Energy Commission through the Inorganic Materials Research Division of the Lawrence Radiation Laboratory is gratefully acknowledged. I am delighted to acknowledge the research efforts of my students who have been involved in the development of many of the applications described here. I would particularly like to acknowledge the contributions of Dr. W.L.Bell.

References

[1] S.Kikuchi, Japan J. Phys. 5 (1928) 83.
[2] G.Thomas and W.L.Bell, Proc. Rome Eur. Electron Microscopy Congress, 1968, p. 283.
[3] Y.Kainuma, Acta Cryst. 8 (1955) 247;
    T.Tan, W.L.Bell and G.Thomas, Phil. Mag. 24 (1971) 417.
[4] M.Von Heimendahl, W.L.Bell and G.Thomas, J. Appl. Phys. 35 (1964) 361.
[5] O.Johari and G.Thomas, The Stereographic Projection and Applications (J. Wiley and Sons, New York, 1969).
[6] E.Levine, W.L.Bell and G.Thomas, J. Appl. Phys. 37 (1966) 2141.
[7] P.R.Okamoto, E.Levine and G.Thomas, J. Appl. Phys. 38 (1967) 289.
[8] P.R.Okamoto and G.Thomas, Phys. Stat. Sol. 25 (1968) 81.
[9] P.B.Hirsch et al., Electron Microscopy of Thin Crystals (Butterworths, London, 1965).
[10] P.R.Okamoto and G.Thomas, Acta Met. 15 (1967) 1325.
[11] G.Thomas, Trans. AIME 233 (1965) 1608.
[12] S.Amelinckx, Direct Observation of Dislocations (Academic Press, 1964) p. 193.
[13] Z.S.Basinski, Proc. Fifth Int. Congress Electron Mic., Vol. 1, B13 (Academic Press, New York, 1962).
[14] E.Levine, G.Thomas, J.Washburn, J. Appl. Phys. 38 (1967) 81, 87.
[15] M.Wilkens, These Proceedings.
[16] W.L.Bell and G.Thomas, EMSA (1969) St. Paul, Minn. Claitor's Publishers La., p. 158.
[17] R.Uyeda, M.Nomoyma and M.Kogiso, J. Elect. Mic. (Japan) 14 (1965) 296.
[18] R.E.Villagrana and G.Thomas, Phys. Stat. Sol. 9 (1965) 499.
[19] G.Thomas, These Proceedings.
[20] D.Watanabe, R.Uyeda and A.Fukuhara, Acta Cryst. A24 (1968) 580; A25 (1969) 138.
[21] J.S.Lally, C.J.Humphries, A.J.Metherell and R.M.Fisher, Phil. Mag. 25 (1972) 321.
[22] W.L.Bell, Proc. HVEM Conference, AERE Harwell (England) 1970, p. 35.
[23] W.L.Bell, EMSA, 1971 (Claitors Publishers, Baton Rouge, La.) p. 184.
[24] L.E.Thomas and C.J.Humphries, Phys Stat. Sol. 3 (1970) 599.
[25] J.S.Lally, L.E.Thomas and R.M.Fisher, EMSA, 1973 (Claitors Publishers, Baton Rouge, La.) p. 4.
[26] E.P.Butler, Phys. Stat. Sol. 18 (1973) 71.
[27] W.L.Bell and G.Thomas, in: Electron Microscopy and Structure of Materials, ed. G.Thomas (Univ. of Calif. Press, 1971) p. 23.
[28] R.M.Fisher, in: Electron Microscopy and Structure of Materials, ed. G. Thomas (Univ. of Calif. Press, 1971) p. 60.
[29] D. Watanabe, R. Uyeda and M. Kogiso, Acta Cryst. A24 (1968) 249.
[30] G.Thomas and J.-C.Lacaze, J. Microscopy 97 (1973) 301.

Diffraction and Imaging Techniques in Material Science,
eds. S. Amelinckx, R. Gevers and J. van Landuyt
© *North-Holland Publishing Company, 1978*

STUDY OF SUBSTITUTION ORDER-DISORDER BY MEANS OF X-RAY AND ELECTRON DIFFRACTION

R. DE RIDDER

Rijksuniversitair Centrum, Antwerpen, Belgium

1. Introduction

Imperfect crystals irradiated by X-rays, electrons or neutrons, produce diffracted radiation which is not as well localized as that produced by perfect crystals. Apart from the strong Bragg beams, which can be considered as resulting from diffraction by the "average" ideal lattice, one observes radiation diffracted in other directions i.e. there is no longer complete destructive interference between wavelets emitted by individual atoms out of the Bragg directions. If the diffracted intensity is appreciable in directions remote from the Bragg beams, the term *diffuse scattering* is used.

This chapter will be devoted to the study of diffuse scattering effects originating from two types of structural imperfections: substitutional disorder and displacement disorder.

For X-rays the *kinematical theory* is adequate to describe the scattering proces. In this theory it is assumed that a phonon is scattered once at most. In the framework of the kinematical treatment a direct technique is available to obtain information about the ordering state of the system (see also the contribution of Guinier in this volume). This technique will be treated in section 2.

In electron diffraction the scattering proces is more complicated since an electron, travelling through the crystal, may undergo multiple scattering events. For instance an electron of the incident beam can be scattered in a Bragg direction and rescattered in or out of other Bragg directions. Or an electron of the incident beam is scattered out of the Bragg directions and rescattered over a reciprocal lattice vector. Thus in the case of electrons one has to account for contributions to diffuse scattering originating from many primary beams which are *dynamically* coupled. Moreover one has to account for a redistribution of the diffuse intensity due to rescattering of the electrons over all vectors of reciprocal space, the most probable vectors being reciprocal lattice vectors however. General expressions for diffuse scattering of electrons, including dynamical interactions through Bragg reflections have been proposed by Gjønnes [1–3] and Cowley, Pogany and Murray [4,5]. Since these expressions are cumbersome for use and since moreover a technique for measuring beam current intensities in the electron microscope has not been developed as yet, only the X-ray and neutron diffraction technique is appropriate to furnish accurate quantitative results. However in one particular situation the kinematical theory will be adequate to explain diffuse scattering effects in electron diffraction. This is the case where the diffuse intensity is confined in reciprocal space to a geometric locus (surface or curve) exhibiting the translation symmetry of the reciprocal lattice. As far as the geometrical features of the diffuse intensity patterns are concerned the simple kinematical approach will be appropriate since the only effect of the dynamical interactions is a redistribution of the diffuse intensity on the locus if one neglects successive scattering events in non-Bragg directions.

In section 3 a model will be proposed which allows to describe the substitutional order in a system which produces a diffuse intensity locus; also applications of the model to experimental examples will be presented.

2. Kinematical diffraction in substitutional disordered systems

2.1. General expressions for n-component systems

A substitutionally disordered system can be defined by a regular lattice occupied by atoms of different kinds. The kinematical expression for the diffracted X-ray or electron amplitude is given by:

$$A(\mathbf{g}) = \sum_j f_j(\mathbf{g}) \exp(2\pi i \mathbf{g} \cdot \mathbf{r}_j) . \tag{1}$$

$\mathbf{r}_j$ represents the position vectors of the lattice sites, $\mathbf{g}$ the general position vector in reciprocal space and $f_j(\mathbf{g})$ the scattering amplitude of the atom at the position $\mathbf{r}_j$ in the direction defined by the vector $\mathbf{g}$. From the expression (1) it is seen that the diffracted amplitude contains information about the average lattice and about the occupation of the lattice sites; it is easily shown that these two types of information can be uncoupled.

Let n be the number of different atom species of the system occurring with respective fractions:

$$m_1, m_2, \dots m_i, \dots m_n ,$$

so that:

$$\sum_{i=1}^{n} m_i = 1 , \tag{2}$$

and with scattering amplitudes:

$$f^1, f^2, \ldots f^i, \ldots, f^n$$

which are functions of $\mathbf{g}$.

The mean scattering amplitude is defined by:

$$\bar{f} = \sum_{i=1}^{n} m_i f^i , \tag{3}$$

so that:

$$f^i = \bar{f} + \Delta f^i , \tag{4}$$

with:

$$\Delta f^i = f^i - \sum_{i=1}^{n} m_i f^i . \tag{5}$$

One has:

$$\sum_{j} \Delta f_j = \sum_{i=1}^{n} N m_i \Delta f^i = N \left[\sum_{i=1}^{n} m_i f^i - \bar{f} \sum_{i=1}^{n} m_i \right] = 0 , \tag{6}$$

where N is the total number of atoms.

Substitution of (4) in (1) gives:

$$A(\mathbf{g}) = A_B(\mathbf{g}) + A_D(\mathbf{g}) , \tag{7}$$

with:

$$A_B(\mathbf{g}) = \bar{f}(\mathbf{g}) \sum_{j} \exp(2\pi i \mathbf{g} \cdot \mathbf{r}_j) , \tag{8a}$$

$$A_D(\mathbf{g}) = \sum_{j} \Delta f_j(\mathbf{g}) \exp(2\pi i \mathbf{g} \cdot \mathbf{r}_j) . \tag{8b}$$

The term $A_B(\mathbf{g})$ of (7) contains the information about the regular lattice (occupied by atoms with average scattering amplitude) and consists of delta functions at the reciprocal lattice points whereas the term $A_D(\mathbf{g})$ contains information about the occupation of the lattice sites.

From (6) it follows that:

$$A_D(\mathbf{g}_k) = 0 , \tag{9}$$

for all reciprocal lattice vectors $\mathbf{g}_k$ so that:

$$A_B(\mathbf{g}) A_D(\mathbf{g}) \equiv 0 , \tag{10}$$

for all $\mathbf{g}$.

As a consequence the intensity $I(\mathbf{g})$ is given by:

$$I(\mathbf{g}) = |A(\mathbf{g})|^2 = I_B(\mathbf{g}) + I_D(\mathbf{g}) \tag{11}$$

where $I_B(\mathbf{g}) = |A_B(\mathbf{g})|^2$ represents the Bragg intensity and $I_D(\mathbf{g}) = |A_D(\mathbf{g})|^2$ the diffuse intensity. The uncoupling expressed by (11) allows to study the ordering of the system from the contribution $I_D(\mathbf{g})$ only.

The expression (8b) for the diffuse scattering amplitude can be uncoupled in a factor containing information about the nature of the atoms in the system and in a factor describing the placement of these atoms on the crystal lattice. Introducing the scattering vector $\mathbf{F}$:

$$\mathbf{F} = \underline{f^1 f^2 \dots f^i \dots f^n} \tag{12}$$

and the occupation vector $\boldsymbol{\sigma}^i$:

$$\boldsymbol{\sigma}^i = \begin{bmatrix} 0 \\ 0 \\ \vdots \\ 0 \\ 1 \\ 0 \\ \vdots \\ 0 \end{bmatrix} - \begin{bmatrix} m_1 \\ m_2 \\ \vdots \\ m_{i-1} \\ m_i \\ m_{i+1} \\ \vdots \\ m_n \end{bmatrix} = \begin{bmatrix} -m_1 \\ -m_2 \\ \vdots \\ -m_{i-1} \\ 1-m_i \\ -m_{i+1} \\ \vdots \\ -m_n \end{bmatrix} , \tag{13}$$

the expression (5) for Δf^i can be written as:

$$\Delta f^i = \mathbf{F} \cdot \boldsymbol{\sigma}^i ,$$

and from (8b):

$$A_D(\mathbf{g}) = \mathbf{F} \cdot \sum_j \boldsymbol{\sigma}_j \exp(2\pi i \mathbf{g} \cdot \mathbf{r}_j) , \tag{14}$$

expressing the uncoupling of the physical and the structural parameters.

2.2. Diffuse scattering from binary systems exhibiting short range order

A binary system of atoms A and B is said to be *long range ordered* if the atom placements on the lattice sites are such that one can distinguish between two types of sublattices: A- and B-sublattices. The sites of the A and B sub-lattices are preferentially occupied by A- and B-atoms respectively. Long range order is revealed in the diffraction pattern by the presence of Bragg reflections (superlattice reflections) which cannot be indexed on the basis of the original lattice. Above a critical temperature, termed *"ordering temperature"*, the super-lattice reflections disappear and the structure becomes disordered, which means that it is no longer possible to distinguish between two types of sublattice. The probability for occupation of a given site by — let say — an A atom is now given by the atom fraction m_A of A atoms. Although there is a quasi random distribution of A and B atoms over the A and B sublattices, there may still exist a preference in the kind of close neighbours about each atom. This depar-ture from randomness in the kind of close neighbours is called *short range order*. Short range order is reflected in the diffraction pattern by a three-dimensional distribution of diffuse scattering in reciprocal space.

For the case of a binary system the occupation vector (13) reduces to:

$$\boldsymbol{\sigma}^A = \begin{pmatrix} m_B \\ -m_B \end{pmatrix} \text{ and } \boldsymbol{\sigma}^B = \begin{pmatrix} -m_A \\ m_A \end{pmatrix} . \tag{15}$$

From (14) one obtains for the expression of the diffuse scattering amplitude:

$$A_D(\mathbf{g}) = [f_A(\mathbf{g}) - f_B(\mathbf{g})] \sum_j \sigma_j \exp(2\pi i \mathbf{g} \cdot \mathbf{r}_j) , \tag{16}$$

where σ_j is now a scalar operator which takes the value m_B if the site $\mathbf{r}_j$ is oc-cupied by an A atom and the value $-m_A$ if this site is occupied by a B atom.

The expression for the diffuse intensity $I_D(\mathbf{g}) = |A_D(\mathbf{g})|^2$ becomes:

$$I_D(\mathbf{g}) = |f_A - f_B|^2 \sum_j \sum_{j'} \sigma_j \sigma_{j'} \exp\{2\pi i \mathbf{g} \cdot (\mathbf{r}_j - \mathbf{r}_{j'})\}$$

and assuming that the atoms are arranged on a lattice with primitive unit cell such that $\mathbf{r}_j - \mathbf{r}_{j'}$ is a new lattice vector $\mathbf{r}_l$, one obtains:

$$I_D(\mathbf{g}) = N m_A m_B |f_A - f_B|^2 \sum_l \alpha_l \exp(2\pi \mathbf{g} \cdot \mathbf{r}_l) . \tag{17}$$

The coefficients α_l in the Fourier sum are the *Warren–Cowley short range order parameters* [6] defined by:

$$\alpha_l = \alpha_{\mathbf{r}_l} = \frac{1}{m_A m_B} \frac{1}{N} \sum_{\mathbf{r}_j} \sigma_{\mathbf{r}_j} \sigma_{\mathbf{r}_j + \mathbf{r}_k} = \frac{\langle \sigma_j \sigma_{j+l} \rangle}{m_A m_B} . \tag{18}$$

These coefficients are directly related to occupation probabilities. Let $P_l^{A\ A}{}_0$ be the probability that the sites with position vectors $\mathbf{r} = \mathbf{0}$ and $\mathbf{r}_l$ are occupied by A atoms. Introducing the scalar operators $\bar{\sigma}_l^A$ and $\bar{\sigma}_l^B$ defined by:

$$\bar{\sigma}_l^B = 0 \text{ and } \bar{\sigma}_l^A = 1 \text{ if an A atom is at the site } \mathbf{r}_l ,$$

$$\bar{\sigma}_l^B = 1 \text{ and } \bar{\sigma}_l^A = 0 \text{ if a B atom is at the site } \mathbf{r}_l , \tag{19}$$

one has:

$$P_l^{A\ A}{}_0 = \langle \bar{\sigma}_l^A \bar{\sigma}_0^A \rangle .$$

Since $\bar{\sigma}_l^{A,B}$ is related to $\bar{\sigma}_l$ by:

$$\sigma_l = \bar{\sigma}_l^A - m_A = m_B - \bar{\sigma}_l^B , \tag{20}$$

and moreover:

$$\langle \sigma_l \rangle = \langle \bar{\sigma}_l^A \rangle - m_A = 0 , \tag{21}$$

if follows that:

$$P_l^{A\ A}{}_0 = \langle (m_A + \sigma_l)(m_A + \sigma_0) \rangle = m_A^2 + \langle \sigma_l \sigma_0 \rangle ,$$

or:

$$P_l^{A\ A}{}_0 = m_A(m_A + m_B \alpha_l) . \tag{22a}$$

In an analogous way one finds:

$$P_l^{A\ B}{}_{0} = m_B(m_A - m_A\alpha_l) , \tag{22b}$$

$$P_l^{B\ A}{}_{0} = m_A(m_B - m_B\alpha_l) , \tag{22c}$$

$$P_l^{B\ B}{}_{0} = m_B(m_B + m_A\alpha_l) . \tag{22d}$$

For a completely disordered crystal (random distribution) of A and B atoms on the lattice sites, all short range order coefficients are zero, except $\alpha_0 = 1$.
In this case one has a diffuse intensity background:

$$I_D(\mathbf{g}) = Nm_A m_B |f_A - f_B|^2 , \tag{23}$$

which exhibits a smooth monotonic behaviour (*Laue monotonic scattering*).
The short range order parameters can be determined from intensity measurements which explore a fraction of the reciprocal space. In fact, the reduced diffuse intensity:

$$I_D(\mathbf{g})/|f_A(\mathbf{g}) - f_B(\mathbf{g})|^2 ,$$

is a periodic function with the period of the reciprocal lattice.
From (17) it follows by Fourier inversion:

$$\alpha_l = \frac{1}{Nm_A m_B V^*} \int_{V^*} \frac{I_D(\mathbf{g})}{|f_A(\mathbf{g}) - f_B(\mathbf{g})|^2} \exp(-2\pi i \mathbf{g} \cdot \mathbf{r}_l) \, d\mathbf{g} , \tag{24}$$

where V^* represents the volume of the reciprocal unit cell. In practice one finds that in some cases there are extra modulations which destroy the periodicity of the normalised diffuse intensity so that formula (24) is not valid. These modulations have been attributed to displacements of the atoms from their crystallographic positions. The traditional approach in the analysis of the diffuse intensity is to treat the short range order scattering as the component of interest and to remove the other components by various corrections. This is the subject of section 2.3.

2.3. Displacement disorder

Apart from substitutional disorder there are other sources of diffuse scattering; they are connected with displacements of the atoms from the sites of the "average" lattice.

Thermal vibrations, i.e. dynamical displacements, lead to a diffuse scattering component, called *Debye scattering* [7,8]. It is common to attempt to remove this temperature scattering component by making measurements at two temperatures, assuming that the thermal intensity varies linearly with the temperature, and extrapolating to absolute zero. One can also consider static displacements. These may result for instance from the presence of point defects. The diffuse scattering associated with the strain field arising from these defects was first studied by Huang and is called *Huang scattering* [9]. Using a simple elastic model for a crystal, with no short range order, Huang was able to show that this scattering component was confined to the vicinity of the Bragg reflections. The Huang scattering component is usually ignored or removed from the other components by discarding intensity measurements in the region of the Bragg reflections and extrapolating the diffuse intensity smoothly through the reciprocal lattice points.

In a system, exhibiting substitutional disorder, static displacements may also occur as a result of the difference in size of the atom species. These displacements give rise to a modulation of the diffuse intensity due to short range order; this is known as the *size displacement effect* [10–13]. It was shown by Borie that this component can be separated from the short range order component in an elegant way [14]. We shall present here a more accurate method, which allows to separate the different diffuse scattering contributions. The method is due to Borie and Sparks [15]. No assumptions are made about the nature of the displacements $\pmb{\delta}$, except that they are sufficiently small so that terms beyond the quadratic term in the series expansion of $\exp(2\pi i \mathbf{g} \cdot \pmb{\delta})$ can be neglected. If $\mathbf{r}_j$ defines a site of the "average" lattice and $\pmb{\delta}_j$ the displacement of an atom from this site, one has to replace $\mathbf{r}_j$ in formula (17) by $\mathbf{r}_j + \pmb{\delta}_j$ and:

$$\exp\{2\pi i \mathbf{g} \cdot (\mathbf{r}_j - \mathbf{r}_{j'})\},$$

by:

$$\exp\{2\pi i \mathbf{g} \cdot (\mathbf{r}_j - \mathbf{r}_{j'})\}\exp\{2\pi i \mathbf{g} \cdot (\pmb{\delta}_j - \pmb{\delta}_{j'})\}$$

$$\cong \exp\{2\pi i \mathbf{g} \cdot (\mathbf{r}_j - \mathbf{r}_{j'})\}\,[1 + 2\pi i \mathbf{g} \cdot (\pmb{\delta}_j - \pmb{\delta}_{j'})$$

$$-\tfrac{1}{2}[2\pi \mathbf{g} \cdot (\pmb{\delta}_j - \pmb{\delta}_{j'})]^2 + \dots]\,. \tag{25}$$

Neglecting terms higher than second order in $\mathbf{g} \cdot (\pmb{\delta}_j - \pmb{\delta}_{j'})$, the total intensity can be written as:

$$I(\mathbf{g}) = I_0(\mathbf{g}) + I_1(\mathbf{g}) + I_2(\mathbf{g}) \,. \tag{26}$$

The term $I_0(\mathbf{g}) = \Sigma_j \, \Sigma_{j'} \, f_j f_{j'} \exp\{2\pi i \mathbf{g} \cdot (\mathbf{r}_j - \mathbf{r}_{j'})\}$ represents the intensity one would have observed if there were no displacements from the ideal atomic sites. This zero-order term includes the Bragg reflections as well as the diffuse scattering due to short range order.

The term:

$$I_1(\mathbf{g}) = 2\pi i \sum_j \sum_{j'} f_j f_{j'} \mathbf{g} \cdot (\boldsymbol{\delta}_j - \boldsymbol{\delta}_{j'}) \exp\{2\pi i \mathbf{g} \cdot (\mathbf{r}_j - \mathbf{r}_{j'})\}, \tag{27}$$

gives rise to the atomic displacement modulation first treated by Warren et al. [10].

The term:

$$I_2(\mathbf{g}) = -2\pi^2 \sum_j \sum_{j'} f_j f_{j'} [\mathbf{g} \cdot (\boldsymbol{\delta}_j - \boldsymbol{\delta}_{j'})]^2$$

$$\times \; \exp\{2\pi i \mathbf{g} \cdot (\mathbf{r}_j - \mathbf{r}_{j'})\} \,, \tag{28}$$

accounts for the thermal scattering and Huang scattering. Assuming that the ratio of atomic scattering amplitudes f_B/f_A can be treated as a constant it is easily shown that $I_1(\mathbf{g})$ and $I_2(\mathbf{g})$ can be written in general form:

$$\frac{I_1(\mathbf{g})}{N f_A^2} = g_1 B_1(\mathbf{g}) + g_2 B_2(\mathbf{g}) + g_3 B_3(\mathbf{g}) \,,$$

$$\frac{I_2(\mathbf{g})}{N f_A^2} = g_1^2 C_1(\mathbf{g}) + g_2^2 C_2(\mathbf{g}) + g_3^2 C_3(\mathbf{g}) + g_2 g_3 D_1(\mathbf{g})$$

$$+ g_1 g_3 D_2(\mathbf{g}) + g_1 g_2 D_3(\mathbf{g}) \,.$$

$g_1 g_2$ and g_3 are the components of $\mathbf{g}$ in the reciprocal lattice basis $(\mathbf{a}_1^*, \mathbf{a}_2^*, \mathbf{a}_3^*)$ so that $\mathbf{g} = g_1 \mathbf{a}_1^* + g_2 \mathbf{a}_2^* + g_3 \mathbf{a}_3^*$.

B_1, B_2 and B_3, C_1, C_2 and C_3, D_1, D_2 and D_3 are periodic functions with the period of the reciprocal lattice.

For a statistically cubic system the expressions simplify to:

$$\frac{I_1(\mathbf{g})}{N f_A^2} = g_1 B(g_1, g_2, g_3) + g_2 B(g_2, g_3, g_1) + g_3 B(g_3, g_1, g_2) \,, \tag{29}$$

$$\frac{I_2(\mathbf{g})}{Nf_A^2} = g_1^2 C(g_1, g_2, g_3) + g_2^2 C(g_2, g_3, g_1) + g_3^2 C(g_3, g_1, g_2)$$

$$(30)$$

$$+ g_1 g_2 D(g_1, g_2, g_3) + g_2 g_3 D(g_2, g_3, g_1) + g_3 g_1 D(g_3, g_1, g_2).$$

In order to separate the measured diffuse intensity into its various contributions and to recover each of the periodic functions B, C and D one defines the operator Δ_1:

$$\Delta_1 \left(\frac{I(g_1, g_2, g_3)}{Nf_A^2} \right) = \frac{I(g_1, g_2, g_3)}{Nf_A^2} - \frac{I(g_1 - 1, g_2, g_3)}{Nf_A^2}. \qquad (31)$$

Since the functions B, C and D have the periodicity of the reciprocal lattice one finds:

$$\Delta_1 \frac{I(g_1, g_2, g_3)}{Nf_A^2} = B(g_1, g_2, g_3) + (2g_1 - 1)C(g_1, g_2, g_3)$$

$$+ g_2 D(g_1, g_2, g_3) + g_3 D(g_3, g_1, g_2) \qquad (32)$$

and:

$$\Delta_1 \left[\Delta_1 \frac{I(g_1, g_2, g_3)}{Nf_A^2} \right] = 2C(g_1, g_2, g_3), \qquad (33)$$

$$\Delta_2 \Delta_1 \left[\frac{I(g_1, g_2, g_3)}{Nf_A^2} \right] = D(g_1 g_2 g_3). \qquad (34)$$

Once the functions C and D are known one can directly substitute these functions in (32) and recover function B; from the functions B, C and D the function $I_0(\mathbf{g})$ and the short range order parameters can be calculated. Experimental techniques and applications of this method are presented e.g. in refs. [16–20].

3. Substitutional ordering associated with a diffuse intensity locus in reciprocal space

3.1. The transition state

In the short range order state the diffuse intensity is spread out over the whole of reciprocal space, i.e. the diffuse intensity has a *three-dimensional* distribution. Intensity maxima generally occur at well-defined crystallographic positions. Especially for the case of a binary alloy with an f.c.c. lattice these maxima are found at positions of the type [21]:

$$\langle 1\ 0\ 0 \rangle, \qquad \langle \tfrac{1}{2}\ \tfrac{1}{2}\ \tfrac{1}{2} \rangle, \qquad \langle 1\ \tfrac{1}{2}\ 0 \rangle.$$

Upon ordering the diffuse intensity becomes ultimately concentrated in the superstructure spots, i.e. the diffuse intensity distribution becomes *zero-dimensional.* Here we shall discuss the case where the diffuse intensity is located on a geometric locus — either a surface or a curve — exhibiting the translation symmetry of the reciprocal lattice. In this case diffraction patterns show characteristic sharp intensity contours which are the intersection of the geometric locus with planes in reciprocal space. Upon ordering the superstructure spots will appear at points which are situated on this locus. The ordering state associated with a one- or two-dimensional distribution of the diffuse intensity is termed *transition state.*

The order in the transition state has been described by De Ridder et al. in terms of a *cluster model* [22–27]. This model was first introduced by Brunel and co-workers [28] to explain the diffuse intensity distribution associated with short-range order in $LiFeO_2$. Their model was based on one of Pauling's rules governing the structure of ionic ordered systems [29]. Later Sauvage and Parthé [30] made use of this model to predict the diffuse intensity locus in ternary derivative structures showing substitutional disorder. We shall give here a more general formulation of the "cluster theory" and show that if the diffuse intensity is located on a geometric locus, the order in the system can be described by means of clusters of a specific polyhedral type. In fact we shall show that there exists a linear relation between the occupation operators for the cluster sites. The occupation of the cluster sites is such that this cluster relation is satisfied as good as possible for each of these clusters in the crystal. The ordering in the transition state is thus described in terms of possible predominant clusters of a specific polyhedral type. In some cases the ordering relation is very simple and a physical interpretation in terms of a small cluster is possible.

Since the cluster relation should also be satisfied in the long range ordered state, the transition state can be considered as being a prefiguration of the ordered state. It is clear that since the cluster relation is derived from the geometry of the diffuse intensity locus only — and thus no intensity measurements have to be performed, the model cannot give complete information about the order in the transition state. For instance, the fractions of different predominant clusters cannot be derived from the geometrical data.

In a further stage of ordering reinforcements of diffuse intensity may appear along the locus and finally the intensity may become confined to the positions of the superstructure spots. This means that at this stage some of the possible predominant clusters become favoured against other ones. The rearrangement on the atoms is such that, apart from the first cluster relation, the system tends to obey a supplementary relation. The reinforcements of diffuse intensity and finally the superstructure spots appear at the intersections of the loci associated with all cluster relations in the ordered system.

Let:

$$f(\mathbf{g}) = 0 , \tag{35}$$

be the diffuse intensity locus, which should have the translation symmetry of the lattice. Eq. (35) can be expressed by means of its Fourier representation:

$$f(\mathbf{g}) \equiv \sum_k \omega_k \exp(-2\pi i \mathbf{g} \cdot \mathbf{r}_k) = 0 , \tag{36}$$

where $\mathbf{r}_k$ are lattice vectors.

If the diffuse intensity lies on the locus (35) one has the identity:

$$A_D(\mathbf{g}) f(\mathbf{g}) \equiv 0 .$$

This identity expresses the requirement that $A_D(\mathbf{g})$ can only be different from zero along the geometric locus defined by (35). The identity can be written explicitly (using expression (16) for $A_D(\mathbf{g})$) in the form:

$$\sum_j \sum_k \omega_k \sigma_j \exp \{2\pi i \mathbf{g} \cdot (\mathbf{r}_j - \mathbf{r}_k)\} \equiv 0$$

and assuming a structure with primitive unit cell:

$$\sum_j \left(\sum_k \omega_k \sigma_{j+k} \right) \exp(2\pi i \mathbf{g} \cdot \mathbf{r}_j) \equiv 0 \tag{37}$$

which in turn leads to the set of homogeneous linear relations between the occupation operators:

$$\sum_k \omega_k \sigma_{j+k} = 0 \quad \text{for all } (j) . \tag{38}$$

Relations (38) define a cluster with sites determined by the position vectors

$\mathbf{r}_j + \mathbf{r}_k$ ($k = 0, 1 ..., S_0 - 1$). This relation, called *cluster relation*, which should hold for *all* clusters of the polyhedral type determined by the vectors $\{\mathbf{r}_k\}$, restricts the possible compositions of the clusters. In general, the number of cluster vectors $\mathbf{r}_k$ will be small and the corresponding cluster type will be a simple one.

Conversely, if (38) is satisfied for all clusters of the type defined by the lattice vectors $\{\mathbf{r}_k\}$, it is easily shown that all diffuse intensity is located on the geometric locus (36). In general this locus is a *surface* when $f(\mathbf{g})$ is a real function; if $f(\mathbf{g})$ is a complex function, i.e.:

$$f(\mathbf{g}) = \phi(\mathbf{g}) + i\psi(\mathbf{g}) \quad (\phi, \psi \text{ real functions}),$$

eq. (36) represents a *curve* which is the interaction of the surfaces:

$$\phi(\mathbf{g}) = 0, \quad \psi(\mathbf{g}) = 0.$$

With a centro-symmetric cluster ($|\omega_k| = |\omega_{-k}|$) generally a surface can be associated; a non-centro-symmetric cluster ($|\omega_k| \neq |\omega_{-k}|$) corresponds to a curve [23].

Relations (38) give rise to an infinite set of relations between the short-range order parameters α_{0j}. Indeed, writing (38) in the form:

$$\sum_k \omega_k \sigma_{l+j+k} = 0$$

multiplying by σ_l, and averaging over all sites (l) one obtains the relations:

$$\sum_k \omega_k \alpha_{0,j+k} = 0 \quad \text{for all } j. \tag{39}$$

By squaring (38) and averaging over all lattice sites j one obtains:

$$\sum_k \sum_{k'} \omega_k \omega_{k'} \alpha_{0,k-k'} = 0. \tag{40}$$

It is not always possible to satisfy (38) for a general set of coefficients ω_k. Even when (38) can be satisfied for a given cluster, topological reasons may imply that it is impossible to satisfy the relations for neighbouring clusters. In practice, the cluster relation will not be satisfied for *all* clusters and will lead a residue value defined by:

$$\epsilon_j = \sum_k \omega_k \sigma_{j+k}. \tag{41}$$

It can be noticed that the statistical distribution of the ϵ_j values has a mean value which is necessarily zero:

$$\langle \epsilon_j \rangle = \sum_k \omega_k \langle \sigma_{j+k} \rangle = 0 \quad \text{since} \quad \langle \sigma_j \rangle = 0 \quad \text{from (21)}.$$

From (16), (36), (37) and (41) it follows that:

$$a(g)f(g) = \sum_j \epsilon_j \exp(2\pi i g \cdot r_j) \quad \text{with} \quad a(g) = \frac{A_D(g)}{f_A - f_B}, \tag{42}$$

so that:

$$i(g)|f(g)|^2 = N \sum_j \langle \epsilon_0 \epsilon_j \rangle \exp(2\pi i g \cdot r_j) \quad \text{with} \quad i(g) = |a(g)|^2 ,$$

and:

$$\frac{1}{V^*} \int_{V^*} dg\, i(g)|f(g)|^2 = N\langle \epsilon_j^2 \rangle . \tag{43}$$

If the intensity distribution is closely confined to the vicinity of $f(g) = 0$ the value of the integral will be small and also the variance $\langle \epsilon_j^2 \rangle$ of the distribution of the residue ϵ. Keeping this in mind we are able to propose the most prominent clusters for the transition state; the clusters which may occur with large frequencies are the ones which correspond to the smallest values of $|\epsilon|$. Conversely, if the variance $\langle \epsilon_j^2 \rangle$ is small the intensity should be concentrated in the neighbourhood of the locus $f(g) = 0$.

3.2. Interpretation and application of the cluster relation

In some cases a physical or structural interpretation of the cluster relation is very simple.

(1) If all $\omega_k = +1$, eq. (38) reduces to:

$$\sum_k \sigma_{j+k} = 0 \quad \text{for all } (j) . \tag{44}$$

This relation expresses that all clusters of the considered type have the same composition which is necessarily equal to the macroscopic composition. Indeed, if (44) is satisfied, one has from (20):

$$\sum_k \sigma_{j+k} = \sum_k (\bar{\sigma}_{j+k}^A - m_A) = 0 \quad \text{(for all } j)$$

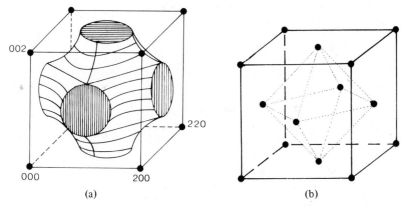

Fig. 1. (a) Locus of diffuse intensity for a f.c.c. system represented by the equation $\cos \pi g_1 + \cos \pi g_2 + \cos \pi g_3 = 0$. (b) Corresponding octahedral cluster of the f.c.c. lattice. The cluster relation expresses that all octahedral clusters should have the macroscopic composition.

so that $\Sigma_k \ \bar{\sigma}^A_{j+k} = m_A S_0$ which expresses that all clusters (j) have the same number of A atoms ($S_0 m_A$ is necessarely integer). It is clear that (44) for a given cluster type can only be satisfied for a discrete set of macroscopic compositions.

Example 1: The locus of diffuse intensity depicted in fig. 1a for an f.c.c. system is represented by the equation:

$$\cos \pi g_1 + \cos \pi g_2 + \cos \pi g_3 = 0 \ .$$

Writing this under exponential form leads to the cluster vectors:

$$\pm \tfrac{1}{2}[1 \ 0 \ 0] \ , \qquad \pm \tfrac{1}{2}[0 \ 1 \ 0] \ , \qquad \pm \tfrac{1}{2}[0 \ 0 \ 1] \ .$$

The cluster corresponding to the locus is an octahedron of the f.c.c. lattice (depicted in fig. 1b). The cluster relation:

$$\sum_{k=1}^{6} \sigma_{j+k} = 0 \ ,$$

expresses that all clusters of the octahedral type should have the macroscopic composition.

Example 2: In the short-range order state the diffuse intensity has essentially a three-dimensional distribution, i.e. is in general different from zero in

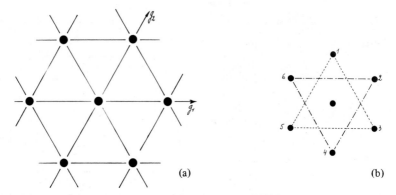

Fig. 2. (a) Locus of diffuse intensity in a two-dimensional hexagonal system represented by the equation $\sin \pi g_1 \sin \pi g_2 \sin \pi g_1 + g_2 = 0$. (b) Corresponding six-point cluster. The cluster relation expresses that the compositions of the triangular subclusters (1,3,5) and (2,4,6) have to be the same.

any point of reciprocal space except at the reciprocal lattice points. From this one can conclude that:

$$A_D(\mathbf{g}) \sum_l \delta(\mathbf{g} - \mathbf{g}_l) \equiv 0 \,,$$

where $\sum_l \delta(\mathbf{g} - \mathbf{g}_l) = \sum_j \exp(2\pi i \mathbf{g} \cdot \mathbf{r}_j)$ is a sum of Dirac delta functions. The corresponding cluster relation:

$$\sum_j \sigma_j = 0 \,,$$

shows that the smallest crystal cluster which can describe the order is the crystal itself. It expresses the trivial fact that the crystal has the macroscopic composition. This relation is equivalent with (21). Applications of the ordering relation (44) can be found in [30] with reference to ordering in ionic systems; in [26] with reference to vacancy ordering in some compounds and in [23] with reference to ordering in Ni–Mo and Au–V alloys.

(2) For some experimental cases $\omega_k = +1$ for half the number of cluster vectors and $\omega_{-k} = -1$ for the other half. Relation (38) becomes explicitly:

$$\sum_k^{S_0/2} \sigma_{j+k} = \sum_k^{S_0/2} \sigma_{j-k} \,. \tag{45}$$

This relation can be satisfied if and only if the composition of the subcluster $\{r_{j+k}\}$ is equal to the composition of the corresponding subcluster $\{r_{j-k}\}$.

Example: The locus of diffuse scattering depicted in fig. 2a, for a two-dimensional hexagonal system is described by the equation:

$$\sin \pi g_1 \sin \pi g_2 \sin \pi(g_1 + g_2) = 0 .$$

Expressing this relation as the sum of exponentials, one finds:

$$\exp\{2\pi i(g_1 + g_2)\} + \exp(-2\pi i g_1) + \exp(-2\pi i g_2)$$

$$- (\exp\{-2\pi i(g_1 + g_2)\} + \exp(2\pi i g_1) + \exp(2\pi i g_2)) = 0 .$$

The cluster vectors are:

$$\pm[1\ 0] , \qquad \pm[0\ 1] , \qquad \pm[1\ 1] ,$$

and the ω-coefficients are:

$$\omega_{11} = \omega_{\bar{1}0} = \omega_{0\bar{1}} = 1 ; \qquad \omega_{\bar{1}\bar{1}} = \omega_{10} = \omega_{01} = -1 ,$$

leading to the composition requirement:

$$\sigma_{11} + \sigma_{\bar{1}0} + \sigma_{0\bar{1}} = \sigma_{\bar{1}\bar{1}} + \sigma_{10} + \sigma_{01} .$$

The prominent clusters are six-point clusters (fig. 2b) which obey the above relation, i.e. the composition of the triangular clusters (1,3,5) and (2,4,6) have to be the same.

Application of this type of ordering relation is given in [25] with respect to the ordering of intercalated copper in $Cu_x NbS_2$ $(0.8 < x < 1.00)$.

(3) In some cases empirical equations for the intensity locus have been put forward which are of the form:

$$f_1(g) + \omega f_2(g) = 0 , \tag{46}$$

where ω is a parameter depending on composition and on heat treatment. The functions f_1 and f_2 are of the form:

$$f_1(g) = \sum_{k_1} \exp(2\pi i g \cdot r_{k_1}) , \qquad f_2(g) = \sum_{k_2} \exp(2\pi i g \cdot r_{k_2}) .$$

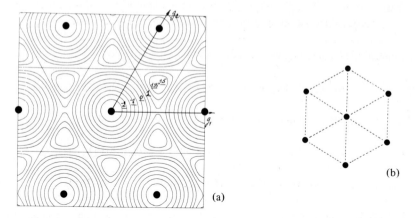

Fig. 3. (a) Loci of diffuse intensity in a two-dimensional hexagonal system represented by the equation $\cos 2\pi g_1 + \cos 2\pi g_2 + \cos 2\pi(g_1 + g_2) + \omega = 0$ for various values of the parameters ω (ω varying from -3.0 to $+1.5$). (b) Seven-point hexagonal cluster associated with the diffuse intensity loci fig. 3a.

The corresponding cluster relation takes the form:

$$\sum_{k_1} \sigma_{j+k_1} + \omega \sum_{k_2} \sigma_{j+k_2} = 0 .$$

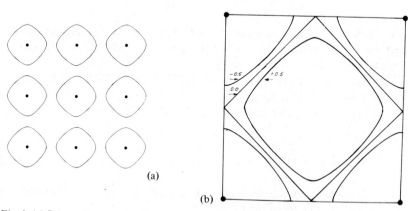

Fig. 4. (a) Schematic representation of the diffuse intensity rings in the $(001)^*$ diffraction pattern. The rings are centered around the Bragg reflections. (b) Representation of the geometric locus $4 \cos \pi(g_1 + g_2) \cos \pi(g_1 - g_2) + \omega = 0$ in a unit mesh of the $(001)^*$ plane for several values of the parameter ω ($\omega = -0.50, 0.00, +0.50$).

Example 1. Let the intensity locus in a two-dimensional hexagonal system be represented by the equation:

$$\cos \pi g_1 \cos \pi g_2 \cos \pi(g_1 + g_2) = \text{const} ,$$

or:

$$\omega + \cos 2\pi g_1 + \cos 2\pi g_2 + \cos 2\pi(g_1 + g_2) = 0 .$$

The loci for varying values of the parameter ω are depicted in fig. 3a. Identification with the general form (36) leads to the planar seven-point hexagonal cluster of fig. 3b. The corresponding relation is:

$$2\omega\sigma_j + \sum_{k=1}^{6} \sigma_{j+k} = 0 ,$$

where σ_j refers to the central site. From this relation the possible prominent clusters are derived.

Use of this cluster relation was made to describe the ordering of Cu atoms in $Cu_x NbS_2$ $(0.07 \leqslant x \leqslant 0.80)$ [25].

Example 2: Fig. 4a shows a schematic representation of the intensity contours

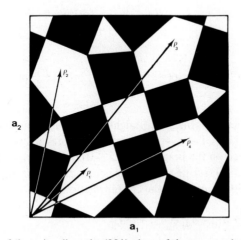

Fig. 5. Projection of the unit cell on the (001) plane of the tungsten bronze structure. The possible position vectors ρ_i (i = 1, 2, 3, 4) for the niobium–oxide strings in the pentagonal tunnels are indicated.

observed in the $(001)^*$ diffraction pattern of a crystal with nominal composition $17 \, Nb_2O_5 \cdot 48 \, WO_3$. The crystal exhibits a tetragonal tungsten bronze
structure [31]; the projection of the unit cell on the (001) plane is presented
in fig. 5. The unit cell contains four pentagonal tunnels in the [001] direction;
these tunnels are partly vacant and partly filled with niobium—oxygen strings.
It has been shown that the observed diffuse intensity contours can be attributed
to ordering of these strings in the matrix tunnels [32]. The high resolution
[001] image published by Iijima and Anstis, fig. 7b can directly be interpreted
in terms of vacant and occupied tunnels. This offers an excellent opportunity
to compare the results derived from the geometry of the diffuse intensity locus
to the actual arrangement of the atom strings in the tunnels of the WO_3-matrix.
This arrangement is related to substitutional ordering of two components
(niobium—oxide strings and vacancies) on a two-dimensional square lattice.
Since the unit cell for this structure is non-primitive (the position vectors of the
tunnels are $\boldsymbol{\rho}_i$, $i = 1, 2, 3, 4$) the results of section 3.2 have to be extended. Assuming the four sublattices with primitive unit cell to be equivalent, it is easily
shown that the cluster relation can be written as:

$$\sum_k \omega_k \sigma_{j+k}^{(i)} = 0 \quad \text{for all } (j) \text{ and } (i) .$$

$\sigma_j^{(i)}$ is the occupation operator for the site which position vector $\mathbf{r}_j + \boldsymbol{\rho}_i$.
The intensity locus is well described by an equation of the type:

$$\cos \pi(g_1 + g_2) \cos \pi(g_1 - g_2) + (\omega/4) = 0 ,$$

or:

$$\exp(2\pi i g_1) + \exp(-2\pi i g_1) + \exp(2\pi i g_2) + \exp(-2\pi i g_2) + \omega = 0 . \tag{47}$$

For $\omega = 0$ the locus is formed by straight lines connecting points of the type
$(\frac{1}{2} \, 0 \, 0)^*$ and $(0 \, \frac{1}{2} \, 0)^*$. For $\omega \neq 0$ the equation represents pseudo-circles which
are either centered on the Bragg spots $(\omega < 0)$ ore centered on positions of the
type $(\frac{1}{2} \, \frac{1}{2} \, 0)$ $(\omega > 0)$ (see fig. 4b). In the actual case ω corresponds to a negative
value $(\omega \cong -0.50)$. From (47) the cluster relation:

$$\sigma_{10} + \sigma_{\bar{1}0} + \sigma_{01} + \sigma_{0\bar{1}} + \omega\sigma_{00} = 0 , \tag{48}$$

is derived.
The cluster which characterizes the ordering is formed by a site and its four

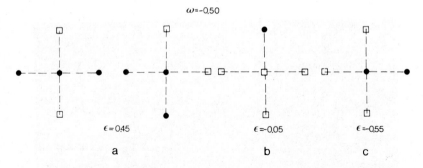

$\omega = -0.50$

$\epsilon = 0.45$ $\epsilon = -0.05$ $\epsilon = -0.55$

a   b   c

Fig. 6. The predominant clusters describing the arrangement of niobium–oxide strings on a same sublattice. The numerical values of the residue ϵ defined by relation (41) have been indicated. From clusters 4a linear arrays of occupied tunnels in the a_1 and a_2 direction are formed. At the ends of this arrays clusters 4c occur. Clusters 4b are responsible for the relative positions of an array with respect to the neighbouring ones.

nearest neighbours. Predominant clusters will be those for which the left-hand side of (48) is as small as possible. From the high resolution image it was concluded that the fraction of occupied tunnels amounts to 30% and thus $\sigma = -0.30$ (vacant site) or $\sigma = 0.70$ (occupied site). The possible predominant clusters are illustrated in fig. 6. A characteristic feature of this ordering model should be the occurrence of linear arrays of occupied tunnels in the a_1 and a_2 direction on a same sublattice. These arrays are formed of clusters (a) with at

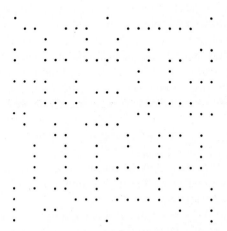

Fig. 7a. Two-dimensional grating constructed from the clusters of the 6a, b and c.

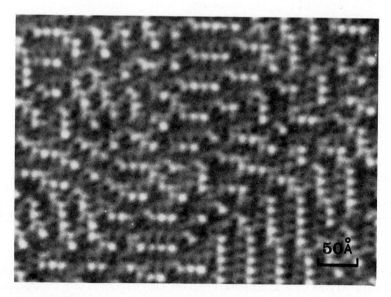

Fig. 7b. Dark field image taken from a part of a diffuse intensity ring (Courtesy : Iijima).
Pairs of occupied tunnels are imaged as white dots. Notice the resemblance with the theoretical model of fig. 7a.

the end clusters of type (c). Clusters of type (b) are responsible for the relative
positions of an array with respect to the neighbouring ones. Part of a grating
constructed from these clusters, is shown in fig. 7a. This grating can be compared to the grating depicted on the high resolution image (fig. 7b). The white
open circles represent the positions of occupied tunnels on a same sublattice.
A striking resemblance is found between the theoretical model and experimental distribution of niobium—oxide strings, directly derived from image interpretation.

3.3. The optimal cluster relation

In section 3.2 the ordering in the transition state has been described by a
cluster relation; we shall show that this relation can be derived from measured
short range order parameters.

The variance of the distribution of residue values ϵ_j for a cluster of a given
polyhedral type can be related to these parameters by substitution of (17), (18)
and (36) in (43); one obtains:

$$\langle \epsilon_j^2 \rangle = m_A m_B \sum_k \sum_{k'} \omega_k \alpha_{0,k-k'} \omega_{k'}^* ,$$

or in matrix notation:

$$\langle \epsilon_j^2 \rangle = m_A m_B \tilde{\omega}^* \alpha \omega = m_A m_B \langle \omega | \alpha | \omega \rangle , \tag{49}$$

with matrices:

$$\omega = \begin{bmatrix} \omega_0 \\ \omega_1 \\ \vdots \\ \omega_k \end{bmatrix} \quad \text{and} \quad \alpha = \begin{bmatrix} \alpha_{00} \alpha_{01} \cdots \\ \alpha_{10} \\ \vdots \quad \alpha_{ij} \end{bmatrix} . \tag{50}$$

The elements of the *cluster vector* ω are the coefficients of the Fourier expansions of $f(g)$; the elements of the matrix α are defined by:

$$\alpha_{i,j} = \alpha_{r_j - r_i} = \alpha_{j-i} .$$

The α matrix is real and symmetric.

If the two atom species are placed at random on the lattice sites, α reduces to the unity matrix and hence:

$$\langle \epsilon_j^2 \rangle_{\text{random}} = m_A m_B \langle \omega | \omega \rangle , \tag{51}$$

expressing Parsivals theorem.

Defining the normalised variance s^2 by:

$$s^2 = \langle \epsilon_j^2 \rangle / \langle \epsilon_j^2 \rangle_{\text{random}} , \tag{52}$$

one has from (49), (51) and (52):

$$s^2 = \langle \omega | \alpha | \omega \rangle / \langle \omega | \omega \rangle . \tag{53}$$

The knowledge of the α parameters allows to test a given cluster relation; the optimal relation is this one which corresponds to the smallest value (s^2 is necessarily positive) of the normalised variance. Thus, one has to look for the absolute minimum of

$$\langle \omega | \alpha | \omega \rangle / \langle \omega | \omega \rangle .$$

This problem is similar to the problem in quantum mechanics of finding the lowest energy level (ground state) and the corresponding wave function for a given Hamiltonian. It can be solved by means of the variation principle:

$$\delta s^2 = \frac{\langle \omega + \delta\omega \,|\, \boldsymbol{\alpha} \,|\, \omega + \delta\omega \rangle}{\langle \omega + \delta\omega \,|\, \omega + \delta\omega \rangle} - s^2 = 0 \quad \text{for all } \delta\omega \quad ,$$

which leads to the eigenvalue-eigenvector equation:

$$\boldsymbol{\alpha} | \omega \rangle = s^2 | \omega \rangle \tag{54}$$

similar to the Schrödinger equation.

The optimal cluster vector ω is the eigenvector of $\boldsymbol{\alpha}$ corresponding to the lowest eigenvalue. If a set of α-parameters $(\alpha_0, \alpha_1, \alpha_2 \dots \alpha_r)$ has been measured with sufficient accuracy it should be possible in principle to determine from (54) a cluster relation which characterises the ordering in the transition state. A more detailed account of this method as well as some applications will be published in a forthcoming paper by Van Dyck et al. [32].

3.4. Conclusion

In the latest years several authors have interpreted diffuse intensity contours observed in X-ray, neutron and electron diffraction patterns of some alloys and non-stoichiometric compounds in terms of coupling between concentration waves and the system of conduction electrons [33, 34]. The coupling involves a relationship between the Fermi-surface and the diffuse intensity locus; this relationship has been examined for different systems [35, 38]. It was shown in section 3 that in some cases a structural model can also account for the geometry and the sharpness of observed contours. The relation between these two views is not clear at present.

References

[1] J.Gjønnes, in: Proc. International Conference on Electron Diffraction and Crystal Defects (Melbourne, 1965) IH-4.
[2] J.Gjønnes, Acta Cryst. 20 (1966) 240.
[3] J.Gjønnes and R.Høier, Acta Cryst. A27 (1971) 166.
[4] J.M.Cowley and A.P.Pogany, Acta Cryst. A24 (1966) 109.
[5] J.M.Cowley and R.J.Murray, Acta Cryst. A24 (1968) 329.
[6] J.M.Cowley, J. Appl. Phys. 21 (1950) 24.
[7] P.Debye, Verh. Dtsch. Phys. Ges. 15 (1913) 678, 738, 857.
[8] C.B.Walker and D.T.Keating, Acta Cryst. 14 (1961) 1170.
[9] K.Huang, Proc. Roy. Soc. A190 (1947) 102.

[10] B.E.Warren, B.L.Averbach and B.W.Roberts, J. Appl. Phys. 22 (1951) 1493.
[11] B.Borie, Acta Cryst. 10 (1951) 1493.
[12] B.Borie, Acta Cryst. 12 (1959) 280.
[13] J.M.Cowley, Acta Cryst. A24 (1968) 557.
[14] B.Borie, Acta Cryst. 14 (1961) 472.
[15] B.Borie and G.J.Sparks Jr., Acta Cryst. A27 (1971) 198.
[16] M.Hayakawa, P.Bardhan and J.B.Cohen, J. Appl. Cryst. 8 (1975) 87.
[17] S.C.Moss, J. Appl. Phys. 35 (1964) 3547.
[18] J.E.Spruiell and E.E.Stansbury, J. Phys. Chem. Solids 26 (1965) 811.
[19] B.Chakravarti, J.Cullie, G.J.Sparks Jr., Starke Jr. and R.O. Williams, J. Phys. Chem. Solids 35 (1974) 1317.
[20] R.O.Williams, Met. Trans. 5 (1974) 1843.
[21] P.C.Clapp and S.C.Moss, Phys. Rev. 171 (1968) 754.
[22] R.De Ridder, Physica 79A (1975) 217.
[23] R.De Ridder, G.Van Tendeloo and S. Amelinckx, Acta Cryst. A32 (1976) 216.
[24] R.De Ridder, G.Van Tendeloo, D.Van Dyck and S.Amelinckx, Phys. Stat. Sol. 38 (1976) 663.
[25] R.De Ridder, G.Van Tendeloo, D.Van Dyck and S.Amelinckx, Phys. Stat. Sol. 39 (1977) 383.
[26] R.De Ridder, D.Van Dyck, G.Van Tendeloo and S.Amelinckx, Phys. Stat. Sol. 40 (1977) 669.
[27] R.De Ridder, G.Van Tendeloo, D.Van Dyck and S.Amelinckx, Phys. Stat. Sol. 41 (1977) 555.
[28] M.Brunel and F.De Bergevin, J.Phys. Chem. Solids 30 (1969) 2011.
[29] L.Pauling, The Nature of the Chemical Bond, 3rd Ed. (Cornell Press, Ithaca, 1960, 547.
[30] M.Sauvage and R.Parthé, Acta Cryst. A30 (1974) 239.
[31] J.Allpress, Mat. Res. Bull. 10 (1969) 707;
     S.Iijima and J.Allpress, Acta Cryst. A30 (1974) 22;
     S.Iijima and J.Allpress, Acta Cryst. A30 (1974) 29.
[32] D.Van Dyck et al., Phys. Stat. Sol., to be published.
[33] M.A.Krivoglaz, Theory of X-ray and Thermal Neutron Scattering by Real Crystals (New York, 1968).
[34] L.M.Roth, H.J.Zeiger and T.A.Kaplan, Phys. Rev. 149 (1966) 519.
[35] S.C.Moss, Phys. Rev. Lett. 22 (1969) 1108.
[36] S.Hashimoto and S.Ogawa, J. Phys. Soc. Japan 29 (1970) 710.
[37] K.Ohshima and D.Watanabe, Acta Cryst. (1973) 520.
[38] J.R.Castles, J.M.Cowley and A.E.C.Spargo, Acta Cryst. 27A (1971) 376.

SUBJECT INDEX TO VOLUMES I AND II *

* Diffraction and Imaging Techniques in Material Science is published in two volumes:
  page numbers 1–454 refer to Volume I and page numbers 455–848 refer to Volume II.